The Library of
DRUMMOND
of Hawthornden

Wits, howsoever pregnant and great,
without Books, are but as valiant
Soldiers without Arms, and Arti-
zans destitute of Tools.

William Drummond
of Hawthornden,
'Of Libraries'
Works,
1711

✳

The Library of
DRUMMOND
of Hawthornden

Edited with an introduction by
ROBERT H. MACDONALD
for the University Press
Edinburgh

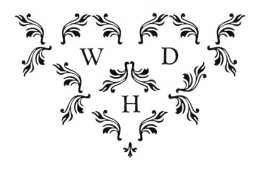

EDINBURGH UNIVERSITY PRESS
22 George Square, Edinburgh
ISBN O 85224 019 8

North America
Aldine Publishing Company
529 South Wabash Avenue, Chicago

Library of Congress
Catalog Card Number 68–22845

Printed in Great Britain by
Aberdeen University Press

Foreword

Thirty years ago I remarked, in the preface to a volume containing a reconstruction of the library collected by Edward Gibbon, that, though the mind of Man is recorded in his books, it was seldom profitable to list the books owned by a single person. The collector's mind must have been of very unusual distinction for the exercise to be of any real value. This view was supported by the small number of individual libraries that had been studied in this way, obvious examples being those of Dean Swift, Dr Johnson and Gibbon. The superficiality of my observation has now been demonstrated by Dr R. H. MacDonald in his reconstruction and fruitful study of the library collected by William Drummond of Hawthornden. It is clear that Drummond's mind was not of the order of distinction possessed by the great men mentioned above; nevertheless it is equally clear that the task of listing his books has been superlatively worth while when carried through with the learning, industry and perception applied to it by Dr MacDonald. By taking advantage of the rare chance of having access to materials adequate for making a reasonably complete reconstruction of the library, he has provided a body of evidence more than large enough to prove how wrong I was. Drummond was certainly a much more cultivated man than the average of the society in which he moved. He was a good classical scholar and a man of wide interests, who had profited by brief travel in Europe. He had a number of volumes of English poetry to his credit and from these he was careful to eliminate any trace of the provincialism into which a Scottish laird might have fallen. He enjoyed the friendship of men such as Sir William Alexander and Ben Jonson, who had visited Drummond when he came on foot to Scotland in 1619.

Drummond's mind was therefore far from commonplace, though Dr MacDonald is careful not to make any exaggerated claims on his behalf. Indeed, he rather emphasizes that Drummond, though a melodious versifier, was an acknowledged borrower and imitator; even his best known prose piece, *A cypresse grove* (1619), is characterized as 'a mosaic of echoes'.

Drummond was, in fact, pre-eminent as a book collector who put his books to such good use that he became one of the best read men of his time. A number of his 'reading lists' for successive years have survived and provide convincing evidence of the pleasure he took in reading widely in English, French, Italian and Spanish literature, as well as very extensively in Latin, using both classical and neo-Latin texts.

Having compiled his catalogue of Drummond's books and manuscripts to a total of 1405 titles, thus accounting, by his own estimate, for 85 per cent of the whole, Dr MacDonald is able to take a wide and interesting survey of its implications, and he rightly sums up the result as providing 'a slice of intellectual history' and a rarely appetizing slice it is in view of the period covered by Drummond immediately after the year 1600.

Geoffrey Keynes

Contents

Preface

This book owes more than most to the knowledge of others. My deepest debt is to the late Professor John Butt: it was his idea that a catalogue of Drummond's library should be printed; it was with his guidance that I began work, and with his encouragement that I planned to do what I have done.

I have gone on accumulating debts. My detective work on Drummond's book titles would have been quite haphazard had I not been helped by many scholars. Mr C. F. Finlayson of Edinburgh University Library was a fund of knowledge; Professor I. D. McFarlane, Professor Dominica Legge and Mr Peter Sharratt told me the authors of many of the French titles, and others I had from Professor V. L. Saulnier and Mme J. Veyrin-Forrer. Professor Mario M. Rossi and Mr Denis Rhodes traced some of the more obscure Italian works. The late Professor William A. Jackson threw open his files on the revised *Short-title catalogue* to my enquiries, and later Miss Katherine Pantzer carried on the spirit of Harvard generosity by not only identifying a dozen or more titles but also providing the latest bibliographical information on them and a score of others.

The catalogue would have been much thinner had not scholars both in this country and in the United States answered my requests for information on the location of Drummond's books in other libraries. The late Dr F. S. Ferguson generously sent me his entire dossier on Drummond and I at once had eight new titles listed in old sale catalogues. Dr John Durkan told me of two of Drummond's books lying unnoticed under my nose, on the shelves of Edinburgh University Library. Others I would like to thank are H. M. Adams, J. R. Barker, N. W. Bawcutt, J. M. G. Blakiston, Richard J. Durling, Bent Juel-Jensen, Sir Geoffrey Keynes, James G. McManaway, Dr J. H. P. Pafford, Dr R. A. Sayce and those private collectors mentioned in the catalogue. One fact emerged from my enquiries around the major libraries: very few librarians, either here or in the United States, have made a systematic search of their older stock for interesting provenance.

I was saved from a host of errors and solecisms by those who read all or part of my typescript: Professor Denys Hay, Miss Winifred Maynard, Professor John MacQueen, Dr Eric Forbes and Dennis Walder. To Hugh Cullen, for much assistance generously given, I am very grateful. The following I imposed upon by asking them to check parts of the catalogue itself: Margaret Allan, Peter Berwick, Dr Robert Donaldson, Glynne Heywood and Ronald Thompson. Alan Bell provided me with some valuable, last-minute information.

I would like to thank the Edinburgh Bibliographical Society for permission to include in my text the bulk of a paper read before them. Finally, I owe a debt to the University of Edinburgh for supporting me over the three years I took to find out who Drummond of Hawthornden was, and just which books he had in his library.

R. H. MacDonald
Carleton University

List of Illustrations

ACKNOWLEDGEMENTS
The publishers are grateful to the University Libraries of Edinburgh
and Dundee, and to the National Library of Scotland for permission
to reproduce items from Drummond's books and manuscripts.

1. William Drummond of Hawthornden. Drummond
holds a scroll of *Flowres of Sion*; his philosophical
work, *A cypresse grove*, stands open on the left, while
behind him can be seen his library. From an
anonymous painting on wood, dated 1623.

AVCTARIVM

BIBLIOTHECAE

EDINBVRGENÆ,

ſive

Catalogus Librorum quos

Guilielmus Drummondus ab

Hawthornden Bibliothecæ

D. D. Q. Anno. 1627.

EDINBVRGI,

Excudebant Hæredes Andreæ Hart, 1627.

Introduction

The main part of this book is a catalogue of a private library collected in the first quarter of the seventeenth century. Its owner, William Drummond of Hawthornden, has nowadays the misfortune of being a well-established footnote, familiar to students of English literature, if at all, as the recorder of Ben Jonson's opinions. His own poetry finds its way into anthologies, though as a whole it is seldom read. Drummond is a name, but his fame is dim.

Why then should one be troubled with a catalogue of his books? Certainly there is some interest in investigating his literary education, and in discovering the models for his poetry. But this one may take as gratuitous, and look instead at the wider importance of this collection.

Drummond's library is a sample of early seventeenth-century taste, one man's choice, but balanced and satisfyingly complete. It was collected in an age when it was still possible to take all learning for one's province, and when all that learning could be assembled without great expense on the shelves of one room. Drummond's interests were typically catholic. His command of languages was unusual, but if in this he had more ability than had his intellectual contemporaries, his taste was nevertheless representative. He followed the fashions, but he did not forget the academic authorities in each field of learning. Nor can he be regarded as eccentric or especially scholarly: his considerable knowledge of the classics was commonplace at the time, and other educated men followed the courtly fashion by adding fluency in Italian, French and Spanish to their accomplishments.

This catalogue is important as a slice of intellectual history: here we can see, without the distortions of modern taste, the sort of books that were read by a contemporary of Shakespeare and Jonson; the collection is small enough to be manageable, and large enough to cover the (then) major departments of knowledge. Beyond this Drummond's library can tell us much else. It is a reminder of the new conditions of the book trade—it is full of cheap, small, second-hand books. It shows where most books came from at the time—the great centres of Frankfort, Paris, Lyons or Venice—and how little of worth was actually printed in London. The library is full of the products of the great humanist, scholarly printers: Aldus, the

3. Hound. Henri de Ferrières, *Le roy modus* (Cat. 1039).

2. Title-page. *Auctarium bibliothecae Edinburgenae . . .* (Edinburgh 1627). This is a catalogue of Drummond's first donation to Edinburgh University Library.

1

1. The basic work on English libraries is Sears Jayne *Library catalogues of the English Renaissance* (Berkeley 1956), which surveys institutional and private libraries and their catalogues between the years 1500 and 1640. Jayne found most of his catalogues in Oxford and Cambridge college inventories—a natural place for them to be preserved—and his survey, admirable as it is, has the disadvantage of quantitative statistics: printed books are printed books, there is no distinction between the classics and ephemera. Jayne includes only a few Scottish catalogues. Much information can also be found in Archer Taylor's *Book catalogues* (Chicago 1957) and Raymond Irwin's series on the English library, *The origins of the English library* (London 1958), *The heritage of the English library* (London 1964) and *The English library* (London 1966). See also Julian Sharman *The library of Mary Queen of Scots* (London 1889); G.F. Warner 'The library of James VI' in *Publications of the Scottish Historical Society, Miscellany* I (1893) xxxi-lxx; W.O. Hassall 'A catalogue of the library of Sir Edward Coke' in *Yale Law Library Publications* XII (1950); G.R. Batho 'The library of the "Wizard" Earl: Henry Percy Ninth Earl of Northumberland' in *The Library* XV, 246-61. Knyvett's catalogue of about 1,500 printed books (my count; 300 less than Jayne's) is in Cambridge University Library MS. Ff. 2. 30. Articles describing smaller collections have appeared frequently in *The Library*; see, for example, Andrew Anderson 'The books and interests of Henry, Lord Stafford (1501-1563)' XXI (1966) 87-114 and Vernon F. Snow 'An inventory of the Lord General's library, 1646' XXI (1966) 115-23. See also Sears Jayne and Francis R. Johnson (eds.) *The Lumley library* (British Museum Publications, London 1956) and Andrew G. Watson *The library of Sir Simonds D'Ewes* (British Museum Publications, London 1966). Numerous notes have been printed on the books of literary and academic owners of the period, though few of these collections are large. Notable are Adam Bothwell's library of some 400 books in 1594, Annie Cameron (ed.) in *Warrender Papers* II (Scot. Hist. Soc., Edinburgh 1932) 396-413; Scipio Le Squyer's 492 printed books in *Bulletin of the John Rylands Library* XXV (1941) 137-64. Part of Dr John Dee's large collection of 2,500 printed books is listed in E.R.G. Taylor *Tudor geography* (London 1930). Continental libraries of the time were on the whole considerably bigger, for example the famous De Thou library. More comparable in

Estiennes, Plantin. It shows that cheapness did not mean inaccuracy, or lack of beauty, and by contrast with their French and Italian fellow craftsmen, it shows the inadequacies of the English artisans. It shows the still-strong position of Latin as the learned tongue, and how in each of the learned branches of knowledge (theology, philosophy, law, medicine, poetry and belles-lettres) Latin guaranteed an international audience. It shows what was printed in the vernaculars, and how the readers of literature, trained through Latin to discount national barriers, were eager to read, understand and imitate from the Italian and French authors. It shows—far better than any academic or public collection—the wider variety of popular stuff printed, bought, and read (but excluded from formal libraries like Sir Thomas Bodley's): here is everything from satires on the Jesuits to travel guides; from the account of the capture and hanging of a pickpocket to a description of the manufacture of silk. Here are accounts of the voyages of discovery and the settlements in America, romances, controversies, sermons, dictionaries, handbooks of health and of letter-writing, the secrets of Merlin, astrologies, prognostications, catechisms—a choice of the trivia and refuse of the time, but valuable as much for its rarity as for the interest and information it adds to the library.

Drummond's library was not unusually large for his time, but because it is a rare survival with few if any rivals, it is especially valuable today. To add to its importance, more than half the library still exists, mostly on the shelves of Edinburgh University Library. It is in good condition (such addenda as maps and diagrams are usually extant), and from a bibliographical point of view there are many rarities in the collection.

Very few libraries or their catalogues have survived from the sixteenth and early seventeenth centuries, and, of those that have, none is quite like Drummond's. Lists of the books of Mary Queen of Scots and James VI have been printed: these are interesting for what they reveal of the education and taste of their royal owners, but these owners were hardly typical. More comparable collections to Drummond's are those of Sir Edward Coke and Henry Percy, ninth Earl of Northumberland, or that of Sir Thomas Knyvett—but of these only Coke's catalogue has been published. The Lumley library stands alone, and its catalogue has been edited and printed; but again, it is hardly the typical private library, for it represents the accumulations of several immensely rich and aristocratic owners. And the same may be said of the library of Sir Simonds D'Ewes, with its huge manuscript and antiquarian section, and its rather small and ordinary group of printed books.[1]

The records of private libraries survive for a number of reasons: if the owner was an important or famous man he was probably wealthy, so that his property was secure (after his death); again, an owner of some standing might donate all or some of his books to an institution which would preserve them; or the owner might have been a writer, from whose works scholars could deduce which books he must have read. In the first of these categories are the royal libraries; in the second the collections of Clement Litil at Edinburgh or of Thomas Reid at Aberdeen; and in the third, the books of Ben Jonson, John Donne or Robert Burton[1]—to mention only a few examples. These are all so different, and their owners so different, that it is extremely hard to compare them with Drummond's. As far as the number of titles is concerned, Drummond's library was quite extensive; but this total includes many small pieces such as congratulatory poems (but then Knyvett had many duplicate copies). Drummond's books would be certainly outweighed by those of his contemporaries; Clement Litil's, though less than a fifth in number, would be quite as heavy, being nearly all solid theological folio volumes. Drummond bought his books to read, not to display on his shelves, and with little money he made the best of two new features of the book trade: small, cheap editions of classical and scholarly books, and the second-hand market.

This catalogue of Drummond's library has been made up from the following sources: first, the books Drummond gave to Edinburgh University Library that still exist, and are still at Edinburgh; second, those that were given to Edinburgh but are now lost—the titles of these have been identified from the catalogue made of his first donation to the university library in 1626[2]; third, books with Drummond's signature now in other libraries; fourth, books signed by Drummond entered in sale catalogues; fifth, the MS catalogue of his library made by Drummond himself in 1611; sixth, other lists also preserved in the Hawthornden MSS; and seventh and last, information in the old shelf catalogues and notes of the University Library. I think that from these various sources I have accounted for about eighty-five per cent of Drummond's library. It is fortunate that he had the habit of writing his name in his books.

The arrangement of the catalogue is based on Drummond's own catalogue of 1611, all books from every source being placed together within language and subject in alphabetical order. I have tried as far as possible to put books where Drummond would have put them. This was not always easy—the line between theology and philosophy is not always distinct; and if there are some odd choices here and there they all (I hope) follow Drummond's own inventory, and can be explained in terms of Drummond's own logic.

I have appended to the catalogue some lists of books Drummond read between 1606 and 1614, his *List of Comedies*, and the titles of the books he made notes on. These fill out this picture of one man's pleasure and study.

I have tried in the essays that accompany the catalogue to describe briefly the intellectual world of the educated man of Drummond's time: what he would learn in school and university, what he would read, what he would believe and accept as common knowledge. I have not given an exhaustive account of theology, law, medicine or any of the other subjects, but only indicated which were the usual Renaissance authorities in each field.

My method has been this: I have used the modern authorities in their respective disciplines to establish the basic facts, and I have then illustrated these facts from Drummond's books (sometimes Drummond's books raise a question or two, and here I have to use

size and content to Drummond's is that of Philip van Marnix, whose sale catalogue of 1599 is reprinted in *Godsdienstige en kerkelijke geschriften* (The Hague 1871-8) III, 123-80, or that of Garcilaso de la Vega, José Durand (ed.) 'La biblioteca del Inca' in *Nueva revista de filologia hispánica* II (1948) 239-64.

1. An inventory of Litil's books is in the *Maitland Club Miscellany* I (1834) 287-301. Reid, who was Latin secretary to James VI and I, gave his library to Marischal College, Aberdeen, in 1624. According to Gordon of Rothiemay in his *History of Scottish affairs* it was 'the best library that ever the north pairtes of Scotland saw', Spalding Club (Aberdeen 1841). An MS catalogue of Reid's books is in Aberdeen University Library. About 1,350 titles are listed, mostly Latin and Greek classics, Renaissance criticism, natural and moral philosophy, with some history, grammar, theology and poetry. There are a few books in English. Ben Jonson's library has been partially reconstructed by C.H. Herford and Percy Simpson in their edition of the *Works of Ben Jonson* (Oxford 1925) I, pp. 250-71 and XI, pp. 593-603. Some of Donne's books are listed in Geoffrey Keynes *Bibliography of Dr John Donne* (2nd ed., London 1932) and in Geoffrey Keynes 'Books from Donne's library' *Proc. CBS* I (1949) 64-8. Burton's collection is printed in S. Gibson and F.R.D. Needham 'Two lists of Burton's books', *Proc. CBS* (1925) 222-46. Burton left his books to the Bodleian and to Christ Church, Oxford, and most of them have survived, though they are dispersed. For a survey of Literary libraries, see A.N.L. Munby *The libraries of English men of letters* (Esdaile Memorial Lecture, The Library Association 1964). Three other MS catalogues make useful comparisons with Drummond's: that of John Rainold (Bodleian MS Wood D. 10), about 1,800 books, mainly printed, mostly theological and classical and split up in parcels of gifts to students, etc.; that of William Branthwaite (Gonville and Caius College MS 735/783), about 1,750 books, mainly printed, the large majority being theological, including many tracts, with some philosophy and classics; that of Sir Thomas Knyvett's collection (see fn. 1, above), about 1,500 printed books, some two-thirds in Latin, the rest French, Italian and English, with a few Spanish.

2. *Auctarium bibliothecæ Edinburgenæ siue catalogus librorum quos Gulielmus Drummondus ab Hawthornden bibliothecæ D.D.Q. anno 1627* (Edinburgh, heirs of A. Hart, 1627) STC 7246.

them as qualifying evidence in critical controversy). I have not limited myself to the titles in Drummond's library, but often mentioned others, particularly if they were important for a balanced view of the period. Drummond had a remarkably representative collection, but he had his gaps, such as Pliny's *Natural history* and Shakespeare's *Hamlet*. On the other hand, because a book is not listed in the catalogue, this does not mean that it is unrepresented in the library, for it may be hiding piecemeal in some anthology or collection. Drummond had many of these: Santa Cruz' *Floresta española*, the *Flores doctorum*, the *Sphinx philosophica*—collections of *sententiae* and pithy truths from writers old and new. Such works were popular. In fairness to Drummond we can assume he read much more than was in his library, yet, on the other hand, we can hardly be sure he even read all that was on his shelves. I have attempted too to point out tastes now forgotten—such as that for neo-Latin poetry—and to bring attention to books once popular and now ignored. At the same time I have looked for the gaps in the library. It is easy when examining catalogues to see those books one knows and to neglect those one does not: by intention, I have said nothing about such as Homer, Plutarch, Dante, Rabelais, More, Machiavelli, Montaigne or Bacon: Drummond owned their works, and this is important, but it seemed superfluous to do more than mention it.

Drummond like many of his contemporaries treated his Greek and Hebrew books as ornaments in his library—books a man liked to have, though perhaps not to read; I have, therefore, described them only incidentally. Significantly, most of the Greek books are either in an edition with a Latin translation, or there is a Latin or vernacular version of the same work. The few Hebrew books are an adjunct to theology. I have similarly examined specialist books printed in the vernaculars only where they fitted into my discussion of their Latin counterparts, for with one or two exceptions (like Edward Wright's *The description and use of the spære*) they are translations or popularizations of the Latin works. Music I have neglected, for though Drummond was interested in the subject—he knew the Italian madrigal books, as his notes in his manuscripts show—the only survival of this diversion is Nicholas Yonge's *Musica transalpina*.

Drummond's manuscripts are only an appendage. He was certainly interested in collecting historical records (in the University Library at Edinburgh are his copies of some royal letters), but though there are some interesting pieces—Sidney's Astrophil and Stella or Fowler's Triumphs of Petrarch, for example—there are few things of much note.

The popular material in Drummond's library needs less introduction, and here the catalogue can speak for itself. It would have been pleasant to investigate the history of the giant Theutobocus, or to look into the French silk industry, or to trace the route from Venice to the Holy Land, but this was beyond my self-set purpose. Not that these books should be ignored: they are all part of the evidence, all part of what an intelligent man might be interested in and be able to buy; but they are curiosities, and they do not need so much explaining as, for instance, the *Emerald tables* of Hermes Trismegistus.

4. Zanitonella and the author.
Merlinus Cocaius,
Opus macaronicorum
(Cat. 1214).

4

Drummond would have been surprised by this present publication of his catalogue: he had no illusions about his library's merit; it was adequate; if he had been richer he could have afforded bigger books and more of them. He might have been flattered at being celebrated as a wise collector; yet, with his patrician sympathies, he would be alarmed at being thought ordinary or typical, and at his books being labelled a sample of his contemporaries' taste.

5. The making of silk. Jean-Baptiste Le Tellier, *Memoires et instructions pour l'establissement des meuriers* (Cat. 1088).

PART I

Drummond and his Books

Life and Interests

William Drummond was born in 1585 and died in 1649.[1] His father had a minor position at court; his uncle was secretary to the queen. Drummond graduated from the 'Tounis College' (Edinburgh University) in 1605, and the next year went to London and on to France. He visited Paris and studied law at the university of Bourges until he returned to Scotland in 1608; he made one more trip to London in 1610, but came back before the death of his father that year. As the eldest son he inherited the family estate of Hawthornden, which lies on the river Esk seven miles south from Edinburgh.

The rest of his life Drummond seems to have spent managing his house and lands, leading the life of a laird of modest income. From the surviving legal and administrative papers of the estate we can gather the familiar information of the routine of this life: rents being collected, loans being sought, tithes and taxes rendered. Hawthornden lands were not extensive, but the Drummonds had property at Linlithgow, and their coalmines must have yielded some ready cash; certainly Drummond found enough to buy books and to build himself a new house at Hawthornden. To this unexceptional example of the small Scottish laird must be added Drummond the literary man, the poet, historian, and pamphleteer. Traditionally Drummond has been portrayed in the most romantic terms—the scholar poet in his study, the writer of posed, polished, sweet-sounding verse, a recluse from the vulgar world. Disappointed in love, descending to a philosophic melancholy, scorning worldly ambitions—Drummond has always fitted conveniently into the conventional ideal of the gentleman poet.

This fantasy is inherently implausible, but it is hard to disprove it convincingly. In the first place, Drummond himself played the romantic part in his youth; for him, being a poet involved more than writing poetry. He was a gentleman fashioning himself to the Renaissance pattern; he had read Castiglione, della Casa and Guazzo. He admired Sidney, and he imitated Petrarch. His own poetry carefully followed the poetic conventions, and as far as he was able his own life was modelled on the convention of the humanist poet. He wrote and published his poetry before he was thirty-five, then turned to history and politics. He did not write much, and what he wrote was excessively imitative; but he spent hours in his study, and

1. Bishop John Sage's short life which prefaced his edition of Drummond's *Works* (1711) is the first source of biographical detail. His facts however are not to be trusted. David Masson's *Drummond of Hawthornden* (London 1873) is readable, reliable and judicial, though Masson gives way too much to conjecture when facts are scarce. Drummond's own Memorials—a MS. record of family data and important personal events—has not been printed, having only recently turned up in a small collection of his books found in the Brechin Diocesan Library. Other details on Drummond's life can be deduced from the private accounts and legal records of the family: the legal records are complete, but only some fragments of personal trivia—debt discharges, bills and records of tithes received—survive in the poet's hand. Drummond's literary remains survive in abundance; known as the Hawthornden MSS, they contain a manuscript history of his education and literary interests, draft copies of his *James the I, II, III, IV, V* and literary notes of his uncle, William Fowler. The Hawthornden MSS are now in the National Library of Scotland. They are described in some detail by David Laing in *Archaeologia Scotica* IV (Trans. of the Society of Antiquaries of Scotland, Edinburgh 1857), 57-116.

his inclinations were sincerely literary. He read extensively, and he took detailed notes of much that he read: the Hawthornden MSS are full not only of his lecture notes from Edinburgh and Bourges, but of his comments on plays, poems and curiosities. Here is the fruit of years of scribbling, the record of a dedicated pursuit of the usual trifles with which gentlemen then filled their leisure: the courtly pastimes—anagrams, impresas, devices and genealogy.

In the second half of his life Drummond abandoned poetry in favour of history, and passed his study hours in writing his history of *The Five James* and a number of political pamphlets (which though not printed until after his death seem to have been circulated among his friends). Politically he was a conservative, a monarchist, bitterly opposed to the new democracy, to all opponents of order, unsympathetic to the levellers in the Kirk. Reluctantly he was forced to accept the Covenant. Like other lairds he must have suffered from the economic confusions of the 1640s; the legal records show that the estate began to be heavily mortgaged at this time. At the age of forty-six Drummond married and subsequently had five sons and four daughters; his preoccupations towards the end of his life seem to have been increasingly domestic.

Drummond did little in matters of state affairs and so, although the public records during his lifetime have survived, he makes only trivial appearances in them. He did much private business, and left a mass of manuscripts to prove it, but these only fill out what is already known of his education and his literary and intellectual pleasures. This vacuum has been filled by his biographers in their various ways, and a good part of this filling is invention. The first of these writers, Bishop Sage, made Drummond into a Cavalier poet and man of letters, whose early retirement from law was all that prevented him from decorating the highest offices of that profession, a romantic lover whose grief for his dead betrothed sent him on a Grand Tour of Europe to forget, who on his return kept scholarly company with the best wits of the land, who was an intimate of Jonson and Drayton and their fellows and was yet equally familiar with nobility, who was not one for dancing but played his lute 'to Admiration'. More important in 1711 and for an editor of Sage's political persuasion, Drummond was 'a true Tory, and seriously concern'd about the HEREDITARY RIGHT and MONARCHY'.[1]

In his full-length life David Masson was forced to follow Sage for want of a better source of information, though he did this with reservations. To fill out his pages he fell back upon conjecture and speculation: his Drummond is a misty, retiring figure, a sweet Petrarchan poet and conservative pamphleteer, who pops up now and again among the interminable and complicated controversies of seventeenth-century Scotland, to deliver congratulatory verse and rather feeble polemics.[2] More recently French Rowe Fogle has made much of Sage's story of Miss Cunningham—the 'Beautiful young Lady' who was betrothed and about to marry Drummond when 'she took a Fever, and was suddenly snatch'd away by it, to his great Grief and Sorrow'. Drummond is supposed to have written his *Poems*, the first half to celebrate her in life, the second, in death.[3]

1. *The works of William Drummond, of Hawthornden*, ed. by Thomas Ruddiman and John Sage (Edinburgh 1711), from the *Preface* supposed to be by Sage.

2. David Masson *Drummond of Hawthornden* (London 1873).

3. French Rowe Fogle *A critical study of William Drummond of Hawthornden* (New York 1952). The phrases quoted are Sage's.

It is difficult to know how much of this to believe. As I show later (when discussing Drummond's poetry) the romantic story of his love has no relation to his poems, for Drummond wrote his funeral sonnets some time before Miss Cunningham actually died. Bishop Sage's account is full of invention: in fact Drummond never travelled through Europe to Rome, never joined Jonson and Drayton in London, and certainly never composed witty little verses in their company. He may have played the lute—he says so in one of his formal 'Familiar Letters'—but he was more the laird than the complete gentleman.

In spite of its speculative content, Masson's biography does fill out the picture, though some of the facts revealed fit neither the conception of laird or poet. What, for instance, are we to make of Drummond's patent, granted to him in 1627, to cover the invention and construction of sixteen mechanical and military contrivances? Admittedly they seem more or less fanciful, decorated with imposing Greek names, ranging from the *Glasses of Archimedes*, by which fleets at sea could be set on fire, to the *Ship-Fountain*, an instrument for turning salt water into fresh. Needless to say, these inventions, including the one which mastered perpetual motion, were never developed. There is no record that Drummond did anything more about them.

To Masson's vague poet some everyday detail can be added, for a diary of Drummond's (though it is disappointingly only a record of births and deaths and illnesses and not much else) has recently turned up.[1] These Memorials give an impression of a thoroughly humourless, painstaking and unimaginative man, quite unliterary, recording for his family's sake their entrances into and exits from a hostile world. (In his private writing Drummond was strikingly ingenuous, but then he was certainly not writing such trivia for posterity.) Added to these statistics of family history, which incidentally include a startling picture of the uncertain and too often short life of children, and of the ravages that smallpox could make upon whole families, is a record of events in Drummond's own life. Apart from the occasions when he was made a burgess of various towns, these events are misfortunes, mostly accidents and illnesses, so that this part of the Memorials reads very much like a hypochondriac's diary. In September 1602 'by reading Heliodorus and other bookes the 17 yere of my age I had a pain in myne eyes for the space of eight dayes' and became nearly blind. A day in 1604 was 'fatall' (disastrous) 'by bonfires'. On 13 November 1608, 'about twelfe a clocke in the night not 20 miles from Scarsbrough returning to Scotland' his ship collided with another, and he was in danger of drowning. In 1620 he had 'pleurisie' on his right side; in 1621 while at supper he 'euanished in a sown almost dead'. On 12 March 1625 he 'suspected my selfe to haue beene poysoned', and the next year he fell from a high stair and was in danger of his life. In 1629 he suffered a blow on his right hand; in 1630 he almost broke his collar bone by the fall of a horse; in 1631 his horse miscarried over coalpits. The 9 January 1631 was mysteriously 'fatall but happy'. From this time on his illnesses became more serious and more severe. In September

1. MS at Dundee University Library. It covers most of Drummond's adult life, and appears to have been begun by him some time before he reached thirty, and continued until shortly before his death, though only in the barest detail.

1632 he had colick—'more terrible than death'—which came again in July 1636 and continued 'in extremitie 12 houres' nor ceased until a month later when he 'voyded a great grauell stone'. In April the next year 'I first knew what the gutte was' (it stayed fourteen days on his right foot)—and so on. The catalogue continues, with gout, fevers and colicks recurring, until the last entry, when in August 1647, two years before his death 'of a sort of grauell' (as his son, who continued the Memorials, records), his horse again fell, and again he almost broke a collar bone.

Apart from this recital of illness there is little else in the Memorials. On 21 May 1634 at ten in the evening Drummond (presumably gambling) lost 'many obligationes' whose interest alone was above 3,000 merkes; it was, as he noted, 'fatall'. The days on which he was made burgess—of Edinburgh, the Canongate, Haddington and Linlithgow—stand out, for those are the only entries of public events. From their isolation it seems he was proud of being so honoured: his burgess ticket from Edinburgh was given to him in gold letter, and his admission was celebrated at a banquet beginning at seven and lasting till almost ten o'clock. (This happened on 8 December 1626, which must have been shortly after his gift of some five hundred of his books to the Tounis College.)

The little that one can add to the sparse detail already known about Drummond does nothing to add to his stature, although it makes him more recognizably human. From his library and his manuscripts he is clearly the scholarly, pedantic, surpassingly well-read literary man, the 'Master and Judge of all polite learning' of Bishop Sage's eulogy. He is the lover of 'courtly trifles'—anagrams, impresas, poems in curious shapes; the collector of vocabulary, wonders, lore, and medicines. To his friends and fellow lairds he seems to have served as a literary arbiter: for them he gave critical opinions on books, and when asked he wrote their epitaphs. He was something of a snob. He flattered his social superiors by presenting them with gilt bound copies of his poems, by explaining the intricacies of devices to the Earl of Perth, and for that same nobleman (head of the Drummonds) writing an involved genealogy. At his marriage he took satisfaction that Lady Jane Mackenzie, 'daughter to the Earle of Seafort who was after marryed to the Earle of Catnesse eldest sone', was his wife's bridesmaid.[1]

Yet this side of Drummond—the self-consciously lettered gentleman using his learning and taste to make his place in society, the poet honoured and called upon to supply verse for the great occasion, the linguist, historian and benefactor—is in a way only the public personality that Drummond aspired to. His biographers picture him as a retiring contemplative man, who retreated by choice from the status that his genius would naturally have won him. To me this seems false: Drummond's purse was too small to permit him great ambitions; his burgess tickets are some proof that he exploited what local position he could. Nor was he always the philosopher hermit, the romantic scholar poet locked in his study from the affairs of this world—he seems to have been a man as other men, to have quarrelled with his mother over his inheritance, and to have raised a family of

1. From the Memorials.

bastards in the years before his marriage.[1]

It is, however, his character as a book collector that should really concern us now, and in many ways Drummond here has no rival. He had enough money to buy books — at least cheap books — and he had the education and discrimination to choose well. His isolated position as a literary man in the cultural poverty of Scotland meant that he had to supply himself with what he wanted, and together with his natural conservatism ensured that he bought in depth as well as in quantity. He looked for accepted opinion, and though he knew the latest ideas still he valued the old. Thus in astronomy he had read of Copernicus, but he trusted Ptolemy.[2] In medicine he owned Fernel, but also Galen; in philosophy Plato as well as Aristotle. He liked a little of everything; he was interested in medieval writers, in the ancients, in the men of his own day. He liked to read both sides of the controversies: his Protestant books are balanced by his Catholic ones. In literature his own inclination towards Petrarchanism 'smelled too much of the schools' (as Ben Jonson told him[3]); it shows up strongly among his Italian and French books, but it is balanced by his up-to-date selection of English poets: Marlowe, Shakespeare, Drayton, Daniel, Peele, Donne and a great many lesser lights. Nor was Drummond without discrimination in his book-buying and his reading, for his marginalia on, for instance, Alexander's *Monarchicke tragedies* prove that he knew his books very well, read them critically, and took great delight in detecting borrowings and literary imitation.

1. For the quarrel with his mother see the *Register of the Privy Council of Scotland* IX, 704-5 and IX, 686. His natural children, two girls and a boy, are mentioned in the Memorials. They were born between 1625 and 1628 (while Drummond in Sage's account was on his Grand Tour of Europe). Only the boy Lodovick survived infancy.

2. Drummond read of the 'new astronomy' some time between 1618 and 1632 when he had printed his *Cypress grove*. See R. Ellrodt (ed.) *A midnight's trance* (Luttrell Society Reprints, Oxford 1952) p. xxi.

3. 'Informations be Ben Jonson to W.D., when he cam to Scotland upon foot 1619', from a MS. copy made by Sir Robert Sibbald, printed in Herford and Simpson, I, pp. 128-78.

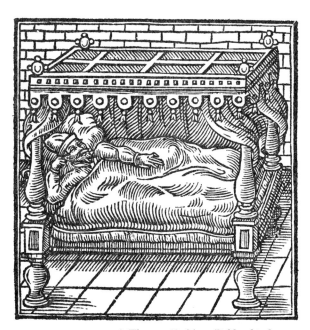

6. Thomas Dekker, *Dekker his dreame* (Cat. 745).

1. For Scottish education see Alexander Morgan *Scottish university studies* (London 1933) and the histories and records of the universities quoted below. W.H. Woodward *Studies in education during the age of the Renaissance* (Cambridge 1906), is still useful for general information, as is Stephen d'Irsay *Histoire des universitiés françaises et étrangères* (Paris 1933). The essays by Craig R. Thompson 'Schools in Tudor England' and 'Universities in Tudor England' in *Life and letters in Tudor and Stuart England* (Folger series, Ithaca 1962) are a useful introduction.
For more detail see Joan Simon *Education and society in Tudor England* (Cambridge 1966), Mark Curtis *Oxford and Cambridge in transition* (Oxford 1959), Lawrence Stone *The crisis of the aristocracy* (Oxford 1965 ch. XII, and Jack Hexter 'The education of the aristocracy in the Renaissance' in *Reappraisals in history* (London 1961). Without entering into the controversy over university education—particularly that of the arisocracy—in England, which is outside the scope of this essay, it is worth noticing that the thesis put forward by Mark Curtis has not gained complete acceptance, and some historians feel that much less cultural change took place at Oxford and Cambridge than he suggests. The routine of a university should not be judged by its brilliant eccentrics, and Gresham College, as Christopher Hill has shown in *Intellectual origins of the English revolution* (Oxford 1965) has much better claims as the cradle of English scientific thought. Kenneth Charlton *Education in Renaissance England* (London 1965), in which the author doubts whether humanism did have much effect on the English universities, is a most useful corrective to those who have perhaps over-emphasized the new at the expense of the old. His findings agree with my own conclusions.

Drummond was educated at Edinburgh's High School and then at its newly founded university, the Tounis College, from which he graduated in 1605 at the age of twenty as a Master of Arts. We have a great deal of information about the education of this time: we know the curricula of the Scottish universities, we know most of the texts which were used, we know the teaching routine and the way the students lived. Some lecture notes from the period have survived, and we have the printed copies of a number of the group theses presented by the classes upon graduation. Also we can compare what we know of Scottish education with that of other countries—and much has been written recently on the subject, particularly on English education.[1] We should thus be in a position to decide fairly precisely just what sort of education a man of Drummond's time did have, were it not that in spite of the amount of information available (or perhaps because of it) there is still some disagreement about the nature of late Renaissance education, and especially, about the quality of the teaching and the general enlightenment or otherwise of educational attitudes.

At heart this boils down to an argument about the amount of humanism or scholasticism in the curriculum, and at its more sophisticated levels, an argument on the nature of humanism and scholasticism, and whether the first can be regarded as progressive, and the second as reactionary. The problem begins with the basic facts of higher education in the last half of the sixteenth century and the first half of the seventeenth, when, in contrast to the usual conception of that age as one which enjoyed the first fruits of humanist scholarship and thought—the classics appreciated anew, Greek and Hebrew studied and read, textual criticism done scientifically with historical insight—the universities continued to teach to the exclusion of almost everything else the one author traditionally associated with scholasticism: Aristotle. Some historians have tried to play down this evident supremacy of Aristotle in the curriculum by stressing the additions made by humanist reformers, such as the teaching of Greek and Hebrew, the new use of scholarly texts which presented an Aristotle stripped of the customary commentaries of the Doctors, and the inclusion of classical literature and the latest medicine or geography. Some have seen the enthusiasm for the

teaching of Ramus at the universities as a hard blow against scholasticism and Aristotelianism; for had not Ramus supposedly begun
his career by putting forward the astounding proposition that everything that Aristotle said was false? Other scholars have wondered
whether there was in fact much change at all, and whether (in spite
of every evidence that this was so) Aristotle was not in fact as
supreme in 1600 as in 1500. To this last group I adhere, since the
details of Drummond's experience at Edinburgh seem clearly to
strengthen their case.

In Drummond's day the systems of higher education in Europe
were not markedly different from country to country, and since
Latin was used generally as the language of instruction, a student
could attend any university with equal ease. (Scots, following George
Buchanan, prided themselves that their pronouncement of Latin was
more correct than the common English usage; in this as in other
matters such as law, their outlook was continental.) The chief
differences in Scottish education were due to two facts: Scotland's
religion and her poverty. Religion—as is discussed below—meant
that education was organized on formal Calvinist lines, although, as
is clear from Drummond's library, this policy did not mean that
Scottish universities were able to do without textbooks written by
Catholic scholars. In England a man might be given an education to
suit his social status. Those who could afford it bought what they
wanted, and the aristocracy were able to read the liberal arts, go on
the Grand Tour, and have private tutors. Oxford and Cambridge
welcomed them whether or not they intended to take their degrees.
Scottish universities were in contrast more like strict seminaries, and
social differences between students had little effect on the programme
of studies. And as in other universities all over Europe, these studies
were based on Aristotle.

The Protestant reformers of the Scottish Kirk had recognized the
importance of education in training the ministers and schooling the
laity, and after the Reformation was established the universities were
their first concern. In 1574 Andrew Melville came back from Geneva
to set about reorganizing education on Genevan lines. Given the
choice of becoming principal master of Glasgow or St Andrews, he
chose Glasgow and immediately began to plan a new curriculum
drafted on the best humanist principles. He trained his own faculty
at Glasgow and with their help the new learning spread to St
Andrews and Aberdeen. By 1582 when Edinburgh Town Council
was granted a charter to found their college, Melville's reformation
had quite established itself at the Scottish universities.[1]

Briefly this reformation broadened the traditional scope of
university education. There was now much emphasis on Greek, and
on its application to the textual study of both the ancient philosophers
and (which Melville in his holy zeal would have considered more
important) to the scriptures. Hebrew was studied to this same end.[2]
These innovations added to the curriculum; as important was the
stress now laid on pure and correct Latin. In the best humanist
manner more attention was paid to grammar and the proper use of
rhetoric; the slovenly Latin of the scholastics and the slangy speech

7. The scholars. Nicodemus Frischlin,
Priscianus vapulans (Cat. 289).

1. Morgan, pp. 133-4. For the early
history of Edinburgh university see
David B. Horn 'The origins of the
University of Edinburgh' in *The
University of Edinburgh Journal*
XXII (1965-6) 213-15 and 297-312.

2. Lectures were also given on
Syriac; Morgan, p. 137.

15

of their pupils were both attacked.

In the matter of formal instruction in philosophy Melville made a more controversial innovation. He had been a student in Paris under the great French logician and mathematician, Peter Ramus (Pierre de la Ramée).[1] Ramus had devised his own system of logic in opposition to the traditional Aristotelian dialectic; this system had met with much opposition from the ruling scholars of the Sorbonne and it had been the subject of bitter controversies for over a decade before the quarrel was partially resolved in Ramus' favour. Ramus' method does not on the face of it seem to merit the kind of bitter abuse it received, for as Father Ong has so decisively shown, it was essentially merely a re-organization of the same material for the sake of simplification.[2] Scholasticism was not replaced, it was instead made fit for another century of use. But Ramus was writing in an atmosphere where any tampering with Aristotle was seen as heresy, and indeed when his *Institutiones dialecticae* was first printed in 1543 it was at once banned.

In the light of Father Ong's work, Ramus' work and his influence on his contemporaries has had to be reconsidered. The famous thesis denouncing Aristotle — if it ever existed — must be taken as just another of the usual academic exercises, a routine practice in ingenuity and logic. Drummond, as I describe later, was busy at just the same game when he graduated in 1605. Ramus' humanism, too, must be taken with reservations. He was much influenced by humanist ideals, he admired Cicero and Virgil, and conducted numerous scholarly quarrels on such topics as the question of correct pronunciation, or the literary merits of Quintilian. He quoted the classics to reinforce his opinions and spurned the traditional medieval authorities, but behind this façade of humanism he was more indebted to standards of scholastic Aristotelianism such as Peter of Spain than to Plato or Cicero. Ramus was important because he was thought by his contemporaries to be important, especially for his opposition to the exclusive authority of Aristotle. His popularity in England, Scotland and Germany was due to men like Melville, who saw in Ramism a way of introducing humanistic principles into the schools of logic. It is now clear, however, that Ramism did this only to a very limited degree.

We can study the effect of Melville's reforms in the Scottish universities, by looking at the curriculum of Edinburgh, which has survived from the instruction given to the college by the Town Council in 1628 (some twenty-three years after Drummond graduated, but it is clear there was no significant change in the interval).[3] It is worth examining this curriculum closely, for not only does it provide an example of the formal (philosophy) education given at the time, but it is also reflected — not surprisingly — in almost every detail in Drummond's books.

The normal course of instruction in the university lasted four years, preceded by a year's course in 'humanitie'. The scholars entered the college from the High School at fourteen or fifteen (Drummond was fifteen in 1600, when he entered the Humanity class). This preliminary year was by way of a formal preparation for

1. For Ramus, see especially Walter J. Ong *Ramus, method, and the decay of dialogue* (Cambridge, Mass. 1958). Father Ong's work is invaluable for its detailed information on the actual, as against the apparent, nature of sixteenth-century education. In particular his re-assessment of Ramism as a different version of scholasticism makes a curriculum such as Edinburgh's more understandable.

2. It has been characterized by a modern scholar, as 'the old system applied perhaps more systematically'; T. W. Baldwin *William Shakspere's Small Latine and Lesse Greeke* II (Urbana 1944) p. 6. About the only real difference between Ramus' logic and Aristotle's, apart from its organization, was that of brevity, as Milton was to point out in his *Artis Logicae*. See Harris F. Fletcher *The intellectual development of John Milton* II (Urbana 1956; 1961) pp. 143-4. Father Ong, of course, expands this point with his usual pungency.

3. *University of Edinburgh: Charters, Statutes, and Acts of the Town Council and the Senatus 1583–1858* (Edinburgh 1937) pp. 110-17. Edinburgh's curriculum, it should be emphasized, was a normal one for the time. Much the same texts were used in other universities. In 1647 the curriculum of King's College, Aberdeen, was almost the same as Edinburgh's; *Fasti Aberdonenses* p. liv. For Cambridge see William T. Costello *The Scholastic curriculum at early seventeenth-century Cambridge* (Cambridge, Mass. 1958). For Padua see Paul Oskar Kristeller *La tradizione Aristotelica nel Rinascimento* (Padova 1962).

8. Amended orthography, William Bullokar, *Bullokars booke at large* (Cat. 715).

a.b.c.c.d.d.e.æ.e.f.g.g.h.i.k.l.l.m.m.n.n.ñ.o.ω.
p.ph.q.r.rſ.ſh.t.th.t.th.v.v.v.w.wh.x.y.z.z̃.&c.

A.a:B.b:C.c.c:Ch.ch:D.d:E.e.æ:E.e:F.f:G.g:G.g:
I.i:H.h:l.i.y:K.k:L.l:l.ſ:M.m.m:N.n:ñ:O.o:ω:P.p:
Ph.ph.f:Qu.q:R.r.r:S.ſ.ſʒ:Sh.ſh.ſh:T.t:Th.th:Th.th:
V.v.u:V.v.u.o.ω.ω:V.v.u:W.w:WH.wh:X.x:Y.y:Z.z.z̃:

He lyk adicionʒ ár vzed in this new amendment,
With lyk ſtrykʒ, prikʒ, & nótʒ alſo, with lyk vc of accent,
In wrytĩ hãd, az in the print, no-thing wantĩ but cõſent.

a.b.c.c.d.d.e.æ.e.f.g.g.h.i.k.l.l.l.m.m.n.n.ñ.o.ω.p.ph.
g.r.rſ.ſ.t.th.th.v.v.v.w.wh.x.y.z.z̃.&c.

A.a:B.b:C.c.c:Ch.ch:D.d:E.e.æ.E.e:F.f:G.g:G.g.g.
J.i:H.h:J.i.y:K.k:L.l.l.l:M.m.m:N.n:ñ:O.o:ω:P.p:
Ph.ph.f:Qu.q:R.r.r:S.ſ.ſʒ:Sh.ſh.ſh:T.t:Th.th.th.th:V.v.
u:V.v.u.o.ω.ω:V.v.u:W.w:WH.wh:X.x:Y.y:Z.z.z̃.&c.

Howʒ thæz figurʒ vnto your ſiht at first ſém too be ſtrang,
Ye may ſoon find by lyk hed, that dò no far way rang,
From the old vzd ortographʒ grét gayn iz in the chanʒ.

He vn-lerned woƦd may be excuzed,
Not wryting the nótʒ in grammar vzed.

The names of the letters according to this amendment of oƷtography, appéré in this Table, by the which ƥe map name the letters in the wƦitten Copies following.

a / a	b / b	cé / c	hé / c	ché / ch	d / d	e:ea / e:æ	æ / e
f / f	gé / g	ga / g turſí a into é.	hé / h	i / i	l / l	bl / l	
m / m	hñ / ñ	ñ / n	hñ / ñ	o / o	o:t:t between / ω	p / p	phé / ph
qué / q	r / r	rr / r	t / t	t / t	thé / th	thé / th	
p / p	oų / p	bé / u	to hé / u	tohé / u	r / r	pé / y	ʒé / ʒ

HEre haue ye, gentle Reader, the vſe of this amended oƷtography, in the Romaine, Italian, Chauncerie, and Secretarie handes, by the examples of which, any other hande may eaſily be framed with this oƷtography: aſſuring you that the ſame handes, being wƦitten with the pen, dœ excell theſe printed, which wƦitten handes, and the Court hand alſo, you map at any time hereafter ſé, at the houſe of the Ƥinter of this bœke, who (as alſo the Auƥoƶ of this bœke) deſireth to be boƦne withall foƦ a time, if any figure oƶ letter be not in his perfectneſſe, foƶ the charge is not ſmall, that bƦingeth all thinges to perfectnes in ſuch caſes. Ƥereafter (by the grace of God) and your gœd accepting of this greater char= ges ſhall not want to the full per= fecting hereof

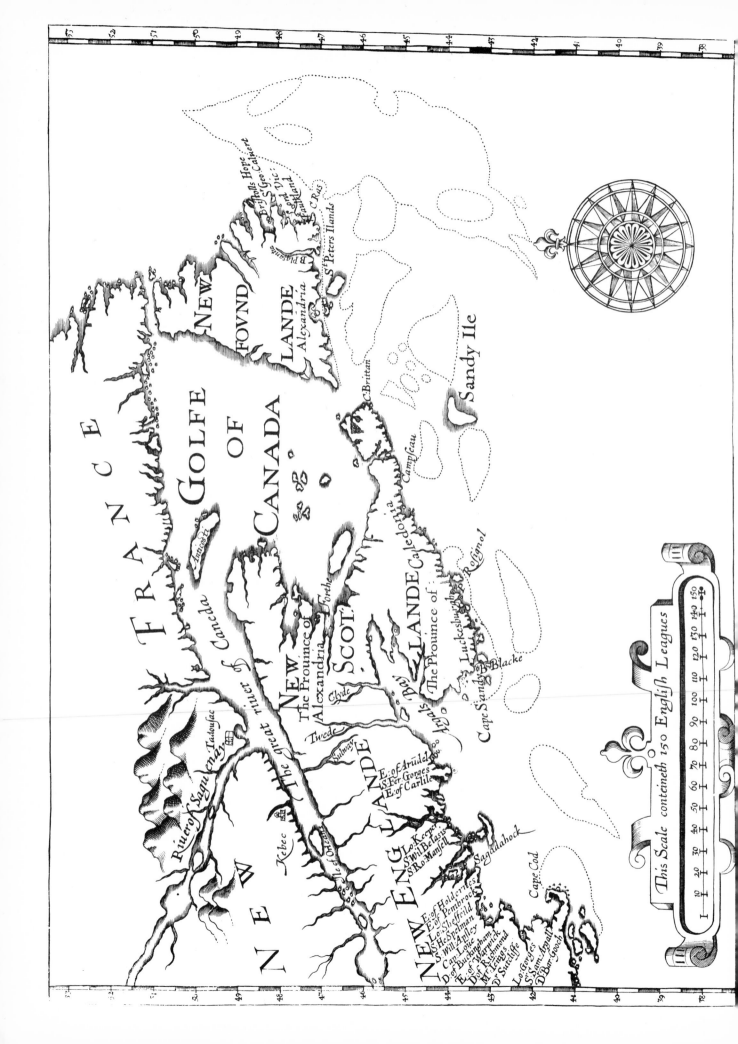

the course proper. During it the scholars were drilled in their Latin and introduced to Greek, and they would be given some further reading in such classical authors as Horace, Juvenal, Plautus and of course, Cicero.[1] They were also taught rhetoric from the work written by Peter Ramus' disciple, Omer Talon.

The first year proper of the university course continued the routine practice of Latin grammar and translation, but the scholars would now turn to Greek in earnest, beginning with the New Testament or Isocrates, then Homer or Theocritus. They would be introduced to logic according to Ramus' system. They would be instructed in theology and drilled in the dogma of the Kirk, for Melville's plan had in Genevan fashion the reformed religion as its heart. Thus the students spent all their Sabbaths in the Kirk or at their Catechism, nor were they allowed to idle, for they were examined after the service on both of the day's sermons.[2]

During the second year they would move on to a more systematic study of rhetoric, using Cassander, Cicero and Demosthenes organized according to the Ramist system with Talon's text. Their training in logic now began with the *Organum* of Aristotle in a Latin text, accompanied by Porphyry's *Categories*. Before ending the year with 'dispute on the logicks' the students were instructed in arithmetic (probably from Ramus' text). In the third year after repeating the logics (the previous year's classes were always rehearsed and the students examined on them) they would be introduced to Hebrew grammar. They then worked through the rest of Aristotle's logic (the *Posterior analytica*) and were lectured on his ethics. By the end of the same year Aristotle's natural science (the *Physica*) was begun, and as cream the scholars were given a little human anatomy from such an author as Fernel.[3] In their fourth and final year they would finish what was left of the *Physica* (such as the *Meteorologia*), and the *De anima* (psychology), then learn some astronomy and general science from Sacro Bosco and some geography from Honterus' cosmography. The year would end in the usual way with repetitions, examinations and as a climax the public disputations in logic.

What was the value of this education? At first sight it seems thoroughly scholastic in its organization, with Aristotle still providing the bulk of the text in almost all the categories of knowledge, and the only apparent 'modernizing' influences being Ramus' dialectic, Talaeus' rhetoric, Honterus' geography and Fernel's anatomy. Even astronomy was still being taught from Sacro Bosco, whose *Sphaera* had been a standby since the thirteenth century. And in spite of the good intentions of Melville and his disciples, one must doubt whether their reforms succeeded in changing the substance of what was taught to any great extent. Certainly—to judge by the books in Drummond's library—the texts used were now those of the humanists: Aristotelians such as Francisco Piccolomini, Zabarella and Toletus, and from what can be deduced from Drummond's notes and from such sources as Mead's recommendations to his students at Cambridge, such commentaries were in fact occasionally studied by the students themselves. But it is hard to believe that the peripatetic texts could be presented to schoolboys in anything like

1. From the books listed for the Humanity class and from some in Drummond's library it would seem that instruction in the High School was limited, typically, to a grounding in Latin and the rudiments of Greek. In his epitaph on his Humanity regent, John Ray, Drummond mentions Quintilian, Plautus, Martial, Virgil and Cicero—but the names may have been chosen with scansion in mind. See Kastner, II, p. 249.

2. 'The forme of discipline' *Charters* p. 119.

3. Spelled 'Servelius' in the printed version of the *Charters* (which are taken from the Burgh records). This is clearly wrong, and the manuscript supports the reading 'Fernelius.' Fernel's medicine was taught by Andrew Melville at Glasgow in 1574. See *The diary of James Melville* (Bannatyne Club, Edinburgh 1929) p. 39.

9. The northern colonies of North America. William Alexander, *An encouragement to colonies* (Cat. 697).

their full complexity, or that the regents did not rely upon the old simplifications that were such a part of scholastic philosophy. The attraction of the scholastic system was that it could be taught as a set of formal rules, divisions and terms: Ramist re-organization of the system simplified and adjusted the matter taught, but the method stayed essentially the same. It is difficult not to make the error of equating humanism with progress and scholasticism with pedantry, yet it would be as foolish to acclaim the few humanist innovations at Edinburgh as anything save well-meant adjustments. Melville and his supporters were hostile to the supremacy of Aristotle, but they recognized that there was no suitable alternative, and as long as the *Organon* and the *Physica* were to be studied, then—for the sake of the students—they had to be studied in a simplified, systematic way.[1] On the other hand, what was grafted on to the traditional curriculum did have the effect of raising the standards, for these innovations were in line with the usual aims of humanist scholarship.

There is a danger, I think, that we may be too much in awe of the kind of education a man like Drummond was given. Nowadays we usually do have small Latin and less Greek, and when we come to read the roll of the classical authors in a curriculum like Edinburgh's we do so with the reverence of the ignorant. We perhaps assume that these Renaissance students always understood what they were taught, or that their professors themselves were uniformly learned men. We forget the facts. The universities were called universities,[2] but they were normally what we would now term high schools or at best sixth-form colleges. The students were not young men, but adolescents, and they normally finished their four year course before they were out of their teens. Their instructors were often no more than a year or two older.[3]

It is worth remembering that the youth of the students made simplification inevitable: in spite of the grandeur of the names of Aristotle, Cicero and Demosthenes their complex arguments would be served up in easily memorized tags, and even these could not always be readily digested by a thirteen year old. James Melville tells how at that age he entered St Andrews and 'was cast in sic a grieff and dispear because I vnderstood nocht the regent's language in teatching, that I did nathing but bursted and grat at his lessones, and was of mynd to haiff gone ham agean. . . .' His regent however took pity on him, and taught him the terms of philosophy, and tutored him in private.[4] This was a problem that was well recognized by sixteenth- and seventeenth-century writers on education. Henry Peacham talks of the 'disproportion' between the childish capacities of the young university students and Aristotle's *Categories*,[5] and Bacon in his *Advancement of learning* says much the same: logic and rhetoric—these 'gravest of sciences'—were degenerated by 'childish sophistry and ridiculous affectation'.[6]

The Tounis College of Edinburgh was a small and spartan place, but certainly it was no worse than other universities. The students studied long and hard, from six in the morning in winter and five in summer, and scarcely finished when prayers were called at six p.m. The regents had to act less with the dignity of professors than with

---

1. Early dreams of including Plato and Cicero in the curriculum had been largely abandoned, probably because no way could be devised to reducing these to the usual formulae. Melville himself went further in the humanist direction than his educational heirs, teaching much Cicero, some of Plato's Dialogues, Sleidan and Melanchthon; *Diary* pp. 38-9.

2. The Tounis College seems to have actually acquired proper university status only in 1621, when King James' patronage was ratified, and the college called 'King James College'. But it had granted degrees from its foundation.

3. Not only in the Scottish universities. John English, Dean of Law at St John's Oxford till 1614, was appointed when he was twenty, and this was not unusual.
See W. C. Costin 'The inventory of John English' *Oxoniensia* XI-XII (1946-7) pp. 106-16.

4. *Diary*, p. 20.

5. Henry Peacham *The compleat gentleman* (London 1634) p. 33.

6. Quoted by Ruth Kelso in *The doctrine of the English gentleman*, University of Illinois Studies in Language and Literature XIV (Urbana 1929) 132.

the punctiliousness of schoolmasters, for they were instructed to take frequent roll-calls and to report, fine or punish absentees. Even the prescribed two hours of play on the fields were monitored. The list of 'Lawes to be Observit by the Schollers in the Said College' again shows that these undergraduates were far from adult, and needed the strict regulation of the schools.

'That none weare long haire.

That none depairt frome the rest in goeing to the kirk in the morning nor in returning to the scoolles efternoone, bot all to goe up with the Regents both the tymes.

That none go to the tavernes or any uther unseemlie plaices for schollers to be fund in'.[1]

The youthfulness of the students was as common elsewhere. At Paris in the sixteenth century a regulation was supposed to ensure that no student acted as master before the age of twenty (that is, had completed his studies, and was ready to teach). Yet Ramus himself bragged that he was producing masters of arts as young as fifteen at the College de Presles.[2]

Thus we might rightly suppose that the quality of such learning was suspect, and that much Renaissance education was better in theory than in practice. But it would be equally wrong to under-estimate the earnestness of the age. The students were drilled thoroughly, and there was no nonsense about pandering to the unintelligent. Those who could understand profited, and those who could not were thrashed.[3] There are many contemporary references to fine scholarship at an early age : James Melville himself relates that his uncle Andrew, a 'seikle tender boy', learned Greek before any in Scotland and studied Aristotle in that language at St Andrews while still of an age for the provost of New College, Mr John Dowglass, to hold him between his legs before the fire, pet him, and call him 'my sillie fatherless and motherles child'.[4] James the Sixth, too, became a good scholar at an early age, and rewarded the efforts of tutors so excellent as George Buchanan. These two are favoured examples, yet it is certainly a mistake to compare the attainments of a sixteenth-century thirteen year old with that of the teenager of today. We may question whether the students understood what they were taught in anything save the most superficial way, though we can hardly doubt that they were forced to remember their lessons.

The substance of the texts studied was reduced to formulae which could be parrotted by a schoolboy. Traditional logic and physics lent themselves to such treatment, and the method was extended to cover such subjects as ethics and metaphysics; this is discussed below in the essay on philosophy. It is worth noticing here that such a method inevitably relied upon simplification. The usual system at the Scottish universities was for the students to remain under one teacher or regent throughout their entire four years. Melville had tried to do away with the regent system at Glasgow, but he was unsuccessful; for at universities as small as those of Scotland it had its uses — for one thing, it was economical. Each regent conducted his own class through the four years study (Drummond was 'bred under' Mr James Knox)[5] and instructed them in the set books. Only

1. *Charters*, pp. 123-5. See also David B. Horn *Short history of the University of Edinburgh* (Edinburgh 1967) pp. 28-30, which gives a picture of student conditions.

2. Ong *Method*, p. 137.

3. But the best teachers, according to Peacham, were those who held that the only punishment was shame, and the best reward praise. Peacham, p. 24. Ramus himself, though, was a notorious flogger. Ong *Method*, p. 34.

4. *Diary*, p. 31.

5 Thomas Craufurd *History of the University of Edinburgh* (Edinburgh 1808) p. 63.

the Professor of Humanity—'Regens humanicorum literarum'—saw new faces each year, although, after some time, the Principal himself became the first to be freed from the routine of the system (he was usually the Professor of Divinity, and as such found himself enjoined at frequent intervals by the Town Council to give sufficient instruction in Hebrew).[1]

All this—the youth of the students, the youth of the instructors, the system of regents, and teaching by formulae—makes one wonder whether such education did not in fact fall far short of the ideals of its designers, Melville and his Genevan brethren. These ideals, we might remember, were strictly utilitarian, and the first task of the universities was to produce men who would make good ministers of the Kirk, who would know the foundations of their faith, who would be able to interpret the Scriptures correctly and refute all heretical opinion. The classical poets and historians might be studied, although their chief merit was that they, too, taught morality, and so could serve as an uncomplicated introduction for the younger student before he reached the dogma of the Kirk.

As a product of this kind of education Drummond dispels many of our doubts. His library shows that an Aristotelian education did not prevent him from acquiring essentially humanist tastes; it is reassuring in that it makes clear that, while remaining scholastic in method, academic instruction did little to stifle literary interests. Drummond's collection of Latin books is the heart of his library, and it is significant that he continued to buy and read academic books long after he left the Tounis College. As is shown in the essays that follow, any man who was interested in learning had to keep up his Latin: the professions used it, the theologians used it, the scientists and philosophers used it. And though Drummond chose to be an English poet, he was well able to appreciate the efforts of his many friends and fellow-countrymen who wrote Latin verse.

His notes in the Hawthornden MSS reveal that he could cope with Greek quite usefully[2]; they follow his usual practice of extracting passages from texts which particularly interested him. His collection of Greek books can be seen as a supplement to his Latin. It seems to have been the custom at Edinburgh to have referred to Aristotle in Greek, while still using a Latin translation for a text; Drummond had several Aristotelian works in Greek, sometimes—like those of Pacius—with commentaries in Latin.[3] He had, too, some other Greek authors who were probably studied in the curriculum, such as Isocrates and perhaps Plutarch, some poets like Homer, Anacreon, and Oppian, and historians such as Herodian and Xenophon. Long after he left the Tounis College, he was still buying Greek books (such as his copy of the Greek Anthology). The most significant thing about these books is the large number that must have an accompanying Latin translation, and this does suggest that Drummond needed a crib.

As for Hebrew, the main purpose of learning that tongue was for the sake of scriptural study. Thus all Drummond's small group of Hebrew works are either books of the Scriptures or dictionaries to help him read them, and from the evidence in the Hawthornden

1. *Charters*, p. 109.

2. It is Ong's opinion that Greek and Hebrew were but sketchily known by all except a few of the university professors that taught them; Ong, pp. 137-8. James Melville claimed to be the first regent in Scotland to teach Aristotle's logic and ethics from the Greek; this was in 1576; *Diary*, p. 43. Yet by Drummond's time the repeated mention of Greek works in the curriculum seems to indicate that Greek, at least in the Scottish universities, was normally taught to an advanced level.

3. In 1648 one of the reforms at St Andrews was that the Regents 'recommendit . . . that everie student have the text of Aristotill in Greek'; *Fasti Aberdonenses*, p. iv.

MSS he clearly reached a moderate level of understanding. He continued going to lectures on Hebrew while at university in France, and one set of notes that he took there was on grammatical problems of a not unsophisticated nature.[1]

When Drummond graduated he presented with his fellow students a thesis for public disputation.[2] It was, typically, on a subject from the *Physica*, namely the matter of first principles and whether or not there were contradictions in Aristotle's statements concerning these. It followed the usual method, that is, it picked several relevant texts from different books of the canon which raised apparent anomalies, using these as a foundation for the student's argument. Drummond, in accordance with the teaching of his faith, resolved the formal argument by appealing to the highest authority: Aristotle, he claimed, had been dreaming when he denied that the world took its origin from God, and the Aristotelian arguments in favour of absolute first principles were consequently invalid. We may well see this thesis as symptomatic of late Renaissance education: its subject Aristotle, its organization scholastic, and its conclusion Christian.

1. I am indebted to Mr Al Sorem for his advice on this matter.

2. Hawthornden MS 2059 ff.24–6.

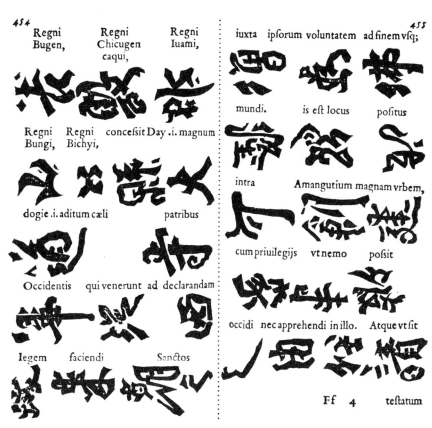

10. Specimen of Japanese script. *Rerum a Societate Iesu in Oriente gestarum volumen* (Cat. 523).

21

Drummond as a Writer

Drummond was not a prolific poet. His first major piece was printed in 1613, his last in 1623. His chief works are these: *Teares on the death of Meliades* (1613), *Poems* (1616), and *Flowres of Sion* (1623). He wrote besides a number of verses for the entertainment of King Charles on his visit to Edinburgh in 1633, and 'A pastorall elegie' of 138 lines on the death of Sir William Alexander's son Antony. His works have a confused printing history; they appeared in several editions, in collections, and under different titles. Thus the *Poems* of 1616 were preceded by a trial edition probably as early as 1614; *Forth feasting* came out as part of the *Poems* (1616) and was reprinted by itself the following year and again (together with some pieces by other authors) in *The muses welcome to the high and mighty Prince James* in 1618. Drummond liked to see his work in print. He encouraged the Edinburgh printer Andrew Hart to bring out new and different editions of his poems, and he may have borne some or all of the expense of this himself. Certainly, he had Hart or his heirs make up a quantity of his books in special gilt bindings, suitable for presentation to his friends and those he wished to impress or flatter.[1]

We must read Drummond as he wished to be read, as an English poet, and resist judging him by the mass of private verse he suppressed, which has only been added to his canon by diligent editors. When young he wrote some sonnets after the Scottish fashion, in the manner of the Castalian school of poets that had gathered around James VI. In these he borrowed considerably from the work of his uncle, William Fowler. Then, towards the end of his life, he wrote numerous squibs, lampoons and epigrams against the extremists of Kirk and State, as well as a number of ribald verses. None of this stuff — including the early sonnets — saw print in his lifetime, for Drummond, like Alexander, turned his face to the south and sought to be accounted as accomplished a wit as those English poets he admired so much.

His poetical reputation rests on his *Poems* of 1616. As their title says, these are 'Amorous, Funerall, Diuine, Pastorall, in Sonnets, Songs, Sextains, Madrigals'. They are divided into poems of the first part (amorous), poems of the second part (funeral), *Urania* (poems spiritual), *Madrigals and epigrammes*, and in some editions,

1. A bibliography of Drummond's works can be found in Kastner, I, pp. xlv-xcvi. Nothing of note can be added to this. Two further pieces of evidence can be brought forward to show Drummond's close relationship with the printers: first the way in which he had his sonnet 'This Beautie, which pale Death in Dust did turne' printed on a single sheet 'In Pious Memorie of the right Worthie and Vertuous Euphemia Kyninghame', as though to distribute to his friends; secondly, his habit of correcting his poems by pasting in printed slips cut from earlier editions (see Kastner) might suggest he had ready access to a printer's surplus. Drummond had at least some of his works printed at his own expense: in a letter dated 1623 to Sir David Lindsay he mentions 'having caused print only some copies [of *Flowres of Sion*] equalling the number of my friends and those to whom I am beholden . . .' See Lord Lindsay's *Lives of the Lindsays* (London 1849) II, pp. 4-5.

Forth feasting, A panegyricke to the Kings most excellent Majestie.
These — together with *Flowres of Sion* — are the poems which earned
Drummond his usual epithets: sweet, sensuous, thoughtful, exotic.

The critical problem with Drummond has always been to judge
him against his sources. It is generally agreed that he had a happy
facility with verse, a good ear and a smooth way with a phrase. He
could paint a pretty picture, use the conventions of love neatly and
strike the appropriate Petrarchan poses. He affected a decent melancholy, tinged with neo-Platonism. He may well have been 'the most
delicate and accomplished artist in the Italian style our literature has
known'.[1] It is agreed, too, that he was a faithful follower of Petrarch,
an imitator of Ronsard, a paraphraser of Sidney, and a translator or
thief of a host of other poets, Italian, French, Spanish, English and
Scottish.

The difficulty is to decide whether Drummond's borrowings are
legitimate. The critical opinion that bears most weight is that of the
editor of the definitive edition of his poems, L.E. Kastner, who
pronounced that 'A full third of Drummond's compositions are
translations or close paraphrases, and betray in no uncertain manner
the imitative temper of his Muse. The rest are best described as
adaptations from foreign models. Though the source of a small
number of them has not yet been revealed, we may reasonably expect
that one day the totality of his poems, with few exceptions, will be
found to have been composed according to a given pattern, more or
less vividly present in the poet's mind. All claim to originality he must
forgo....'[2] Since a short excursion into this question of
Drummond's plagiarism is bound to reveal the extent of his reading
and the quality of his poetical taste, it will be relevant to our study
of his library.

It is well known that critics of the Renaissance encouraged
imitation; none disputed the principle, although few agreed on its
limits. Theories ranged from the advice that only the classical forms
should be copied, to straightforward encouragement to theft in the
grand manner, the more thoroughgoing the better.[3] By Drummond's
time critical opinion in England had moved towards the Italian
position: imitation was essential, with the ancient authors as the
best models, but it should be imitation not of detail, but of concept.
The controversy was most complex, with each critic putting forward
his own interpretation of what Aristotle had really meant, and what
Horace had really intended. The best synthesis of the arguments can
be found of course in Sidney's *An apologie for poetrie*, where at the
heart of Sidney's opinion is the idea that poetic imitation consists of
arriving at 'that Idea, or fore-conceit of the work', not in reproducing the work itself.[4] Some Elizabethans were as scornful of those
that stole other men's verse as modern critics are of today's literary
thieves: Puttenham said of Soowthern's thefts from Ronsard's *Odes*
that 'this man deserues to be endited of pety *larceny* for pilfring
other mens deuises',[5] and Sidney himself spoke for the self-respecting
poet when he claimed 'I am no pick-purse of another's wit'.[6]
Drummond, too, made the distinction quite clear: Sidney and
Alexander approached Petrarch not 'in following his Invention, but

1. John Purves, in *The works of William Fowler* (Edinburgh 1940) III, Scottish Text Society p. cxlix.

2. Kastner, I, p. xliii.

3. See Harold O. White *Plagiarism and imitation during the English Renaissance* (Cambridge, Mass. 1935)

4. See the critical edition of the *Apology* (Edinburgh 1965) where this passage is discussed by Geoffrey Shepherd, the editor, p. 60. Drummond had James VI's *The essays of a prentise, in the divine art of poesie*, and James' ordinary opinion would have been received sympathetically by him: James asked for originality of expression in particular details, but recommended following (and borrowing from) other authors. White, pp. 64-6.

5. *The arte of English poesie* (Cambridge 1936) p. 253. This passage is discussed in the intro-duction by the editors Gladys D. Willcock and Alice Walker, p. lx. Puttenham went on to say 'I would wish euery inuētour which is the very Poet to receaue the prayses of his inuention, so would I not haue a trāslatour be ashamed to be acknowen of his translation'.

6. *Astrophil and Stella*, Son. lxxiv, 1.8. See Kastner, II, p. 372.

1. From 'Character of several Authors'. *Works* (1711) pp. 226-7.

2. See his sonnet to the author of *Penardo and Laissa* (Patrick Gordon) Kastner, II, p. 162.

3. See Kastner, I, p. 208.

in forging as good'.[1] But Drummond excepted himself from the rule, though he was ready, in the best of other poet's phrases, to maintain it :' Thy Syre no pyick-purse is of others wit'.[2] Roughly, then, we can make a distinction between imitation (or borrowing) of phrase and language, which was considered reprehensible, and imitation of certain ideas, conceits, and figures, which was thought admirable. This is what was usually conceded to be the chief rule of poetic imitation, though in fact it was often broken. Following Bembo—who imitated Petrarch closely, and told others to do the same—many poets were less than scrupulous. Du Bellay first and later Desportes were enthusiastic borrowers; Lodge translated Ronsard and Constable adapted Desportes. In Scotland Fowler and Alexander had gone to the Italians, and Montgomerie to Ronsard. But even in an age that saw much 'pilfring,' when the practice of imitation was generous however ambigious the theory, the scale of Drummond's plunder was exceptionally ambitious. Garcilaso's sonnet

> Oh hado esecutivo en mis dolores,
> ¡Cómo sentí tus leyes rigurosas !

he translated as

> O Fate ! conspir'd to powre your Worst on mee,
> O rigorous Rigour, which doth all confound, *etc.*[3]

and followed it with a translation from Sannazzaro :

> O vita, vita no, ma vivo affanno,
> Nave di vetro in mar di cieco errore

which became

> O Woefull Life ! Life, no, but liuing death,
> Fraile Boat of Christall in a rockie Sea, *etc.*[4]

There is no need to illustrate further ; the student can find all the examples he needs in Kastner's notes ; the point is that Drummond made the most of his fluency in languages and of his wide reading, while exploiting the liberality of current theories of imitation.

To the Elizabethans it was quite legitimate, even essential, to follow the conventions of the kind of poetry that one set out to write. England had seen a vogue of amorous pastoral verse ; sonnet-sequence upon sonnet-sequence had been produced after the style of the Italians and the French. If Petrarch had celebrated his Laura, so had Sidney his Stella, Daniel his Delia, Lodge his Phillis, Fletcher his Licia and Constable his Diana. *Astrophil and Stella* in 1591 marks the beginning of the English craze for sonnet writing ; by 1597 the taste had staled. Shakespeare, Greville, Alexander, and Drummond were the only poets of any stature to have their sonnet-sequences printed for the first time after that date, and of these four Shakespeare and Greville wrote most of their poems while the vogue was still at its height. In 1616 Drummond (celebrating his Auristella) was practising a genre quite out of fashion in England.

The conventions of the Petrarchan sonnet are well known, and can be found with little variation in any of the sonneteers, in Sidney,

Daniel or Drummond.[1] The poet was in love. He was without serious hope, but his passion was undying. He was distracted, he suffered, he could not sleep. His mistress was the fairest of the fair, but indifferent to his distress, and often even cruel. He frequently wished he could approach her through the objects she touched or used: if only he were the rose she kissed he would be in very heaven. She would be immortalized in his verse; she might die, her beauties fade, but yet she would live, for she had inspired his poetry.

The language of the Petrarchans was also stylized. The poet's mistress was described in terms of perfection, not realism. Certain epithets were used again and again: hair was golden, eyes were suns, or bright as topaz, neck and breasts were milk-white, lips red as coral, teeth pearls, bearing humbly-proud.

Such charms could come only from the gods:

> When first sweet Phillis (whom I must adore)
> Gan with her beauties blesse our wondring skie,
> The sonne of Rhea, from their fatall store
> Made all the Gods to grace her Maiestie.
> Apollo first his golden rayes among,
> Did form the beauty of her bounteous eyes . . .[2]

> *Mars* and *Apollo* first did Her aduise
> In Colour Blacke to wrappe those Comets bright . . .
> Chaste Phebe spake for purest azure Dyes,
> But IOVE and VENUS greene about the Light
> To frame thought best, as bringing most Delight . . .[3]

Often, however, perfection hailed from far-off and exotic places:

> Restore thy tresses to the golden Ore,
> Yeeld Cithereas sonne those Arkes of loue;
> Bequeath the heauens the starres that I adore,
> And to th'Orient do thy Pearles remoue,
> Yeeld they hands pride vnto th'Iuory white,
> Th' Arabian odors giue thy breathing sweete:
> Restore thy blush vnto Aurora bright,
> To Thetis giue the honour of thy feete . . .[4]

So did her rare cruelty:

> The *Hyperborean* Hills, *Ceraunus* Snow,
> Or *Arimaspus* (cruell) first thee bred,
> The *Caspian* Tigers with their Milke thee fed,
> And *Faunes* did humane Bloud on thee bestow. . . .[5]

which could be contrasted with her beauty in neat antitheses:

> More fayre, but yet more cruell I thee deeme,
> (Though by how much the more thou beautious art,
> So much of pittie shouldst thou more esteeme)
> Fayrer then Phoebe, yet a harder hart.[6]

The poet was enslaved, and his mistress was careless of his suffering:

> In vaine I seeke and sew to her for grace,
> And doe myne humbled hart before her poure:

1. But not in Petrarch, who lacks many of his followers' accretions. My summary of the Petrarchan sonnet is not intended to do more than outline the genre and it omits the considerable development which took place as the sonnet went from Italy to France, Spain and England. For a fuller account, see for instance the essay 'Petrarch in England' in Mario Praz *The Flaming Heart* (New York 1958) pp. 264-86, or the short summary in Ernest H. Wilkin *Studies in the life and works of Petrarch* (The Medieval Academy of America, Cambridge, Mass. 1955) pp. 280-96, which has a selected bibliography.

2. Lodge *Phillis*, Son. 33. Drummond noted in his copy that this sonnet was adapted from Ronsard.

3. Drummond *Poems*, Son. 18. Kastner, I, p. 22.

4. Daniel *Delia*, Son. 19. Daniel adapted this sonnet from Du Bellay. See Joan Rees *Samuel Daniel* (Liverpool 1964) p. 27.

5. Drummond *Poems*, Son. 35. Kastner, I, p. 31.

6. *Zepheria*, Canzon. 7.

The whiles her foot she in my beck doth place,
And tread my life downe in the lowly floure.[1]

But if she was cruel, that was only the price of her beauty, and the poet who worshipped beauty was ready to pay the cost.

For had she not bene faire, and thus vnkind,
My Muse had slept, and none had knowne my mind.[2]

Antithesis was the very core of Petrarchanism, and prompted the best conceits

Faire is my Yoke, though grieuous bee my Paines,
Sweet are my Wounds, although they deeply smart . . .[3]

that could be developed in the most delicate thoughts. Neo-Platonism was a favourite resource (especially with the Italians):

My Minde mee told, that in some other Place
It elsewhere saw the *Idea* of that Face,
And lou'd a Loue of heauenly pure Delight.
No Wonder now I feele so faire a Flame,
Sith I Her lou'd ere on this *Earth* shee came.[4]

The very rigidity of the conventions ensured repetition, and laid the genre wide open to the satirists: 'My Mistres eyes are nothing like the Sunne' was Shakespeare's response to the Petrarchan epithet, and he added that 'If Snow be white, why then her Brests are dunne', music sounds more pleasing than her voice, roses are redder than her cheeks, and perfumes sweeter than her breath.[5] Drummond must have read this, but he turned a blind eye to its obvious message. Twenty years after the fashion he was still apostrophizing the heavens, the earth, the sea to 'vaunt not' their glories, for these his mistress surpassed:

Pearle, Iuorie, Corrall, Diamond, Sunnes, Gold,
Teeth, Necke, Lips, Heart, Eyes, Haire, are to behold.[6]

This conservatism of Drummond needs some explanation. He was writing as though he belonged to an earlier generation; writing, it must be admitted, extremely well, but not originally. Writers, it is said, lead their readers in taste; what is *avant garde* one year becomes the property of the common reader not in the next, but in twenty or thirty years. This I think explains Drummond: he was a most sensitive reader. He could appreciate Donne, but not imitate him; he had an instinctive distrust of the way Donne broke the good rules of prosody. He was more at home among the sonneteers, and their artificiality was much more to his liking. There his reading could serve him well, from *Astrophil and Stella* he could go to Petrarch, from Daniel to Ronsard. Immediately before him was the example of Sir William Alexander, another Scot, who in the best courtly manner had offered his *Aurora. Containing the first fancies of the authors youth* to the public in 1604. The neo-classical way was still the best, and Drummond had only the deepest scorn for reformers: 'What is not like the Ancients and conform to those Rules which hath been agreed unto by all Times, may (indeed) be some-

1. Spenser *Amoretti*, Son. 20.

2. Daniel *Delia*, Son. 6.

3. Drummond *Poems*, Son. 4. Kastner, I, p. 5.

4. Drummond *Poems*, Son. 7. Kastner, I, p. 6.

5. Shakespeare *Sonnets*, Son. 130. See Patrick Cruttwell *The Shakespearean moment* (London 1954), chapter one et seq. for a discussion of the contrast between the conventional amorous lyric and Shakespeare's sonnets. Drummond read Shakespeare's sonnets (since he comments on their recent publication in his 'Character of several Authors') but he seems to have been quite uninfluenced by them.

6. Drummond *Poems*, Son. 6. Kastner, I, p. 6.

thing like unto *Poesy*, but it is no more *Poesy* than a Monster is a Man.'[1]

Drummond's sonnet-sequence has been singled out as the one sonnet-sequence in the Petrarchan fashion which is a personal love story: the poems of the First Part are a 'little history of love', and those of the Second Part 'a fell sequel', recording the poet's 'desolation and sorrow'.[2] According to his first biographer, Drummond was in love with a Miss Cunningham of Barns, and this love (according to a modern critic) 'gives to the poems a depth and intensity which lift them above the level of the conventional exercise of poetic wit'.[3]

It may matter to modern critics whether or not the *Poems* were autobiographical; it was simply not relevant to Drummond's own contemporaries. We have seen that his poems are in the Petrarchan manner, that his conceits, figures and epithets were taken from the Italians, the French, the Spanish and the English Petrarchans, and that in imitating, adapting and even translating he was following precedents. All writers of amorous lyrics needed a poetic mistress: whatever the identity of Stella, Sidney could not have done without her. And her identity hardly matters, for the mistress was as conventional as the epithets that described her.

Thus, it is no surprise to find that Drummond's *Poems* do not form the one exception to the rule: it is most unlikely that they are autobiographical. Drummond may have been in love with Miss Cunningham, but if he wrote the *Poems* in her honour he must have had second sight, for the poems 'Funerall' were completed at least a year before her death. Miss Cunningham died on the 23 July 1616; most of the poems Funerall were completed for the early edition of the *Poems*, which Kastner dates to 1614 (if that dating is wrong, we are left with the improbable, unreasonable possibility that Drummond composed and had printed two editions in the last six months of 1616). The conclusion seems clear: the *Poems* were not a memorial (as Bishop Sage claimed) of Drummond's love and sorrow, and Auristella was as conventional an invention as Delia or Aurora.[4]

Drummond drew his poesy from his reading, and few poets can have been so well read. To refer again to his editor's statement, that 'a full third of Drummond's compositions are translations. . . . The rest are best described as adaptations from foreign models'; if we look at his sources we will be able to tell exactly how he used this part of his library. He imitated William Fowler and Sir William Alexander. Of the English poets, he borrowed or adapted from the following: Sidney, both from his *Astrophil and Stella* and the *Arcadia*, Daniel, from *Delia*, Drayton, from *Idea*, and from Shakespeare, Spenser, Peele and Watson. To the French he owed even more. He translated, borrowed or adapted from Passerat, Desportes, Ronsard, Pontus de Tyard, Tabourot, Pasquier, and Jodelle. He took something from the Latin of Volpi, Zanchi, Castiglione and Horace, and much from the Spanish of Boscan and Garcilaso. The Italians provided him with most of all, and he translated and adapted the verse of almost all the notable poets: Petrarch, Bembo, Luigi Groto, Sannazzaro, Paterno, Guarini, Bonardo, Belli, Guazzo,

1. Letter to Dr Arthur Johnston, *Works* (1711)) p. 143. Although the general sense of Drummond's remarks here are clear—that he was against innovation—it is by no means certain just who were the reformers he was attacking. He says 'In vain have some Men of late (transformers of every Thing) consulted upon her [Poesie's] Reformation, and endeavoured to abstract her to Metaphysical Ideas and Scholastical Quiddities, denuding her of her own Habits, and those ornaments with which she has amused the World some Thousand Years. . . .' Kastner took this to mean Malherbe and his followers; Fogle felt that Donne and Jonson were the reformers attacked. Drummond is referring to matter rather than manner: he is objecting not to new techniques in style and versification but to the inclusion of what he feels is non-poetic material into poetry to the exclusion of natural and traditional diction. His rough draft of his letter to Johnston (Hawthornden MS 2062, f. 228v) makes the point a little clearer: 'Metaphisicall matter, and scholastic theologie is not to be set downe in verses, which are better vnderstood in prose. . . .' This seems to rule out Malherbe, whose innovations were mostly technical. Drummond bought, read, and took notes on the first production of Malherbe's circle, the *Nouveau recueil des plus beaux vers de ce temps*, and might be supposed to welcome Malherbe's approach to 'correct' prosody. On the other hand, though Drummond's remarks on this new poetic matter seem more applicable to Donne than anyone else, I am not certain that Drummond would have wished to attack Donne. He praised his epigrams and lyrics, and went to the trouble of transcribing two satires, some letters and the epigrams. The songs and sonnets—the more likely target—he transcribed too, but piecemeal. See Kastner, I, p. xxxiv, and Fogle, p. 19, for their opinions on his conservatism.

2. Masson, p. 46.

3. Fogle, p. 45.

4. See my article 'Drummond of Hawthornden, Miss Euphemia Kyninghame, and the *Poems*', *MLR*, LX (1965) 494-9.

Torquato Tasso, Marino, Moro and a number of lesser figures. Scholars are still turning up more examples of Drummond's debt to his books; but there can be little profit in adding to the inventory, for the point has been made.[1]

Were one to pick one poet above all as Drummond's favourite, it would have to be Giambattista Marino. Marino is now considered decadent, sugared, artificial, exaggerated. In his day he was thought the supreme poet of Italy, he was idolized, fêted, and given the title of Chevalier. His collected lyrics were first printed in 1602, and his fame was at its height while Drummond was writing his poetry. Marino took the poetic conceit to extremes of extravagance in his efforts to maintain his new poetic creed: to astonish his readers. The most ordinary sentiments he frames in extraordinary language. His verse glitters with ornament, he loves the exotic, the precious, the euphuistic. (Lyly and his imitators exploited in England the taste for the baroque simultaneously, but independently.)

We have already quoted one sonnet Drummond took from Marino; the one beginning

> Te l'Hiperboreo monte, ò l'Arimaspe
> Produsse, Elpinia, il Caucaso, ò l'Cerauno:
> Te frà l'Hircane tigri, e frà le Caspe
> Sol di tosco nodrì Centauro, ò Fauno.[2]

This startling imagery, this summoning-up of exotica, is all to emphasize one thing—the cruelty of the poet's mistress.

A considerable portion of Drummond's poetry was religious or philosophical, and here Marino's influence is quite dominant. The second part of the *Poems* (1616) are 'funerall', and they are followed by 'Urania, or spiritual poems'. The *Flowres of Sion* are also subtitled 'Spiritual poems'.[3] There is no very marked change in these from the amorous and pastoral poems: the object of the poet's love is no longer physical, but spiritual, he withdraws from the world, and settles into a quiet and philosophic melancholy. Much of the verse is religious, that is, vaguely mystical feeling is expressed, but there is little attempt to ask or explore theological questions. 'Metaphisicall matter, and scholastic theologie is not to be set downe in verses. . . .' Drummond breaks this rule once or twice, but for the most part he keeps the *Urania* and the *Flowres of Sion* firmly within the realm of divinity, and is content to hymn those mysteries revealed by God to man. His mood is adoration, not speculation. Neo-Platonism runs through the sonnets: the contemplation of the higher existence, the feeling that earthly beauty is but a pale reflection of some more absolute beauty that exists outside the world of sense, and that love of such beauty is the means of freeing the poet from his subjection to the corruption and decay of his present state.

In his religious verse Drummond occasionally employs a conceit that should let us call him a metaphysical poet. He describes the Magdalene before Jesus:

> These Lockes, of blushing deedes the faire attire,
> Smooth-frizled Waues, sad Shelfes which shadow deepe,

1. W. C. Ward, in his edition of Drummond's poetical works (London 1894) was the first to document Drummond's sources in detail. Kastner in his notes recorded almost all the rest (that is, apart from Drummond's prose sources; see below). I am indebted to Dr. R. Jack for information on Drummond's Scottish sources.

2. Kastner, I, p. 193.

3. With his usual economy, Drummond republished ten of the thirteen poems of the *Urania* with little modification in *Flowres of Sion*.

Soule-stinging Serpents in gilt curles which creepe,
To touch thy sacred Feete doe now aspire. . . .[1]

The model is Desportes, the mood is Italian.

Drummond drew heavily on Marino for his divine sonnets. Whether it is to name Christ as 'That Heauen-sent Yongling, holie-Maide-borne Wight', or God as 'the Worlds great King', Marino is the inspiration, or rather the source (for the sonnets in which these phrases occur are translations)[2] The resonance, the use of compounded words, the heavy baroque language suited Drummond's taste. The thought is of the simplest; all weight is in the ornament. Consider the sonnet 'To a Nightingale': 'Sweet Bird,' writes Drummond (adapting Marino)

What Soule can be so sicke, which by thy Songs
(Attir'd in sweetnesse) sweetly is not driuen
Quite to forget Earths turmoiles, spights, and wrongs,
And lift a reuerend Eye and Thought to Heauen?
Sweet Artlesse Songstarre, thou my Minde dost raise
To Ayres of Spheares, yes, and to Angels Layes.[3]

It is sweet-sounding verse, but when we remember what Donne was wrestling with at the same time, how vapid it seems!

In summary we can say of Drummond's poetry that though he borrowed more heavily than any other poet of his time, he did find a 'voice' of his own, and a sweet, melodious one at that. In a detailed study of his style in relation to his translation one critic has succeeded in defining Drummond's essence: he adorned Petrarch, made Tasso more explicit, and delighted in Marino.[4] His omissions are as characteristic as his direct translation. When he borrowed a sonnet from Petrarch he intellectualized it, he embroidered the language, increased the adjectives, and generalized the personal statements. In Tasso he left the metaphysical well alone, he translated the elaborate imagery, made the sense more explicit, and indulged in some general sententiousness. With his favourite Marino, although he liked the floriate description he was not willing to stomach all his excesses, and he left out of his translations much he thought in bad taste. Thus in his 'The Woefull Marie' (adapted from Marino's 'Stabat Mater') he omitted the stanzas where the physical imagery is carried to excess, and also those where Marino's Catholic doctrinal opinions proved too much. Drummond's verse emerges less incisive, but more poignant and charming.

Predictably, Drummond as a prose writer followed the same habits he had set as a poet. He wrote some essays — philosophical and political — and a history; they are all derivative. Of these his *A cypresse grove* is the best known. He wrote it first as *A midnight's trance* (printed 1619) and later revised it: it is a remarkable example of baroque style, a mosaic of echoes, phrases and thoughts from a wide range of sources, transmuted by Drummond with considerable skill into a cohesive whole. From it we can see once again how Drummond put his reading to use.

This 'collection of purple patches' was assembled from a variety

1. *Flowres of Sion*, Son. 12, Kastner, II, p. 12. Richard Crashaw (who was similarly much influenced by Marino, and who adapted many of the same of Marino's verses as Drummond) makes an interesting comparison. See the essay on Crashaw by Mario Praz in *The flaming heart*, pp. 204-63.

2. *Flowres of Sion*, Son. 9, Kastner, II, p. 11, and Son. 17, Kastner, II, p. 26.

3. *Flowres of Sion*, Son. 23, Kastner, II, p. 31.

4. Ruth C. Wallerstein, 'The style of Drummond in its relation to his translations', *PMLA*, XLVIII (1933) 1090-107.

1. As R. Ellrodt describes it. A list of critical articles tracing Drummond's sources in *A cypresse grove* can be found in his edition of *A midnight's trance* (Oxford 1951). Besides the introduction and notes in Ward and Kastner, these are: S. Clegg (editor), *A cypresse grove* (Hawthornden Press 1919); G. S. Greene 'Drummond's borrowing from Donne', *Philological Quarterly*, XI (1932) 26-38; G. S. Greene 'Bacon a source for Drummond', *Modern Language Notes*, XLVIII (1933) 230-2; M.A. Rugoll 'Drummond's debt to Donne' *Philological Quarterly*, XVI (1937); Grover Smith 'The influence of Sir John Hayward and of Joshua Sylvester upon William Drummond's *Cypresse grove*', *Philological Quarterly*, XXVI (1947) 69-80; M.P. McDiarmid, 'The Spanish plunder of William Drummond of Hawthornden', *Modern Language Review* XLIV (1949) 17-25. To these can be added Ellrodt's own introduction to *A midnight trance*, and his subsequent articles 'More Drummond borrowings', *Huntington Library Quarterly*, XVI (1953), 305-10; and 'William Drummond's *Cypresse grove* and the *Somnium Scipionis*', *Notes and Queries*, IX (October 1962) 376-7. The last two articles show how Drummond paraphrased passages from the *Somnium Scipionis*, both direct, and *via Purchas his Pilgrimage*.

2. Quoted by Ellrodt in his introduction to *A midnight's trance*, pp. vii-viii. Drummond suppressed this passage in *A cypresse grove*, but, as Ellrodt says, not from shame, for he added some spoils just as outrageous.

3. In STC 23575.

4. See Ellrodt's introduction. Drummond probably also lifted a passage from Beaumont and Fletcher's *Philaster* (which he thus must have read on its first publication in 1620). Ellrodt, pp. ix-x.

of Drummond's favourite authors, notably Bacon, Charron, Donne, Granada, Guevara, Hayward, Montaigne, Ringhieri, Cicero, Purchas and Passerat.[1] Some other authors (such as Sidney and Shakespeare) Drummond used in *A midnight's trance*, and afterwards suppressed in *A cypresse grove*. The piece itself is a discourse on death and the vanities of life on this earth, framed in elaborate rhetoric. In it Drummond advances through a sequence of attitudes from the pagan fear of death, Senecan Stoicism, and Platonism to the Christian doctrine of bodily resurrection.

Much of the philosophical *sententiæ* (particularly the Neo-Platonism) are common to several of the authors that Drummond read, and so it is not always easy to say with confidence which source he used. This had led to some critical arguments, but for the most part the history of scholarly examination of *A cypresse grove* has tended to fix more clearly Drummond's indebtedness, for only too often Drummond used phrases and even whole sentences without any modification. Here, for example, is Drummond at the assembly-line:

> 'The halfe of our Life is spent in sleepe, which (sith it is a release of care, the balme of woe, an indifferent arbiter vnto all) must be the best, and yet is but the shadow of Death: and who would not rather thē suffer the Slings, and Arrows of outragious Fortune, the whips and scorns of time, the oppressors wrongs, the proud man contumelies, sleepe euer (that is, dye) and end the Heart-ake, and the thousand naturall Shocks, that flesh is heire to?'

It is hardly necessary to add that this is a marriage in prose of Sidney's invocation to Sleep (Sonnet 39, *Astrophil and Stella*) and Hamlet's famous soliloquy.[2]

The works that Drummond used that can be precisely identified are these: Pico della Mirandola's *Heptaplus*, Bacon's *Essays*, Donne's *Anniversaries*, Sir John Haywards' *Sanctuarie of a troubled soule*, Pierre Matthieu's *Tablettes de la vie & de la mort*, Montaigne's *Essaies* and *Apologie de Raimond Sebond*, Charron's *De la Sagesse*, and Innocenzio Ringhieri's *Dialoghi della vita et della morte*. In addition he seems to have read Matthieu's *Tablettes* in Joshua Sylvester's English translation,[3] to have paraphrased pieces of Granada's *Guia de pecadores* and *Oraciones y exercicios*, to have lifted an idea from Samuel Purchas' *Pilgrimage*, and some others from Passerat's *Consolation de Madame Givry*. Knowing Drummond's method of composition, and having his reading lists and the catalogue of his library before us, there are few surprises here. We might add that the critic who detected in *A cypresse grove* something of Sir John Davies' *Nosce teipsum*, and of Drummond's direct reading of Hermetic and Platonic philosophy was, to judge by Drummond's books, probably right.[4]

It would be tedious to go into Drummond's sources in any greater detail. It has all been done before, and the evidence is now very clear. Drummond was a borrower supreme, and his distinguished style is all that saves his work from being regarded as pastiche pure and simple. He clearly did read his books, however, and language was no barrier to him. He moved from Latin to French, from French to Italian, from Italian to Spanish with apparent ease, and if his own compositions are but ground-up passages pulled from his commonplace book, they certainly show that books to Drummond were not for show but for use, and his library a mine for the mind.

O F J ET,
Or P O R P H Y R I E,
Or that white Stone
P A R O S *affoordes alone,*
Or thefe in A Z V R E *dye,*
Which feem to fcorne the S K Y E;
Here Memphis *Wonders doe not fet,*
Nor A R T E M I S I A'S *huge Frame,*
That keepes fo long her Louers Name:
Make no great marble Atlas *tremble with Gold*
To pleafe a Vulgar E Y E *that doth beholde.*
The Mufes, Phœbus, Loue, *haue raifed of their teares*
A Cryftal Tomb to Him wherethrough his worth appears.

11. Pyramid poem 'Of Jet.' Drummond, *Teares on the death of Moeliades* (Cat. 767).

Drummond as a Critic

There are few surprises about Drummond's critical opinions, as far as they go. His fluency in languages gave him a fine range, and he was able to keep local reputations firmly in their place. He could judge the merit of a translation, and he knew who had taken what from where. He knew enough terms to find rhetorical figures, and to keep his finger upon proper decorum. Beyond this his natural conservatism put limits on his insight; he read the latest writers, but his opinions remained firmly old-fashioned.

In his 'Characters of Several Authors' which he seems to have written about the year 1615, his views are unremarkable with one exception, that Spenser's *Amoretti* are 'so childish, that it were not well to give them so honourable a Father'.[1] Petrarch he thought the best and most exquisite poet on the subject of love; in English Sidney approached him in matter, and Alexander in manner (by 'approach' he meant not 'in following his Invention, but in forging as good'). Daniel he believed second to none for sweetness in rhyming; Drayton somewhat artificial, writing with the mind, not the heart; Donne 'among the Anacreontick Lyricks' the first.[2] Shakespeare he noted as being lately published.[3] He liked Drayton's *Poly-Olbion*, yet poets should not dwell over much on history lest they forget sometimes to be good poets. He liked Sylvester's translation of Du Bartas' *Judith*.

When Drummond was taking down Ben Jonson's 'Informations and Manners' in 1619 he left his own opinions aside, apart from a few well-deserved corrections (such as pointing out that Jonson was not well read in French and Italian). He was quite well enough read to keep up with Jonson's remarks on literature, which often—as on Donne—confirmed his own judgement. His classical reading was not as wide; he misquoted Martial, and muddled Jonson's story from Pliny.[4]

The 'Informations' have their faults, but Drummond has been hard done by on their account. Critics have complained that they are gossipy, badly organized, inaccurate; that they should not be graced with the name of 'Conversations', since the talk is all Jonson and no Drummond, that Drummond, after picking his guest's brains, then murdered his reputation. Drummond made the notes of Jonson's opinions for his own instruction and delight, and he never published

1. *Works* (1711) pp. 226-7. Drummond's remark is difficult to explain. Spenser's *Amoretti* are a sonnet-sequence in the Petrarchan fashion; the usual conventions are followed. Perhaps some of the sonnets are too simple and undecorated for Drummond's taste.

2. By 'Anacreontick' Drummond means the love lyric not in the Petrarchan style—he is not referring to the metre. He said of Donne that although he excelled, his verse could not compare with that of Sidney or Alexander, since it was of a different kind: 'They can hardly be compared together, trading diverse Paths; the one flying swift, but low; the other, like the Eagle, surpassing the Clouds.' Drummond added that Donne might 'easily be the best Epigrammatist we have found in English; of which I have not yet seen any come near the Ancients.' Drummond was fond of epigrams, and wrote a number himself. His praise of Alexander, a poet noted for his rectitude and decorum, may have been stimulated by his friendship with him.

3. Shakespeare's sonnets were first printed in 1609.

4. The so-called 'Conversations' have been printed a number of times, the best critical edition being in C. H. Herford and Percy Simpson *Ben Jonson* (Oxford 1925) I, pp. 128-78.

12. King James VI and I. From Drummond's poem *Forth feasting* (Cat. 765).

The
High and mighty
Prince, IAMES
KING of great
Britane, Fraunce
and Ireland, &c

HONI SOIT QVI MALY PENSE

P·ALL'AS ARMATA,

OR

Actii. f. 18

Militarie Instructions for the Learned:

And all Generous Spirits, who affect the Profession of Armes.

THE FIRST PART.

Containing the Exercise of Infanterie, as well Antient, as Moderne: Wherein are Clearelie set downe all the Postures and Motions, belonging to Battaillions of Foote.

PRO PRINCIPE ET PATRIA IN VTRVMQVE PARAT

MARTI MVSISQVE

C. dickesonn Sc.

Exc. I. fin Lason

Printed at *Edinburgh* by the Heires of *Andro Hart*, 1627.

them. What he was interested in was Jonson's opinions, not his own; his heading 'Information be Ben Jonston to W.D. . . .' is quite clear; these are not notes of a conversation. His character of Jonson is just:

> 'He is a great lover and praiser of himself, a contemner and Scorner of others, given rather to losse a friend, than a Jest, jealous of every word and action of those about him (especiallie after drink which is one of the Elements jn which he liveth) a dissembler of ill parts which raigne jn him, a bragger of some good that he wanteth, thinketh nothing well bot what either he himself, or some of his friends and Countrymen hath said or done, he is passionately kynde and angry, carelesse either to gaine or keep, Vindicative, but if he be well answered, at himself. . . .'[1]

1. Herford and Simpson, p. 151.

From the 'Informations' and from what is already known of Jonson this seems a temperate and moderate judgement.

Being the kind of man he was Drummond was content to record. The questions he did ask Jonson (that is, the questions he makes a note of in the 'Informations') are trifling, and just the sort he would ask. He wished to know the grammar of 'them, they, those,' and this Jonson told him. It must be remembered that Drummond had made an effort to rid his poetry of Scotticisms, and that he was one of the first of his countrymen to write in English. He was taken with Jonson's wit, but being Drummond he often missed the point of the joke. In his manuscripts he had made a collection of epigrams, witticisms and *bon mots*; he loved a joke, though he handled them clumsily.

It is difficult to judge what effect Jonson's visit had upon Drummond. His own opinions were well formed by the time he heard Jonson's; he was as well read, although in different literatures; what seems to have mattered most with him was the opportunity to hear first-hand gossip. Drummond had read Drayton, Daniel, the poets and the playwrights; Jonson came and gave the names flesh, and to Drummond he must have cut them down to size quite cruelly. He 'thinketh nothing well bot what either he himself, or some of his friends and Countrymen hath said or done'. Is this what made Drummond answer him back, till Jonson became 'vindicative at himself'?

Drummond must have spent hour upon hour copying out passages from his favourite authors, for the Hawthornden manuscripts are full of his gleanings. On the face of it, there seems to be little we can learn from these notes, except perhaps which books he was most fond of. The *Arcadia* is there, the French poets of the Plèiade, some Italian poets, and several selections from English plays, from Marston's *Parasitaster*, Dekker's *Converted courtezan*, Chapman's *All fooles*, or Day's *Law tricks*.

Drummond did scribble in the margins of his books, and here it would seem is the best quarry for his critical opinions. Most of this *marginalia* is unfortunately (but knowing Drummond, typically) quite uninteresting, being mere pointing of special words in the text. And these words are hardly ever themselves particularly significant.

13. Title-page. Sir Thomas Kellie, *Pallas armata* (Cat. 852).

Drummond's usual annotations are these: the translation of words, the picking out of figures of speech, and the overlining of some purple passages.

In two books in his library he goes further. In Alexander's *Monarchicke tragedies* Drummond made notes as he read, on the sources of Alexander's borrowings: these were, according to Drummond (and in order of frequency), from Sidney, Du Bartas, Tasso, Ariosto, Montemayor and Jacques de la Taille. On his copy of Fairefax's *Godfrey of Bulloigne* his notes on sources are just as ambitious, and added to these are numerous comments on the merit of the translation. It may be worth looking at these *marginalia* closely, for besides being interesting in themselves they tell us much about Drummond as a critic.

Drummond's comments on Fairefax are so numerous that for ease I have classified them into eleven types (listed in order of frequency).

1. He notes what is introduced by Fairefax, what differs from the original Italian, and what Fairefax omits.
2. He notes whether Fairefax improves upon Tasso, or falls short in his rendering.
3. He notes the introduction of new characters in the story, special scenes, etc.
4. He notes figures of speech (e.g. *simile*).
5. He notes misprints (e.g. on D5r, 'sinne' for 'sunne').
6. He notes literary indebtedness and other authors' use of the same stories.
7. He notes passages of especial beauty in the original.
8. He notes rhyming schemes (e.g. 2D3v, '*feminius*').
9. He makes comments on the behaviour of the characters and remarks on general truths.
10. He notes failings in the metres (e.g. on H1r).
11. He makes a few comments of general praise which cannot well be classified, such as 'this inuention surpasseth all thes of the former ages' (on 2E4v), referring to the myrtle which gives birth to the nymph (in the eighteenth book).

It is worth quoting a few of Drummond's remarks so that their tone may be felt: against the sixteenth book, the eighteenth stanza, he wrote 'tuo louers alone' and 'this st. matcheth that of Tasso'. The stanza runs:

Her breasts were naked, for the day was hot,
Her lockes vnbound, wau'd in the wanton winde;
Somedeale she swet (tir'd with the game you wot)
Her sweat-drops bright, white, round, like pearles of Inde,
Her humide eies a firie smile foorth shot,
That like sunne-beames in siluer fountaines shinde,
Ore him her lookes she hung, and her soft breast
The pillow was, where he and loue tooke rest.

In the fourth book, stanza 29—the description of the nymph Armida—against the couplet

Yet neuer eie to Cupids seruice vow'd
Beheld a face of such a louely pride,

14. Creation, the fifth day.
Guillaume de Saluste Du Bartas,
La diuina settimana (Cat. 1277).

Drummond wrote 'Beautie' and the first line of the Italian, 'Argo non mai, none vide Cipro o Delo . . .'. Against the comparison of Armida's hair to the beams of the sun, he wrote 'Simile', and beside the last two lines of the stanza, 'this distich is the Translators'. Against the next stanza (which continues Armida's decription) 'which of the tuo hath done best, Tasso or Fairefax'. Two stanzas further on he copies out the Italian for the first two lines

> Come per acqua o per cristallo intero
> Trapassa il raggio, e nol divide o parte,

against Fairefax's

> As when the sun-beames diue through Tagus waue,
> To spie the store-house of his springing gold,

as though to point out the freedom of the translation. Drummond surely read Fairefax with the Italian at his side. His criticism is sensible (though elementary, as far as it goes).

Drummond found literary comparisons in *Godfrey of Bulloigne*, and in Virgil, Heliodorus, Montemayor, and Spenser. He noticed the similarity that Tasso's shepherd (of the seventh book) bore to Spenser's Melibee (*Faerie Queene*, Book six, part 2, canto nine), and how each character relates that once in their youth they had ambitions for wordly things, and spurned the country life and forests sweet. On the stanza which describes Armida looking in the mirror (Book sixteen, stanza twenty) Drummond noted 'See Diana of Montemaior Cireno holding his mistris glas lib. 1.' Here are the two verses for comparison, with Fairefax first.

> Downe by the louers side there pendant was
> A Christall mirrour, bright, pure, smooth and neat,
> He rose and to his mistresse held the glas,
> (A noble Page, grac'd with that seruice great)
> She, with glad lookes; he with enflam'd (alas)
> Beautie and loue beheld, both in one seat;
> Yet them in sundrie objects each espies,
> She, in the glasse; he, saw them in her eies.

When Syrenus holds the mirror to Diana he sings

> For if I enjoy with free
> Pleasure, seeing before me
> Face and eies, where Cupid stands:
> So though seeing in my hands,
> That which in thine eies I see.[1]

1. Jorge de Montemayor *Diana*, trs. B. Yong (London 1598) p. 7.

Had Drummond been living today he would have been well equipped to write scholarly articles of literary history.

It must be clear by now what sort of critic he was. He took pleasure in the depth of his reading, in his languages, in his memory. He trained himself to follow faithfully a school of opinion that was already being rejected while he was a child: his taste was towards the classical, the artificial, the decorative. He liked to keep to the rules and see decorum observed. Within the limits he set himself his taste was excellent. The best illustration of this is his own poetry:

1. Kastner, II, pp. 172-289. Here are four groups of poems, collected from the Hawthornden MSS by previous editors or found there by Kastner himself. Fogle discovered some additional poems in the Hawthornden MSS. See Fogle, pp. 187-209.

he suppressed all that he thought unworthy (and his modern editors and critics have done him no great good by printing all his suppressions).[1] He liked to see his work in print, but he kept back a mass of verse he thought unfit for public view. And like this private verse — which was done for his own amusement — his criticism was for himself and his friends, and was never intended to be seen by outsiders.

One last opinion of Drummond's, again from his copy of Fairefax: against Armida's confession

> I thee enchanted and allur'd to loue,
> Wicked deceit, craft worthie sharpe repriefe,
> Mine honor gaue I thee all gifts aboue,
> And of my beauties made thee Lord and chiefe,
> And to my sutors old what I denaid,
> That gaue I thee (my louer new) vnpraid.

he wrote 'common coustume of women'. Drummond was fond of platitudes.

15. One of Drummond's annotations on his copy of Jonson's *Works* (Cat. 850). The comment on Beaumont, He died ere he told 30 yeeres, was one of the 6 wits at court', echoes Drummond's words in the *Conversations*, and must have come from Jonson himself. See J. R. Barker 'A pendant to Drummond of Hawthornden's *Conversations*' *RES* XVI (1965) 284-8.

Epigrammes. 78[2]

LIIII.

ON CHEV'RIL.

CHev'ril cryes out, my verses libells are;
   And threatens the *starre-chamber*, and the barre :
What are thy petulant pleadings, CHEV'RIL, then,
   That quit'ft the caufe fo oft, and rayl'ft at men ?

LV.

TO FRANCIS BEAVMONT.

HOw I doe loue thee BEAVMONT, and thy *Mufe*,
   That vnto me doft fuch religion vfe !
How I doe feare my felfe, that am not worth
   The leaft indulgent thought thy pen drops forth !
At once thou mak'ft me happie, and vnmak'ft ;
   And giuing largely to me, more thou tak'ft.
What fate is mine, that fo it felfe bereaues ?
   What art is thine, that fo thy friend deceiues ?
When euen there, where moft thou prayfeft mee,
   For writing better, I muft enuie thee.

LVI.

ON POET-APE.

POore POET-APE, that would be thought our chiefe,
   Whofe workes are eene the fripperie of wit,
From brocage is become fo bold a thiefe,
   As we, the rob'd, leaue rage, and pittie it.
At firft he made low fhifts, would picke and gleane,
   Buy the reuerfion of old playes ; now growne
To'a little wealth, and credit in the *fcene*,
   He takes vp all, makes each mans wit his owne.
And, told of this, he flights it. Tut, fuch crimes
   The fluggifh gaping auditor deuoures ;
He markes not whofe 'twas firft ; and after-times
   May iudge it to be his, as well as ours.
Foole, as if halfe eyes will not know a fleece
   From locks of wooll, or fhreds from the whole peece ?

LVII.

ON BAVDES, AND VSVRERS.

IF, as their ends, their fruits were fo, the fame
   Baudrie', and vfurie were one kind of game.
                    Vuu 2   LVIII.

Book Prices

By the time Drummond returned from France in 1608 he had collected at least a third of his library, and in 1611 he set down a detailed catalogue of these books. His father had died the previous year; now at the age of twenty-four, Drummond was the Laird of Hawthornden, and this catalogue was presumably one way of taking stock of his possessions. The catalogue lists 546 titles, and of these only 130 match books that have survived either at Edinburgh or elsewhere. Thus the first importance of the catalogue is that it gives 416 previously unknown titles from Drummond's library. Besides this, it shows how Drummond arranged his books, where he bought them, and what he paid for them. Many a more imaginative or less canny man might not have bothered to keep accounts in such detail; Drummond must have travelled through England and France with his notebook always at the ready. Of the 546 books he listed in the catalogue he was able to record the price he paid for 401 of them, and the remainder were mostly those that he had inherited from his father, his uncle, and his friends. These prices are interesting. They add to the rather scanty information that is in print on English book prices of the time, and they provide comparative French prices, which again, are not readily available.

Drummond bought 323 books in France, and 76 in England. He paid 2,399 sous for his French books (that is, about £10 18s.) and £6 13s. 7d. for his English books. Two prices in Scots money are noted: these amount to 3s. 2d. sterling. In all Drummond paid £17 14s. 9d. for his 401 books.

What, if anything, do these figures reveal? Were books cheaper in France than in England, in London than in Edinburgh? And which particular books were cheap, and which expensive? Is there anything about the individual prices that is surprising? There is only one detailed study of English retail book-prices of the early seventeenth century—by Francis R. Johnson.[1] Johnson's conclusions, based on the prices of 521 books, indicate that book prices between 1560 and 1635 remained remarkably steady, and though the price index doubled in that time book prices hardly moved. Prices in fact stayed below the level set by the Stationers Company in 1598, when they ordered that the maximum price for a printed book be 1d. for 2 sheets set in pica, and 1d. for 1 sheet set in brevier or long primer.

1. 'Notes on English retail book-prices, 1550-1640' *The Library* v (1951) 83-112. In this article Johnson argues that there is only one sensible way to estimate book prices, that is, by the sheet. This, the bibliographer's way of looking at the cost of a book, is calculated simply by dividing the number of leaves in the book by its format— which of course gives one the number of sheets—and then dividing the number of sheets into the price of the book. The point of this operation is that the cost of a book can be reckoned per sheet regardless of the book's size, folio or octavo or whatever, taking into account, of course, the usual printers' costs of composition and proof reading.

Thus, when Drummond was in London, the usual price of a printed book was ½d. a sheet. Books that were much above these rates, Johnson found, were not ordinary books, that is, they were books that would naturally cost the printer more to compose and print. Law books, music books, and illustrated books were all expensive. Other books were priced dear because they sold well — the latest works of the favourite poets, for instance. Erotica was also expensive.

Drummond's English book prices agree with Johnson's figures, although two variables make any exact comparison impossible. In many cases there is no way of knowing whether Drummond bought the book new or second-hand, unbound or bound. We can safely assume that a new book would be bought unbound, and that an old one would already be bound: this accounts for what at first seems surprising — that there is little difference in the prices between obviously old and obviously new books. The books in between — those that are a few years old on purchase, and thus may be second-hand and bound — are those it is impossible to be sure about, and we can only say, when we come to any especially high price, that the binding must have been out of the ordinary. The highest English price Drummond paid for a book was 10s. for Joannes Scapula's Greek dictionary, a large reference work; this seems reasonable. For Samuel Daniel's *Works* he paid 7s.; at 1.14d. per sheet this was expensive, but since it was printed in 1602 it might have been second-hand, in a good binding. (Bindings could cost anything from 2d. or even 1d. for a small cheap wrapper to as much as 15s. or more on a grand folio, stamped and clasped, but a usual price would be 2s. 6d. And Drummond probably followed the usual practice of having several works bound together.) For Sidney's *Arcadia* he paid 6s., for the *Faerie Queene* 6s., for Yong's translation of Montemaior's *Diana*, 7s. Poetry and romance were expensive. He paid 8s. for the *Country farme* (a translation from the French of a practical work on husbandry) a price probably made high by the inclusion of woodcuts and diagrams: this might be either of the quarto editions of 1600 or 1606, but not the later folio edition augmented by Gervase Markham.[1] At the other end of the scale Drummond paid only 4d. each for Spenser's *Shepheardes calender*, *Fowre hymnes*, and *Amoretti* and *Epithalamion*. These were presumably second-hand, although the first, the most popular (five editions between 1579 and 1597), might be new. Small though these works are, the price seems very low. For plays in quarto Johnson found that the usual price was 6d.; Drummond paid 4d. for the second quarto of *Romeo and Juliet* (printed 1599), again, perhaps, second-hand.

French prices turn out to be much cheaper than English; on an average, a book in Paris seems to have cost one half of its price in London or even less. Drummond gives his French prices in two forms: *libs.* (that is, livres or pounds) and sous.[2] The chief values of French currency at the beginning of the seventeenth century were crowns (or écus), livres and sous. In English money the crown was worth a little more than six shillings, the livre about two shillings, and the sou was roughly equivalent to a penny — it is impossible to be more precise, for not only did the number of sous to the crown

1. See F. N. L. Poynter *A bibliography of Gervase Markham* (Oxford Bibliographical Society, Oxford 1962) pp. 148-50.

2. Indicated in Drummond's catalogue by what looks like our shilling sign.

fluctuate, but also the comparative values of the French and English currencies varied from year to year. French money suffered less from inflation, and comparatively speaking was worth more than English; both of course were based on the actual value in weight of the silver or gold in the coinage. Gerard Malynes in the *Lex mercatoria* (1622) says that a French crown might cost an Englishman 6s. 3d.,[1] and we can check this figure by comparing the weight of silver in the two currencies.[2] The value that is most useful for us here is the sou: to Drummond it was worth one English penny, or a little less.

Assuming, then, that Drummond's French prices are typical, it would certainly have been worth a Scotsman's while to go to Paris solely to buy books, if (as is likely) it would be cheaper to take them home in his luggage than to pay the retail price in Edinburgh. A letter written in 1617 by Henry Erskine to his father, John, Earl of Mar seems to confirm this (Henry and his brother were doing what Drummond had done ten years earlier—studying law at Bourges and Paris, and generally completing their education). Henry says: '. . . I will not be prodigall in nothing except in baying of bookes, and yit none bot suche as shall be necessaire, and I asseure myselfe that your Lordship will allow me in this, seeing that it was be your commande that I followed my studies in France. . . .'[3]

In Paris, Drummond paid three livres (6s.) for his copy of the *Corpus iuris civilis*: the usual editions of this, the civil lawyer's Bible, are folios, large and thick. Unfortunately Drummond's copy has disappeared, so there is no way of estimating a price per sheet. For *Memoires de l'estat de France* he paid the highest price recorded: 6 livres (12s.) Again, this book is lost, but it is most likely to have been the octavo edition; printed at Middelburg in 1576 in three large volumes, and so certainly second-hand; the price suggests that the set must have had a handsome binding. For Plutarch's *Lives* (in Latin), he paid 40 sous; for Despauterius' *Grammatica magna*, 30 sous; for *Roland furieux* 20 sous. For Clavius' edition and commentary on Sacrobosco's *Sphæra* he paid the high price of 48 sous; for the works of Plato (in Latin) 50 sous. These, however, are the exceptions, for Drummond bought mostly smaller books, octavos and less. I would guess that he had an eye to their weight, for he would have to think of the cost of taking them home. The normal price for the smaller books is in single figures—3, 5, 8 sous, once as low as 1. Working with those that have survived and can be identified in Edinburgh University Library, the prices come to about a farthing a sheet—an average of one half of an English price. Second-hand prices are only slightly lower, for again the cost of binding would tend to cancel out the difference.

I have not been able to find many comparative French book prices for the early seventeenth century (there is plenty of information about prices in both the sixteenth and eighteenth centuries.)[4] The inventories of Parisian printers and booksellers that appear in Pichon and Vicaire are mostly from the mid-sixteenth century, although a few date from the 1590s, and the prices in there seem much the same as those paid by Drummond.[5] Here again it is hard to be precise, since only in a few cases, when a binding is actually

1. *Consuetudo, vel lex mercatoria, or the ancient law-merchant* 3rd ed. (London 1686) p. 290.

2. There were 20 sous in a livre tournois, and three livres to an écu. The franc—which was coming into use at this time—was equivalent to a livre tournois. Rene Sédillot states that the livre tournois was worth 11.06 grammes of fine silver in 1602. This he derives from Avenel, whose economic history on prices is still the standard work. See Sédillot *Le Franc* (Paris 1953) p. 75. At the same time the English shilling was worth 92 grains of fine silver. See R. W. Cochran-Patrick *Records of the coinage of Scotland* (Edinburgh 1876) pp. lvii-lix.

3. *Hist. Com. Mar & Kellie MSS.* (1930) p. 97.

4. David Pottinger *The French book trade in the Ancien Régime* (Cambridge, Mass. 1958) discusses prices, and indicates the French authorities, who, however, seem to give little or no information on early seventeenth-century prices.

5. Jérome Pichon & Georges Vicaire *Documents pour servir à l'histoire des libraires de Paris. 1486-1600* (Paris 1895). See, for example, the inventories on pp. 161-2, or p. 167.

1. Georges Lepreux *Gallia typographia* (Paris 1911) I, i, p. 226.

2. Pierre de l'Estoile in his famous journal records buying two books in 1607 that Drummond also bought at the same time: Melanchthon's *De pace ecclesiae* and Du Moulin's *Apologie pour la cene*. He paid 4 sous for the first and 18 for the second. *Memoires-Journal*, VIII, 335, 340.

mentioned, can one be sure whether a book is new or second-hand. Lepreux in the *Gallia typographia* gives a few of Robert Estienne's prices —[1] again from the mid-sixteenth century —but nothing for the early seventeenth century. I have, however, found nothing on French book prices that would make me doubt Drummond's figures.[2]

If then it was profitable to buy books in France, what sort of books would a foreign student buy? The obvious answer of course, is books that were printed there, and if one was in Paris, particularly books that were printed in Paris: these would be the cheapest. Thus the most common imprint on Drummond's title-pages is that of Paris. Paris was a great printing centre, and compared with the London printers, standards were much higher. The London printers had the greatest difficulty in composing and printing a learned book, and those they did produce were seldom pleasing to look at; the Parisians, on the other hand, numbered amongst themselves scholars as well as craftsmen, and a considerable proportion of their output was in Latin and Greek, designed for the international market. All this is well known. From Drummond's purchases, however, it is clear that Paris was not only a city of printers, but also a centre of the international book trade. Books from the presses of Venice, Lyons, Geneva, Heidelberg, Leyden, Antwerp or Frankfurt were all for sale in Paris. Most of these imported books must have been second-hand (judging by their date of printing), and possibly these travelled back from Venice or Germany with their first purchasers on the return from some Grand Tour. Others may well have been bought in by booksellers particularly for the French market. There does not seem to have been any effective prohibition of Protestant books in Catholic France, for Drummond bought a number in Paris or Bourges. While he was in Rouen he bought Pollot's *Dialogues contre la pluralité des religions*, a Huguenot work from the presses of La Rochelle.

Apart from English books, Paris plainly had a better (and cheaper) selection in every subject than London or Edinburgh. Drummond bought two Italian books in Scotland, 18 in England, and 39 in France. The figures for other subjects are in the same pattern: in Greek, 20 in France, 11 in England; in Hebrew, 5 in France, none in England; in theology, 10 in France, none in England; in law, 14 in France, none in England; in philosophy, 27 in France, 10 in England; poetry, 30 in France, 6 in England; prose, 69 in France, 11 in England; and of the French books, 102 in France, none in England. These are the figures only for the books priced, so there may be a little distortion, but the inference is clear: though learned and literary books could be quite easily bought at home, they would be the thing to shop for in Paris.

I have only been able to find one piece of information about the prices that Drummond had to pay for books in Edinburgh, and although only four book-prices are recorded in this note, they are interesting, and perhaps worth quoting in full. The note is in Drummond's hand.[3] It seems to have been meant for a friend or a merchant travelling to London and France, for it is a list of books

3. Hawthornden MSS, vol. VIII, f. 152.

for him to buy and bring back. It reads:

The Guide into Tongues
>> by Iohon Minshew. London 1617.
>> or his great Dictionarye in English. 1617.[1]
It will cost 20 marke and aboue.
Famiani Stradæ poemata. 18d.

Summæ Thomæ Aquinatis 16/s ster.
Adone del cauallier Marini.
printed at Venice, or if it can not be found the edition at Paris.
yee know the prize.
>> It will cost at Paris 18/s ster or 20.

The first book here—Minshew's *Guide into tonges*—is a large folio in 6's, 282 leaves, an English dictionary with occasional meanings in eleven languages. The very high price of 20 merks (£1 2s. 2d. Eng.), which works out at just under 2d. per sheet, was probably justified by the expense of composing and printing such a complex work. Passing over Strada's poems (the price is unremarkable) the next item is the *Summa theologica* of St Thomas Aquinas, at 16s. sterling. It is interesting that Drummond should have wanted such a book (considering his country and his religion) and significant that he should be prepared to pay the high price of 16s. for it. I would date this note to about 1625 or 1626: at least two new editions of the *Summa* were then available; that of Rome 1619, or that of Cologne 1622. The cost of the last book, Giovanni Battista Marino's *L'Adone* also seems very high: for these poems Drummond was prepared to pay 18s. sterling or even £1. However, *L'Adone* was a large handsome work, and it is not improbable that it should sell for a high price. As Drummond noted, there were two editions: the one of Paris 1623 was a folio of 575 pages; the one of Venice, 1623 a quarto of 577 pages. It is quite clear from this note that Drummond must have had access to a catalogue. Printers, such as Andro Hart or his heirs, would certainly receive the Frankfurt Fair catalogues, and these would be the most likely source of information on new foreign books. At this time the catalogues were being printed by Sigismund Latomus (until Autumn 1625) and his heirs (from Spring 1626). There were other catalogues, including the unofficial Frankfurt catalogues, Basle catalogues, or those of the Latin Stock of the Stationers Company: Drummond's notes suggest that such catalogues were used by the bookbuyer far from the market.[1]

With the sum of £17 14s. 9d. Drummond bought 401 books, approximately a quarter of his library. Was Drummond's collection uncommonly large for his time, his class, and especially, his country? Was this an unusual amount of money to spend on books? I would say no to both questions. If we give Drummond a library of 1,600 titles—and this is being conservative—then on the face of it he does seem to have had more books than his contemporaries. Sears Jayne in his *Library catalogues of the English Renaissance* records only a few men with more,[2] and these are usually persons with more money and a higher social position than Drummond. However, it is not of much value to compare Lord Lumley's or Archbishop

1. See Graham Pollard and Albert Ehrman *The distribution of books by catalogue* (Roxburghe Club, Cambridge 1965) pp. 70-139.

2. (Berkeley 1956).

41

Bancroft's library with that of a Scottish laird, and to use Sears Jayne's material as a yardstick could be misleading. Jayne's records are chiefly based on will inventories and catalogues of gifts, and they rely heavily on Oxford and Cambridge college benefactors' rolls. Thus, the type of information one gets is a record of how many books a man might have on his death, of who gave what to which college.

The second difficulty about using Sears Jayne is that of quality: are 1,000 theological tracts worth as much as 1,000 solid folio volumes of patristic commentary? Each would appear as 1,000 pb, that is, printed books. Before we can compare libraries, we need to know what books are in the collection, as well as how many.

How could Drummond afford to keep up with the nobles, archbishops and wealthy English gentry? He could not and did not: the Drummonds were far from wealthy. Sir John Drummond on his death in 1610 left his heirs £14,085 6s. 8d., plus his lands and house.[1] The money was to be divided equally between his three sons, and William, the eldest, inherited the house and estate. This seems a considerable inheritance; the money, however, was Scots—worth less than a twelfth of English.[2] In the details of Sir John's will his true status emerges more clearly: he had 'sex scoir of schip', 'fourtene drawin oxin', 'thrie ky', 'thrie work horsis'. Sown on his ground (he died in August) he had £500 worth of oats, £500 worth of beir (barley), and £64 worth of peas. He had 3,600 merks in ready cash, personal possessions of £400, and he was owed the large sum of £9,900. All this is evidence of a modest estate, but not real wealth. The printer, Andro Hart, for instance, left £19,528 12s. (Scots) to his heirs, though admittedly no land.

Drummond himself left only £3,935 (compared to his father's £14,000), but, like many other lairds, he seems to have suffered from the confused economic state of Scotland in the 1630s and 1640s. His lands, however, did stay intact, and he had built himself a new house.[3] All these figures, even if we can make complicated adjustments into modern values, do not give us a clear idea of how a laird like Drummond lived. He had enough money not to work, he was kept two years in France, he could buy books, he was able to build himself a house: this seems comfortable enough. Yet in cash value his library cannot have been worth much more than £90 English. In 1640 Andrew Ainslie gave 240 merks to Edinburgh Tounis College: this gift bought only 42 books (which, at this rate, would cost roughly 6s. English each). If Drummond had bought books of such value and size, he would have had no more than 260 in his library instead of 1,600. Drummond does not seem to have cared for the expensive binding, or if he did, he was not able to afford it. The few books that survived David Laing's wholesale rebinding of the Drummond Collection are bound in an inexpensive calf, and unless his gift to the university was immediately rebound in 1627, many of Drummond's books, judging by the evidence of the 1636 catalogue, were bound together.

Drummond's books are 'guid gear in sma bulk'. They are evidence of the revolution that printing had just made in one of the first applications of mechanical mass-production: books could be small

1. His will was probated on 4 January 1611. *Com. Edinburgh record of testaments*, vol. 46, f. 211.

2. See Cochran-Patrick, I, p. lxxvi.

3. Drummond's will was probated on 22 July 1653. *Com. Edinburgh record of testaments*, vol. 67, ff. 158-9.

and cheap, and one could buy one's culture in quantity. The luxurious folio of Virgil's works, complete with learned commentary, might still be the only fit purchase for the wealthy nobleman, but a gentleman of slender means like Drummond could now buy the same matter from the best presses in octavo at a quarter the price. For £90 sterling he had a library of more books than many wealthier collectors—the same authors perhaps, but in smaller, cheaper editions. We might compare this sum of £90 with the annual pension of £20 which Ben Jonson received from Lord Pembroke for the express purpose of keeping up his library.

In one of the few articles that specifically sets out to consider the reading taste of the early seventeenth century in Scotland, Miss M.A. Bald in 1926 dismissed Drummond's library as an oddity, a freak. It was hardly, she thought, 'evidence of a general Scottish interest in fine literature', and Drummond's taste in books 'was infinitely removed from that of his Scottish contemporaries'.[1] She based this opinion on her study of four kinds of evidence: (i) the wills of the Edinburgh booksellers, printed in the *Bannatyne Club Miscellany*; (ii) the libraries of Queen Mary and King James VI; (iii) the old university catalogues; (iv) the odd references in official documents like the State Papers. I have objections to all four sources, for none of them seem to be an adequate guide to the reading taste of Scots society. The booksellers' inventories are evidence of what they had in stock, for sale. The greater part of this stock was educational and religious books, which would be evidence of what was taught and preached, but not necessarily evidence of what was read, for many buyers, like Drummond, would deal directly or indirectly with foreign markets. The royal libraries are interesting in themselves; to a large extent they, too, are irrelevant as documents of taste: Mary Queen of Scots' private taste was French, and James' books were not those of his own choice, being bought in his youth for his education or presented to him by his subjects. Neither Mary or James was a typical member of educated Scots society. The university catalogues are yet more untrustworthy. They show what books were being studied, and what books were being donated, but again, not what books were being read. It seems ridiculous to judge the taste of the reading public by Clement Litel's formal gift to the Tounis College of 270 works of theology, for like most donations, then and now, these books would be chosen to edify and impress, not to delight. With this very thought in mind, a later donor to Edinburgh University Library, Robert Johnston, expressly excluded his Italian, French and Spanish books from his gift, since he apparently thought them too exotic for Scottish students.[2] The fourth source of evidence that Miss Bald cited—references to titles in official documents—I will ignore, since these are too fragmentary and trivial to be worth considering.

If these sources do not tell us much about the reading taste of Scottish literate society in the early seventeenth century, where then do we look? Miss Bald came to the conclusion that very little literature was read in Scotland at that time, and she found this depressing. But was she right? It is most difficult comparing collections

1. 'Vernacular Books imported into Scotland, 1500-1625,' *The Scottish Historical Review* XXIII (1926) 254-67.

2. He 'ordaynit his italian, frensch and spanish books to be chainged for uthers to be sent to the said colledge.' Johnston's gift was made in 1640. Edinburgh University Library records.

of books, since so many different points have to be considered. Some of these I have already discussed: the books themselves, were they large or small, expensive or inexpensive, finely bound or cheaply wrapped? Their subjects: were they textbooks or literature, law-books or philosophy, practical works or Bibles? And the owners: were they princes or scholars, gentlemen or bishops? The records, too, from this period are most scanty, and the most probable place to find any details of books is in wills, inventories and catalogues of donations made to institutions like the universities. Not much besides these has survived, but then not much was likely to survive. Because we have now very little evidence of the private libraries and reading habits of Scottish society of 350 years ago, it would surely be a mistake to say that few men owned much beyond Bibles, sermons, grammars, and the odd classic, and to reject one very real proof to the contrary—Drummond's library—as the exception that proves the rule.

Besides, there is some evidence that other Scots did own books. The same *Bannatyne Miscellany* that recorded the printers' wills has details of a few private libraries: that of Adam King, an advocate, was valued on his death in 1620 for £1,440 Scots (£120 sterling)—which would be more than Drummond's was worth. King had lived abroad (he was a professor of philosophy and mathematics at Paris) but he returned to practise law in Edinburgh. David Ferguson and Thomas Buchanan, both ministers, had libraries worth £100 and £300 (Scots) respectively.[1] To Aberdeen's Marischal College Thomas Reid, Latin secretary to the King, gave his library of about 1,350 books in 1624; his books were mostly Latin literature, some Greek, some natural and moral philosophy, some theology, history and grammar, with a few English books like the inevitable *Arcadia*.[2] This was, however, reputed to be 'the best library that ever the north pairtes of Scotland saw' according to Gordon's *Scots affairs*.[3] Some of the libraries of the Scottish landowning families go back to this period, and houses like Newbattle, Seton, Tyninghame or the Hirsel have or had many books that were bought by Drummond's contemporaries. The Lindseys had a good library, so too, it seems, did the Dalyells. These we know about because the families have kept their heritage; did the poorer gentry whose posterity has disappeared have nothing?

Miss Bald's opinion that no·one in Drummond's day read literature in Scotland except Drummond, might have some weight if one should show that there was no intellectual commerce between Scotland and the continent, that Scotland had no poets and prose writers, and that Drummond had neither friend nor neighbour with whom he could share his strange enthusiasms. This is not possible. Drummond was sent to France as a young man, and he heard the lectures in law at Paris and Bourges. He was one of many Scots there, for the majority of would-be lawyers had to read their civil law in France—the only alternative was a laborious apprenticeship at home in Edinburgh. In fact, at times there seems to have been so many Scots in the university town like Bourges and Toulouse that a man might have difficulty learning French.[4] Even Paris was

1. *Bannatyne Miscellany* (Bannatyne Club, Edinburgh 1836) II, p. 190.

2. There is a MS catalogue of Reid's library still at Aberdeen.

3. James Gordon, *History of Scots affairs* (Spalding Club, Aberdeen 1841) III, p. 89.

4. Henry Erskine told his father that 'if we had stayed still in Bourges we could not have lernit the France, in respek of the great number of Scotsmen that is there for the present . . .'. Quoted in David Mathews *Scotland under Charles I* (London 1955) p. 201.

over-crowded: John Carnegie wrote to his brother in 1610 that he was quitting Paris for Poitiers 'for be reason of the gryt number of Scottis men I can do no guid here'.[1] France was the Scottish finishing school. It is difficult to believe that of all the hundreds of Scots who came to France to complete their education and their manners, Drummond alone cultivated a taste for literature. And we can hardly say that there were no poets and prose writers in Scotland, or suppose that those who were writing had no audience. There is no need here to go into this; a mere mention of the *Delitiae poetarum Scotorum* suffices; such men as Arthur Johnston, David Hume or John Leech upheld the high standards of Scottish Latin. The court poets — Sir William Alexander, Sir Robert Ayton, Sir David Murray — though they went south with James, still called themselves Scots. Then there is Drummond himself. We have perhaps cause to maintain that Scots literary culture was derivative, but no reason at all to claim that there was none.

1. Mathews, p. 205.

16. Title-page. *The araignment of John Selman* (Cat. 906).

45

17. The death of Bacchus. Ovid *Las,
transformaciones* (Cat. 1315).

Drummond's father was not a reading man, if we can rely on the list of books he left his eldest son. Apart from the *Arcadia*, Lyly's *Eupheus*, the anthology *England's parnassus*, the *Hyperotomachia*, and an English translation of Ovid's *Metamorphoses*, his books were on the practical side: works of popular medicine, devotions, a French grammar and guides on husbandry and letter-writing. Sir John Drummond died in 1610, and by that year Drummond had formed his own tastes and collected a good part of his library.

Drummond seems to have begun his book-buying as soon as he graduated from Edinburgh, notably on his first visit to London in 1606. As his reading lists show he was then discovering the lighter matter of English literature—romances, courtesy books and plays. And so he read *The mirror of knighthood*, *The courtier* and *A midsummer nights dream* and he bought *Zepheria* and Lodge's *Phillis*. In France during the next two years he indulged his appetite for literature (although he did also buy a few books of law, for example in 1607 a *Lexicon juris civilis* in a small cheap edition). He saw (and took notes on) Italian comedies at Bourges; he bought most of his Tasso and Ariosto and the French writers of the Pléiade. Back in Scotland he found Marino. By 1611 he had collected about one third of his library, and it was still nearly all literary or academic. In this year he made his first systematic catalogue. Into his thirties Drummond continued adding to his Italian, French, Spanish and English poets and dramatists, but he appears to have become more and more interested in books of the day, political and religious controversies, mostly in English. From these years there is in his library a wide range of more popular stuff—voyages, travel-guides, news, astrologies, prognostications, English and French satires and polemics—and a quantity of neo-Latin occasional verse, most of it written by his friends and fellow Scots. In middle life Drummond seems to have turned away from poetry towards medicine and theology (as befits a man in bad health). To these years I date his lists of devotional books, his purchase of Fernel's *Universa medicina* and St Thomas Aquinas' *Summa theologica*. And since he was writing his own *History of the five James*, that portion of his library which is missing must include some more works of history.

Judging by his catalogue of 1611 Drummond arranged his books

46

first of all according to language, then according to subject. For his day this was a logical system, and one used by professional librarians and cataloguers, such as Thomas James in his 1605 catalogue of the Bodleian library, or George Draud in his *Bibliotheca classica*. Based on the principle (and practice) of all academic, scholarly or 'serious' works being in Latin, the bulk of a catalogue would be taken up with Latin books, subdivided into the categories of theology; medicine; law; philosophy; mathematics; history, geography and politics; poetry; music. The first four of these divisions can usually be found in all late sixteenth- and early seventeenth-century catalogues[1]; the other subjects, depending on the amount of books in each, are often gathered together. Thus Drummond's five Latin classes—theology, philosophy, law, poetry and prose—suit his library: he had a few medical books, so those he had put in with his philosophy, and his geography books joined them, probably because he was taught geography at Edinburgh as part of the philosophy curriculum.

Books in Hebrew and Greek are sometimes thrown in with the Latin in contemporary catalogues; Drummond preferred to keep his separate. Italian, French, Spanish and English books—if they were admitted to a library—were often lumped together within each language, or sometimes tacked on to the catalogue of the Latin works within each subject. Drummond chose to keep his together by language, not subject, and since they are mostly literary there is good sense in this.

In his 1611 inventory Drummond listed between one quarter and one third of his books. (It is hard to be exact, since an unknown number have been lost.) In 1626 he gave some three hundred and sixty-three printed books and manuscripts from his library to the Tounis College, and between 1628 and 1636 probably as many again. The first donation was catalogued, and the catalogue printed by the heirs of Andro Hart in 1627.

We can only guess why he should have given a good third of his library to the Tounis College. The books themselves tell nothing: they are not all of a kind, or all of a size; in the main they are not suitable for young students, or books to look impressive on the shelf. They seem to be almost a random sample of the whole library. There is a little of everything: some Spenser, Sidney and Shakespeare (but not enough to make it certain that he had given up literature for himself or that he wanted to introduce it to the university), some philosophy, some law, some theology, some poetry. There are little books of popular medicine (like the *School of Salerne*), political pamphlets and pilgrims' directions on the voyage from Venice to the Holy Land; but just when one thinks that the whole donation is made up of such trivia, and that Drummond took the chance to clear his shelves and be generous into the bargain, one comes across books he must have valued, such as the manuscript of Astrophel and Stella. Drummond was friendly with the principal of the college, John Adamson, and Adamson may have asked Drummond to give some books to encourage other donations. Perhaps this was one reason for immediately printing the donations, for the resulting catalogue gives after the title-page a list of ten notable donors to the college

1. James had four chief faculties: Holy Scripture, Aristotle, Law and medicine [see Cat. 521.].

library, and this list is followed by an essay in Latin by Drummond (from the books) to the reader. So something was made of the donation; it was dressed up and publicized.

We can speculate too about Drummond's relations with the Town Council. In the records of the burgh of Edinburgh his donation is recorded on the 22 November 1626; two days later the council ordained him burgess and giltbrother. This was an honour, and one valued by Drummond, and it comes so close on his donation that there is certainly a link between the two. In 1629 the town council asked Drummond to go with John Adamson to Stirling to inspect the library of a Mr David Drummond, presumably with the view to purchasing it. They were both voted expenses for the trip. From such snippets of recorded information we might guess that Drummond enjoyed a semi-official position of literary adviser to the burgh of Edinburgh (as well as that of semi-official local poet, for he was to write the verses of welcome for King Charles' visit in 1633).

The Edinburgh donation must remain a puzzle. What man fond of his books would give so many of them away? If he was tired of them, why did he not give them all to the Tounis College? If he still loved them and used them why did he not keep them till his death? He did rebuild Hawthornden some years later, and he may have been short of space (from the Memorials it seems he lived for a while at Linlithgow, and that is where his first children were born). He may have been embarrassed by some of his youthful tastes, for poetry, for controversy (in particular—though it seems unlikely—he may have wished to be rid of some of his Catholic books). Perhaps the simple explanation is the most likely: he gave a valuable part of his library to the Tounis College because he wished to benefit the college library, and be remembered as a benefactor.

Some of the books that Drummond bought after 1611 and kept at Hawthornden have been lost and their titles will never be known; but some from this period have survived, and because of Drummond's careful habit of writing his name in his books, seventy-eight of those have been traced in public and private libraries, and sales catalogues —and there may well be others.

Bishop Sage says that Drummond's son, Sir William, still owned a number of his father's books in 1707. The last lineal descendant of the Drummonds of Hawthornden was a Barbara Mary Drummond, who died in 1789. Her second husband was a Bishop Abernethy, who at one stage in his life had the charge of the Episcopal diocese of Brechin. Bishop Abernethy, who incidentally presented all Drummond's manuscripts to the Society of Antiquaries of Scotland, seems to have removed a part of what was then left of Drummond's library at Hawthornden with him to Brechin, and this part was discovered when the Brechin diocesan library was given on indefinite loan to Queen's College, Dundee. There are some valuable books among these, including Drummond's copy of Ben Jonson's *Works*.[1] What remained of the library at Hawthornden was probably dispersed shortly afterwards, for throughout the nineteenth century books bearing Drummond's signature turn up in private collections and sale catalogues in both Scotland and England. Thus the book-

1. Described by J. R. Barker 'A Pendant to Drummond of Hawthornden's Conversations' *RES* XVI, 284-8.

18. The Four Monarchies. Johan Nossenio, *Annali* (Cat. 1250).

PERSIA

BABILONIA

GRECIA

Iohan
Kelertaler
Schulpsit

IM. Nolseni ARC Inven

A spice spectator sic me docuere parentes   Me quoque maiores omnes, virtute carentes.

A spice spectator sic me docuere parentes   Me quoque maiores omnes, virtute carentes.

A   Now when into their fenced holdes, the knaues are entred in,
To smite and knocke the cattell downe, the hangmen doe beginne.
One plucketh off the Oxes cote, which he euen now did weare:
Another lacking pannes, to boyle the flesh, his hide prepare.
C   These theeues attend vpon the fire, for seruing vp the feast:
B   And Fryer smelfeast sneaking in, doth preace amongst the best.

3

Who play'th in Romish toyes the Ape, by counterfetting Paull:
For which they doe award him then, the highest roome of all.
Who beyng set, because the cheere, is deemed little worth:
Except the same be intermixt, and lac'de with Irish myrth.
Both Birde, and Harper, is prepard, which by their cunning art,
Doe strike and cheare vp all the gestes, with comfort at the hart.

D

seller Constable writing to Francis Walker (Drummond) of Edinburgh in 1815 describes the copy of Tasso's *Works* (bought in London by Drummond in 1610): 'I purchased the Book in London in 1812 I had no intention of parting with it but do so to you most cheerfully as restoring it to its old abode at Hawthornden . . .'[1] — from where it might be added it has long since disappeared.

1. Constable Letter Books (National Library of Scotland, MS 789. f. 311). Francis Walker later became Sir Francis Walker Drummond, Bart., of Hawthornden.

When Drummond began to give away his books to Edinburgh University he kept enough at home to satisfy his needs and his interests, but after his death his heirs through carelessness or ignorance allowed all these books to leave Hawthornden piecemeal. We can only guess the identity of those that failed to survive, but our guesses will not be pure conjecture, for there are enough clues to fill in at least a few of the gaps.

To start with, it is most likely that Drummond had copies of his favourite poets, particularly those he adapted and borrowed from in his own poetry. In discussing his poetry I have named his important sources, and if these are not in his library catalogue they were nevertheless almost certainly in his library. Drummond must have had all Ronsard's works and most of Marino's, and the probability is that he owned the verses of most of the men he was indebted to. The editor of his poems, L.E. Kastner, has identified many of the actual editions he used; Drummond, for example, read and paraphrased the poets in the collection printed in Venice in 1586, *Delle rime scelte di diversi autori*, Castiglione and others in *Carmina quinque poetarum* (Venice 1549) and the *Madrigali dell' eccellentissimo Sig. Valerio Belli* (Venice 1599). He may have been able to borrow these works from his friends or from the college library, but he owed so much to them he would have found it more convenient to have had his own copies. Similarly, we can be almost certain that he had the second edition of Samuel Purchas' *Pilgrimage*, for he used that in his *Cypresse grove*.[2]

2. See R. Ellrodt 'More Drummond borrowings' *Huntington Library Quarterly* XVI (1953) 305-10.

Another clue to this missing group of books is Drummond's history, the *Five James*, the major work of his later years. Again, it is probable that most of his sources were actually in his own library, and that he collected histories especially to furnish the material of his own history. He had as is clear from the catalogue a full range of classical models, as well as a representative selection of Italian, French, Spanish and English works, but apart from the MS of John of Fordun's *Scotichronicon* (which covers a period before Drummond's own history began) and the books of Hector Boethius there is nothing on Scottish history. From the work that has been done on the particular sources of the *Five James* we can fill in this blank: Drummond must have had Holinshed and Pitscottie (Robert Lindsay of Pitscottie, whose work would then be in MS), and probably also the chronicles of Stow and Edward Hall, and the histories of John Major and George Buchanan.[3] In the Hawthornden MSS are his notes on Bishop John Leslie's *De origine, moribus, et rebus gestis Scotorum*.

3. I am indebted to Dr T.I. Rae of the National Library of Scotland for this information, which forms part of his as yet unpublished study of Drummond's history.

To add to the list still further, we can make a strong case for Drummond having owned every play in the *Catalogue of comedies* (see Appendix I). Some of these appear in his library catalogue, and

19. The Irish rebels hideout. John Derricke, *The image of Irelande* (Cat. 749).

some in his reading lists, but many more are entered in his MS notes. Here he quotes jokes and conceits from *The converted courtesan, Westward Ho, Sir Giles Gooscape, The isle of gulles* and *A mad world my masters*—to name a few. And we can hardly suppose that these notes were for want of the play itself, for his copies of some, such as Marston's *Parasitaster* and Chapman's *All fooles*, still exist.

The Hawthornden MSS are full of extracts from Drummond's reading. It was his habit to précis or copy out passages—even whole chapters—from his favourite authors; there are large extracts or paraphrases from Sidney's *Arcadia*, Warner's *Albion's England* and Pasquier's *Recherches*. Drummond had these three works in his library, but still he liked to write them up, making note of fancy phrases and striking metaphors. (From Pasquier, for instance, he first heard of poets, such as Jodelle, that he later imitated in his own poems.) Knowing these practices, we may fairly assume that if Drummond took notes on a book, that book was in his library. And so we can add to the catalogue Sir John Harington's translation of Ariosto's *Orlando Furioso*, William Camden's *Britain*, George Peele's *Hunting of Cupid*, Francis Davison's *Poetical rapsody*, and Drayton's *Poly-Olbion*.[1]

We might also—though this is less certain—be correct in adding most if not all the books that appear on Drummond's reading lists (see Appendix I). The majority appear in the 1636 shelf catalogue of the university library, and, significantly, these very copies are now lost. It looks as though these books too were presented to the library by Drummond. They may of course be both here and in Drummond's reading lists for other reasons—other donors may have presented them and Drummond may have borrowed them. But this is not so likely as it may seem at first, since the college library had few books in the vernacular until Drummond made his first donation and borrowing was not a normal practice then, even for a favoured patron like Drummond. These books look (in the shelf catalogue) as though they were Drummond's: the editions are correct (Ronsard's *Poems* and *Hymns* of 1604), and they conform to his known taste (there is a considerable group of Spanish books, including authors Drummond is known to have read and imitated, such as Guevara and Granada). If these books listed in the *Press* catalogue were Drummond's, then they would have been given to the university library after the printing of the *Auctarium* in 1627, and they must have been lost some time after 1637.

Finally, we can surely add a group of at least eleven books that carry commendatory verses written by Drummond. Grateful authors would, we might suppose, present copies of their books to the poet; at the least that would be the price of his labours. Of these eleven books three are already in the catalogue: Alexander's *Doomesday*, Kellie's *Pallas Armata* and Vander Hagen's *Miscellanea poemata*. The missing six are Patrick Gordon's *The first book of the famous historie of Penardo and Laissa*, 1615 (STC 12067), William Cowper's *Pathmos: or a commentary on the Revelation of St. John*, 1619 (5931), Archibald Simson's *Heptameron*, 1621 (22566), and his *Samson's seven lockes of haire*, 1621 (22570), Sir William Moore's

1. For a detailed record of Drummond's reading and notes see my unpublished thesis, 'The manuscripts of Drummond of Hawthornden', (Edinburgh 1969).

The true crucifixe for true catholickes, 1629 (18063), David Person's
Varieties : or, a surveigh of rare and excellent matters, 1635 (19781),
and Henry Adamson's *The muses threnodie*, 1638 (135).[1] Drummond
also wrote a sonnet on Sir John Skene's *Regiam Majestatem : the
auld lawes and constitutions of Scotland*, 1609 (22626). He would
have found the book itself useful when he composed his history, so
we should add it to the list.

The collection that Drummond gave to Edinburgh University was
for the most part saved, and those books that did go missing are at
least known. Many of the shorter pieces were bound together while
Drummond had them, according sometimes to their size, sometimes
to their subject, and it is possible to follow these through their early
entries in the university inventories. In 1701 the university librarian
spent four weary months checking the 1627 catalogue against his
stock of Drummond books and, as he noted then, these books were
in a state of confusion. During the next one hundred and twenty
years many books went missing, were stolen or lost, some were
cropped and others lost their bindings, until in 1827 David Laing the
antiquary and scholar arranged that they should all be re-bound and
brought together on the library's shelves as the *Drummond Collection*.
This re-binding saved the books from further serious damage, and
helped to preserve them as a unit, but it did destroy much worth
saving. The old calf bindings are gone, and with them any hope of
reconstructing the physical appearance of Drummond's library.[2] In
spite of this, much of Drummond remains: his annotations (which
without exception are trivial, being either comments on the language
of the text or emphasis of proper names or particular passages) often
show where he put down the book, and in one or two places uncut
leaves suggest that nobody has read any further since.

1. See Franklin B. Williams *Index
of dedications and commendatory
verses* (Bibliographical Society,
London 1962).

2. Worse, if we are suitably grateful
to Laing for his work, we cannot now
undo it, and any errors he may have
made are for ever fixed. If Laing
decided that a certain book now
without any marks of Drummond's
ownership was Drummond's we
must take his word for it that it was,
and that by its previous association in
binding with some other work with a
provenance Laing was right in calling
it a Drummond book, and in binding
it with the Drummond arms. Laing
was a learned and careful scholar,
and his work can usually be trusted,
though I have rejected a few books as
spurious and marked others as
doubtful. (Some error was added
when the Edinburgh University
Library catalogue was printed:
several of the books there marked as
Drummond Collection are not, and
were not named as such by Laing.)

k·3·36 *Gui. Drummond.*

DIALOGVES
CONTRE L·A PLV-
RALITE DES RELIGIONS,
ET L'ATHEISME.

cAj. i. 8 1. *De la Religion de Dieu.*
2. *Des Religions des hommes.*    *P·329·*
3. *Contre l'Atheisme.*

Sur la fin est adiousté, par occasion tres-necessaire, vn
quatriesme D I A L O G V E, contre l'Auarice
de ce dernier siecle de Fer.

*Par Laurent Pollot, du Marquisat
de Saluces.*

*Given to the
colledge of
Edmbrough
by
William
Drummond
1628.*

A LA ROCHELLE,
Par Hierosme Haultin.

I 5 9 5.

a Rouen 1608.

20. Title-page, with Drummond's note of purchase,
Rouen 1608, and record of donation to the University
of Edinburgh, 1628. Laurent Pollot, *Dialogues*
(Cat. 1134).

PART II
Subjects of the Library

Philosophy
Logic, Physics, Mathematics, Medicine, Astrology and Alchemy, Platonism

One of the most striking features of Drummond's collection of philosophy books is the prominence of Aristotle. As we saw in the chapter describing Drummond's education, philosophy was the mainstay of the Edinburgh curriculum, and Aristotle the chief support of philosophy. For Drummond and his contemporaries, philosophy covered most subjects, apart from the learning of the professions, and in all academic subjects Aristotle was supreme. Drummond had the main Aristotelian texts, he had the commentaries of the important scholars, he had compendia. He had Ramist interpretations, and anti-Ramist interpretations; he had tracts from the Middle Ages and the latest synthesis of the day — but almost all of his collection described, supplemented or criticized the books of the Aristotelian canon.

As was suggested earlier, although it is often supposed that Aristotelianism gave way in the Renaissance to the revival of interest in Plato and Platonism, and that scholasticism was superseded by humanism, it is now recognized that what happened was a reinterpretation of Aristotle, since the humanists themselves felt that there was no substitute for the comprehensiveness of Aristotle's survey of human learning. The sum of this assessment (to quote from perhaps its most erudite proponent, Paul Kristeller) is that 'the common notion that scholasticism was superseded by the new philosophy is ... disproved by plain facts'.[1] Kristeller would agree that Edinburgh's curriculum is one of these facts, and Drummond's library another. Kristeller has shown that scholasticism and humanism were in conflict with each other much less than had been supposed; after initial quarrels they settled down in the same curricula and enjoyed a state of coexistence in the universities that lasted well into the seventeenth century. This was first of all because they governed different spheres of influence: scholasticism in logic and natural philosophy; humanism in grammar, rhetoric, poetry and to a lesser extent, moral philosophy. Scholasticism was not essentially a doctrine but more of a method; that is, a type of logical argument, which though firmly anchored in logic could be extended to the other branches of knowledge (such as medicine, for example). As a method it was open to improvement without complete replacement.

This in effect happened during the Renaissance. Aristotle had been

1. Paul Oskar Kristeller *Studies in Renaissance thought and letters* (Rome 1956) p. 576. In this chapter on philosophy I have not tried to examine in any detail the advances or innovations in the subjects covered by Renaissance philosophy, but only to assess the accepted academic and general knowledge available to a man like Drummond. The following authorities are my first sources, after the books in Drummond's library: Marie Boas *The scientific Renaissance, 1450-1630* (London 1962); Ernst Cassirer *The individual and the cosmos in Renaissance philosophy* trs. Mario Domandi (Oxford 1963); Frederick Copleston *A history of philosophy* vol. III, *Ockham to Suarez* (London 1953); Harris F. Fletcher *The intellectual development of John Milton* (Urbana 1956, 1961); Wilbur S. Howell *Logic and rhetoric in England, 1500-1700* (Princeton 1956); Francis R. Johnston *Astronomical thought in Renaissance England* (Baltimore 1937); Paul Oskar Kristeller *The classics and Renaissance thought* (Harvard 1955); Brian Lawn *The Salernitan questions* (Oxford 1963); James R. Naiden *The sphera of George Buchanan* (n.p. 1952); *New Cambridge Modern History* (Cambridge 1957-8) vols. I and II; Walter J. Ong *Ramus, method, and the decay of dialogue* (Cambridge, Mass. 1958); George Sarton *Six wings, men of science in the Renaissance* (London 1957) and *The Appreciation of ancient and medieval science during the Renaissance* (Philadelphia 1955); D.E. Smith *Rara mathematica* (London 1908); E.G.R. Taylor *Tudor geography, 1485-1583* (London 1930) and *Late Tudor and Early Stuart geography 1583-1650* (London 1934); Lynn Thorndike *The Sphere of Sacrobosco and its commentators* (Chicago 1949) and *History of magic and experimental science* (New York 1941) vols. V, VI; William P.D. Wightman *Science and the Renaissance* (Aberdeen 1962).

supreme during the Middle Ages, but he had been increasingly seen only through the eyes of his scholastic interpreters. Peter of Spain in developing the medieval dialectic had unavoidably brought philosophy even further into the realm of theology. Commentators such as Duns Scotus and William of Ockham had obscured Aristotle with their subtle and complex readings, just as their followers, in evolving other theological profundities, had proceeded even further away from his actual philosophy.

The scholars of the Renaissance were able to present Aristotle without always involving themselves in Christian controversy. With the humanistic revival of criticism, Aristotelianism lost much of its lumber: the text was examined again in the Greek, and careful attention paid to its editing and exegesis. The medieval commentators were largely laid aside and their place taken by men who had felt the full force of humanistic scholarship. The fundamental Aristotle, however, was retained. What other philosopher could replace sych encyclopaedic authority? Aristotle covered almost all knowledge, and for the most part, he covered it systematically. His logic was a framework that, shorn of its scholastic accretions, was successfully and profitably taught to a Renaissance mind.[1] Men like Ramus might deny the absolute authority of Aristotle, and seek to simplify his complexities, but though they might alter they could not wholly discard the Aristotelian method, nor hope to imitate the vast range of the Aristotelian canon. The universities were not fighting against the tide in clinging to Aristotle; rather, they were teaching a new Aristotle refurbished by Renaissance scholarship.

Drummond's philosophy books illustrate this revised scholasticism: Drummond had no less than twenty-two separate works or editions of Aristotle in Greek and Latin, either unadorned or accompanied by commentary or *scholia*. He had practically the whole Aristotelian canon with the exception of the *Metaphysics* and surprisingly, the *Poetica*. He had several editions of the *Organum* (logic), either whole or in its parts, with commentaries; from what we would call psychology he had the *De anima* (concerning the mind) and the *Parva naturalia* (which included such subjects as the senses, memory, sleep, life, death); under biology he had J.C. Scaliger's translation of the *Historia animalium* complete with commentary; he had the *Politica* and the *Nicomachean ethics*. Besides these he had a number of works which went under Aristotle's name, like the *Physiognomia* and the little book on colours.

LOGIC

Logic, as we saw, was the foundation of the curriculum both at Edinburgh and at other universities, and thus it is no surprise that the largest group among Drummond's philosophy books is that on logic. Defined simply as the 'Art of reasoning well',[2] logic was the first and lowest of all parts of philosophy, an 'Instrument necessary for the other parts'.[3] As taught in the schools logic was a rigid and organized science, 'a system of precepts for the teaching of learned communication', which provided the student with the procedures for analysing and using logical truths. These procedures 'constituted

1. Judging by the number of works on logic printed in the sixteenth century logic maintained its supremacy. Father Ong has calculated that the 'ratio of dialectic or logic texts to rhetoric texts remains over three to two in favor of dialectic or logic'. And 'in spite of all the fine humanist talk in favor of eloquence, dialectic, not rhetoric, tends to remain the dominant factor in Renaissance linguistic, at least at the level of conscious cultivation'; Ong *Ramus and Talon inventory* (Cambridge, Mass. 1958) pp. 4-5.

2. Petrus Ramus *The art of logicke, gathered out of Aristotle* (London 1626) p. 1.

3. David Person *Varieties, or, a surueigh of rare and excellent matters, necessary and delectable for all sorts of persons* (London 1635) I, p. 3.

a machinery of analysis and synthesis on the level of language—a machinery for assembling materials to prove the truth of an assertion and for combining those materials into complex discourses'.[1]

Without first mastering the language and methods of logic a student could not hope to study the other sciences, for these themselves were organized on logical principles. Logic was thus the key to scholarship.

Scholastic logic was based on Aristotle's *Organon*, and the familiar sets of terms—the two major parts, the five predicables, the ten categories—were taught with direct quotation and reference to the original text. But, as in other sciences, the text was only approached through a mass of interpretation and commentary, and, even after humanist scholarship resurrected the original Greek, Aristotle was treated as the final authority to a system already set out and defined.

In Drummond's day there were three major schools of logic: the Aristotelians, who continued the scholastic tradition, the Ramists, who rebelled against the old scholastic methods, and the Systematics or Syncretists, who tried to compromise between the two by maintaining the scholastic system without ignoring all of Ramus' reforms.[2] These three groups are all represented in Drummond's library, together with a few of the standard texts of the Middle Ages—still evidently read in the Renaissance.

First, there are the Aristotelian commentators. In the Edinburgh curriculum Porphyry's *Isagoge* was a set book: this third century commentary on the *Topics* was a usual introduction to Aristotle's categories, and stayed popular from the Middle Ages onwards.[3] Of the medieval dialecticians Drummond appears to have had only Peter of Spain's *Summulae logicales*, a work that was most influential in the thirteenth century, but which, although it put a new emphasis on language, was basically a restatement of Aristotelian logic. The core of the logic books comes with the Renaissance commentators. There are five of these, ranging from the Jesuit works of the Portuguese University of Coimbra, through those of the Spanish Jesuit, Cardinal Francis Toletus, to those of the Italian Giacomo Zabarella. The list is completed with the *Institutiones logicae* of Julius Pacius, the Italian lawyer and scholar, which was printed in Cambridge in 1597, and the *Dialectica* of Augustin Huens. These works show the strength of the revival of scholasticism in the Renaissance. Toletus and Zabarella are perhaps the most notable authors here, though the Conimbricenses in their day were equally admired for their scholarship. Yet in spite of scholarship these authors seem to look back, not forward. Zabarella was an exponent of the teaching of the Arab Aristotelian Averroes—which may seem odd from a writer of the second half of the sixteenth century—while Pacius at the same time considered himself an expert on the logic of Ramon Lull (whose own attack on Aristotelian logic in the thirteenth century was an attempt to simplify the complexities of the scholastic accretions.) Huens (or Hunnaeus), an obscurer figure, is known only as a strict follower of Aristotle, that is, a traditionalist, and an opponent of Ramus.[4] These scholars are followed by the works of two popularizers: first the *Compendium* of Francis Titelman, which was first

1. Howell, p. 15.

2. Walter J. Ong *Ramus and Talon inventory* (Cambridge, Mass. 1958) pp. 510-33, gives a list of Ramists, Anti-Ramists (or Aristotelians) and Syncretists (or Systematics).

3. Porphyry was still used in Milton's day. From H. F. Fletcher's study of Milton's intellectual background it is clear that there was little difference between the Edinburgh curriculum in 1605 and the Cambridge curriculum in 1625. Only some of the recommended Aristotelian commentators have changed; Fletcher, II, pp. 137-270.

4. Howell, p. 310.

published in 1533, and supposedly designed by this Franciscan for the 'simple brothers' of his order, who had neither the time nor the intelligence to wrestle with the difficulties of Aristotle. According to Titelman his work was written 'lest tender adolescents lose heart, terrified by the prolix multitude and involved difficulty of irrelevant matters.'[1] The other simplification of logic has perhaps a more respectable pedigree, and it is a work that seems to have pandered less to its readers. This is the *Dialectica* of John Seton, first printed in 1545, which then stayed in use in both England and Scotland for over a hundred years. It was essentially an adaptation of Aristotle for university freshmen, and has been described as 'the last major document in the history of scholastic logic in England'.[2] Drummond owned the edition annotated by Peter Carter.

The Ramist logic was taught at Edinburgh, as we saw, and Ramus' importance is of course reflected in Drummond's library. Drummond owned his *Dialectica*, which had a commentary by Ramus' disciple, Omer Talon.[3] This might have been the actual text he used at Edinburgh.

The remainder of the logic books are all affected by the Ramist controversies. When Ramus attacked the supreme authority of Aristotle he began a series of quarrels which were still going on in the early seventeenth century: his system had to be defended by his supporters in England and Germany, and naturally it was attacked by scholastics, especially in France. Inevitably, compromisers or 'Systematics' emerged to stand between the two opposing forces, a typical example being John Henry Alsted, who in his *Harmonious system of logic* attempted to organize and revise the incongruities of formal logic, and to iron out the differences between Ramism and traditional Aristotelianism. For the 'Systematics' the latter was represented by the work of Philip Melanchthon. Thus, typically, Libavius titled his attempt at compromise *Dialectica Philippo-Rameae*. Besides these, Drummond also owned one of William Temple's pamphlets on the Ramist controversy and John Case's *Sum of the ancient interpreters of the entire Aristotelian dialectic*. Case's work, while not strictly speaking favouring either side, does seem to give a qualified endorsement of Ramus' position.[4]

We can do little here except briefly and roughly classify these books of logic, for the subject is so foreign to us now, and it was so complex in its time, that it will not bear summary. The modern reader who tries to work his way through even the most simple Renaissance text-book of logic immediately finds himself in unknown country, and is soon bewildered and cast down with a hundred strange terms and procedures. It is plain what is going on—the analysis by a refined process of linguistic study of the methods of reasoning—but we are no longer conditioned so to organize our thought. But from this distance it is clear that training in logic had a powerful effect on Renaissance methods of thought, not only in the sciences but also in the arts. The extent to which this is so has not yet been fully investigated, although such studies as those by Rosemund Tuve on Ramism and poetry show that logical methods and terms may have governed poetic imagery and poetic imagination.[5]

1. Quoted by Thorndike, v. p. 149.

2. Howell, p. 55.

3. Drummond's edition was almost certainly that which contained Ramus' complete logic, evolved from his earlier works.

4. Howell, pp. 191-2.

5. See Rosemund Tuve *Elizabethan and metaphysical imagery* (Chicago 1946). Miss Tuve's opinions on Ramism are by no means accepted by all critics. See N.E. Nelson *Peter Ramus and the confusion of logic, rhetoric and poetry* (University of Michigan *Contributions in Modern Philology*, Number 2, April 1947) and for a general view of the controversy, Joseph A. Mazzeo 'Modern theories of metaphysical poetry,' *Modern Philology*, L (1952) 86-96.

Logic influenced methods of thinking and it seems at times, paradoxically, to have shackled thought itself. Looking through Drummond's books we can feel its cold hand everywhere, and it is hard not to suppose that though the system may have often helped to organize a man's perceptions, it as often prevented him from exploiting those perceptions to the full. Using the methods of logic he might be a tramcar, so to speak, but not a bus. An example of this is Simon Sturtevant, the inventor of a new method of making metals, and the author of a book on the subject called *Metallica*. Sturtevant's invention was apparently an improved forge which could be fired economically with most common fuels: 'Sea-coale, pit coale, earthcoale and brush-fewell.'[1] (We are not given any details of the forge, although the royal patent is quoted in full.) The *Metallica* itself is a treatise 'comprehending the doctrine of diuerse new metallical inuentions'[2] but any reader hoping to learn the practical details of these inventions will be disappointed, for the treatise proves instead to be a logical dissection of the nature of metals and their properties, with a tedious preoccupation with every linguistic possibility.

It is arranged according to the first elementary rules of logic, beginning with a definition of the 'art', proceeding to definitions of its major parts, and concluding with definitions of their parts. The nature of a thing, it seems, can be discovered by listing and examining these parts. Thus Metallica itself is 'an ignick inuention, for the cheaper making of all kindes of mettles or metalique concotures, by the meanes of cheape firing, and other *metallical,* instruments, wherevpon the materials and things made by this arte, are called *metaliques*'.[3] Metallica depends upon '*heuretica,*' which is defined as the 'art of inuentions', and its two main parts are '*ignemetallica,*' which worketh with fire and hearth', and '*inignemetallica*', 'which' useth not the meanes of fire'.[4] So far so good—this we might think is quite in order, a naming of terms for the treatise which is to follow—but by the time we have won through to the 'Cannons or rules seruing to iudge of the goodnesse of a deriuatiue inuention emporeuticall',[5] we can see that Sturtevant's purpose is not to describe a practical science, but to categorize, to categorize, and again, to categorize. Each (of the aforesaid) rules is 'grounded vpon triplicities of the former vertues or lesser faultes, or intermixt of both',[6] which means that each rule can have sixteen of these virtues or lesser faults. Thus the first cannon—an 'inuention that hath none of the grand faults and hath at least one of the grand virtues ...'—has as its 'triplicitie': '1. More sufficiency, Equi-cheapnesse, Equi-excellence. ... 2. Equi-sufficiency, equi-cheapnesse, more excellency. 3. Equisufficiency, more cheapnesse, equi-excellency.' And so on, to the number of sixteen.[7] This sort of reasoning while logically sound seems to us now tedious and unnecessary, a symptom of a method becoming an end in itself. This is just what Bacon was attacking in his *Novum organum* when he pleaded for a new logic, a method of induction drawn from the method of experiment.[8] Science could not progress while it was content with a logic of linguistics.

1. From the title-page of the *Metallica* (London 1612).

2. Ibid.

3. *Metallica*, p. 35.

4. Ibid, p. 34.

5. Ibid, p. 81.

6. Ibid, p. 86.

7. *Metallica*, pp. 87-8.

8. See Boas, pp. 253 et seq.

PHYSICS

If we think of Renaissance science we think not of Aristotle but of Copernicus, not of Ptolemy but of Kepler. In his collection of books on natural philosophy Drummond had no Copernicus, no Kepler, no Brahe, no Gilbert, no Galileo—none of the great innovators— although by the early seventeenth century their works were available in print. Drummond's scientific books are all traditional, and his view of the physical world must have been Aristotelian.

This was normal. Aristotle and Ptolemy were taught in the universities, and the educated man of the time did not need to question the well-known concepts of scholastic cosmology. As late as 1650 Milton could base the scheme of *Paradise lost* upon the fundamental assumptions of Aristotelian physics, which he had learned at Cambridge from textbooks little different from those used by Drummond.[1] Drummond himself joined John Adamson, the Principal of Edinburgh University, in writing commendatory verses to David Person's *Varieties*, a survey of knowledge printed in 1637 which dismissed Copernicus and his 'franticke and strange opinion'.[2] Copernicus had died almost a century before. Person quotes from Scripture—which tells us that 'the Earth is stablished sure'—and from Archimedes, and holds confidently to safe, accepted, conventional opinion, that the globe of the earth remains firm and immovable, 'whatever fond conceit Copernicus had concerning the motion of it'.[3]

Aristotle's universe consisted of a number of hollow, crystalline spheres, each resting one within another, all eternally moving. Fixed on these spheres were the heavenly bodies. At the centre of the universe was the earth, spherical but immobile; at the outer rim enclosing the universe lay the fixed stars, and between the two the moon, sun, and the five planets, all revolving around the earth. Compared with the sun the earth was insignificant in size. Between the moon and the earth itself (in the sublunary sphere) lay the four elements—earth, water, air and fire—each with their own sphere around the centre of the globe in that order: earth first, then water, then air, and finally, just below the moon, the fiery sphere, where occurred the unusual and transitory celestial phenomena such as comets and meteors. The four elements had simple motions natural to themselves: earth and water downwards to the centre of the universe, air and fire upwards.

The fifth element Aristotle considered to be the ether, whose natural motion was circular. In the ethereal regions—from the moon upwards—all motion was circular, and since this kind of motion had no natural opposite (in contrast to the motions of the elements, upwards and downwards) it was essentially nobler. Ever moving, ever fixed, the heavenly bodies rolled on their spheres in celestial harmony. Below the moon all things were subject to change. Alteration or decay was inevitable, as the motions of the four elements were in opposition.

These Aristotelian theories formed the basis of the accepted Renaissance ideas on cosmology and physics elaborated by the mathematics of Ptolemy and the Arab astronomers. The popular

1. Fletcher, II, pp. 167-81.

2. *Varieties*, v, p. 81.

3. Ibid. I, p. 8.

conception of the universe was now expanded to ten spheres, with God in His eleventh heaven. The other celestial bodies and spheres (according to Henry Peacham) were

> The tenth the first moover.
> The ninth the Christalline heaven.
> The eighth the starry firmament.
> Then the seven Planets in their Order. . . .[1]

1. Henry Peacham *The compleat gentleman* (London 1634) p. 58.

The ordinary educated man of Drummond's time was familiar with the commonplaces of this cosmology: the creatures of the ethereal region eternally moving, eternally unchanged; the sublunary elements inconstant, the earth an 'Orbe of generation and corruption'.[2] Sidney could speak in the *Arcadia* of 'The ever turning spheres, the never moving ground'[3]; and Drummond could profess 'I know that all beneath the Moone decays',[4] and philosophize in *A cypresse grove* on 'our constant mutabilitie'.[5]

2. In *A cypresse grove* Drummond gives the conventional picture of the universe: Kastner, II, pp. 71-2.

3. Quoted by Kastner, I, p. 166.

4. Kastner, I, p. 4.

5. Kastner, II, p. 72.

This is not to say that all ideas on cosmology and physics came from Aristotle, or that alternatives to Aristotelian cosmology were not known and discussed. The revival of interest in Plato and in neo-Platonism brought to the fore Platonic cosmological ideas, principally the animistic conception of a hierarchy of spiritual beings inhabiting the spheres. The theories of the Pythagorean school of philosophers, to whom mathematics was the supreme science, and who placed an almost mystical significance on numbers, were well known and highly thought of, particularly by Renaissance Platonists. In fact, all the known writings of the ancients were printed and read, for if a work was Greek or Roman it was immediately respectable: Heraclitus might be quoted to suggest that the world began with fire, Democritus and Leucippes that it began in atoms, Thales with water.[6] The answer to these ideas was not in more exact observation by contemporary scientists, but in recourse either to Aristotle or Christian dogma—as Person said 'All which opinions in this may be refuted, that they derogate too much from the power of God'.[7]

6. *Varieties*, V, p. 62.

7. Ibid. V, p. 63.

In the schoolroom the use of the *Zodiacus vitae* of Marcellus Palingenius Stellatus—a long didactic poem containing a summary of all learning—was most important in offering qualifications on the Aristotelian system. Palingenius was one of the most enthusiastic Renaissance neo-Platonists, and his astronomical theories owed much to the neo-Platonic conception of the universe, even to the extent of peopling the ethereal regions with a company of immortal spirits:

> . . . creatures doth the Skies containe, and euery Starre beside
> Be heauenly townes & seates of saincts, where Kings & Commons bide,
> Be perfect Kings and people eke, all things are perfect there.[8]

8. Quoted by Johnson, p. 149.

The *Zodiacus vitae* was a most popular school text, and Palingenius' insistent attacks on the infallibility of Aristotle must have had considerable effect in undermining peripatetic predominance.

There was, too, some science written in the vernacular which was often more advanced than that taught by the academics.[1] Men like Robert Recorde and Thomas Digges gave English accounts of the Copernican theory as early as the mid-sixteenth century, so that by Drummond's time its principal parts were common knowledge among the educated. John Donne's interest in astronomy was perhaps exceptional for a layman, but it is significant that even in a satirical work like *Ignatius his conclaue* he should have been able to mention with approval not only Copernicus, but also Kepler and Galileo. Robert Burton was familiar with Copernicus' name, and Drummond in *A cypresse grove* gave a muddled summary of Copernican theory. Yet in spite of the currency of Copernicus' ideas the general effect, as one scholar puts it, of the greatest systematic revolution in scientific thought since Ptolemy, on the learned world of the sixteenth century was fundamentally almost none.[2]

As Kristeller has pointed out, the wealth and breadth of Aristotelian learning in natural science was itself a reason for the slow progress of new knowledge, for it was difficult to improve on so complete a system. In the curriculum at Edinburgh, Aristotle's *Physica* had, as we saw, a central place. The *Physica* do not cover the same ground as our modern science of physics; rather, they were concerned with the philosophical properties of matter, motion and being, all leading from the conception of God as the unmoved first mover to a systematic classification of nature. Astronomy belonged to the ethereal regions where motion was uniform, circular and everlasting; the rest of natural science being sublunar constituted a separate whole. Only in the sublunar zone could change take place, and all sublunar bodies manifested change: meteors, comets, clouds, rain, thunder, the seas, the land, all things either living or dead, all nature. The four elements—fire, air, water and earth—with their contrary motions caused change.

A striking characteristic of Aristotelian physics was thus its comprehensiveness. The study of the sublunar zone covered not only the complex philosophical questions of the causes of the movements of the elements, but also the effects of these movements, which meant the mutability of all nature. Generation and decay, meteorology, and chemistry all properly came within the bounds of physics. The university student hearing lectures on the *Physica* would be given a description of the whole of the world in its parts, from the qualities of the elements to meteors, from the nature of time to the nature of sleep. He would learn a portion of the sciences we now know as geology, botany, zoology and psychology and he could be introduced with little difficulty to such related subjects as human anatomy or geography.[3] For Drummond and his teachers the *Physica* was known as the *Acroamatica* or the 'Lectures [literally hearing] on nature'.[4]

Drummond has his *Physica* in both a Greek and a Latin text. He also owned three very different commentaries on it: one, by Giacomo Zabarella, the learned Aristotelian, whose scholarship has been described as lucid and profound; another, from the school of Peter Ramus, which would be a re-ordering of natural philosophy in the

1. For the peculiarly English interest in science and mathematics, much of it practical, see Christopher Hill *Intellectual origins of the English revolution*, chap. 2. The centre for the English scientists was London, not Oxford or Cambridge, and Gresham College after its foundation became the place where the new science could be taught. The work of such as William Gilbert, Edward Wright and Henry Briggs was of practical importance in fields like navigation, but it did little or nothing to change immediately what was taught in the universities. Educated laymen—if Drummond is a fair example—were sometimes capable of bypassing the conventional science and learning about the new directly from books, but one must doubt whether they were prepared to jettison their acquired academic knowledge.

2. Wightman, I, p. 116. The pious could refute Copernicus from the Scriptures, for Joshua had told the sun to stand still, not the earth. It would be unwise to attach too much weight to the kind of intellectual speculation aroused by the Copernican theories, since they often seem to have been taken as just one more conjecture to add to those already described by the Greeks. Thus Drummond, echoing Montaigne and Donne in his passage on the futility of human thought in *A cypresse grove*, could offer a sampler of theories new and old—but all brought forward to illustrate his point that man's understanding was still imperfect:

> 'The Element of Fire is quite put out, the Aire is but Water rarified, the Earth is found to moue, and is no more the Center of the Vniuerse, is turned into a Magnes; Starres are not fixed, but swimme in the etheriall Spaces, Cometes are mounted aboue the Planetes; some affirm there is another World of men and sensitiue Creatures, with Cities and Places in the Moone ... Thus, Sciences by the diuerse Motiones of this Globe of the Braine of Man, are become Opiniones, nay, Errores, and leaue the Imagination in a thousand Labyrinthes.' Kastner, II, p. 78.

3. See the list of chapter headings of Magirus' textbook given by Fletcher, II, pp. 174-6.

4. As lecture notes of the time in Edinburgh University Library show.

interests of that school, that is, a reorganization of the traditional explanations in the cause of simplification; the third, the *Compendium* by Francis Titelman (whose popular work on logic Drummond also owned). The *Compendium of natural philosophy* is remarkable not only for its popularity, but also for its author's attempts to re-organize natural philosophy on an ostentatiously religious level. This meant serving up Aristotle's outline in a pious form (even to adding psalms written by Titelman himself). But from Titelman's presence among more erudite philosophy books it is fair to conclude that his piety was perhaps regarded as adequate compensation for his lack of learning, or alternatively, to a Protestant reader, his simplifications were worth more than the odium of his religion. Titelman is an easy target for scorn, yet his faults were by no means so obvious to his contemporaries. Many a sixteenth-century work on natural philosophy was no more than a re-hash of existing knowledge, and many an author of such a work had no more qualifications as a philosopher than had Titelman.

The elementary facts of astronomy were taught at Edinburgh from Joannes de Sacro Bosco's *Sphaera mundi*, a simple treatise, popular in the Middle Ages but still evidently considered useful in the universities. Sacro Bosco's treatise gave a straightforward account of Aristotelio-Ptolemaic astronomy, modified only by the addition of some material from the Arab writers. Drummond had a copy with a commentary by one of the most famous scholastics of the Renaissance, the Jesuit philosopher and mathematician Christopher Clavius. In the same class as Sacro Bosco we may put the *Sphaera* of Proclus, again in Drummond's library (in Greek), and again popular more for its authority and reputation as the work of an ancient, than for its actual astronomical data.

While works like the *Sphaera* of Sacro Bosco stayed in the university curriculum—from inertia as much as anything else—it would be a mistake to think that they were not seen as merely utilitarian tracts presenting a roughly accurate simplification of the cosmos suitable for the study of beginners. Serious scholarship—with notable exceptions of the great discoverers, Copernicus, Kepler and Brahe—proceeded from discussion of the work of known authority rather than empirical observation. Renaissance scholars were able to attack the fortress of Aristotle, for they found opposing theories held by his fellow Greeks. There was much controversy on the inconsistencies of the *Physica*, which were sometimes resolved by recourse to alternative authority, and in fact the Renaissance philosopher could hold a scientific investigation without ever moving outside Greek sources.

In Drummond's library the works of the ancients are, as one would expect, numerous, and the works of their Renaissance commentators and disciples are common. Drummond had such standard texts as Seneca's *Naturales quaestiones* (accepted from the Middle Ages as one authority on cosmology, and especially notable for its references to theories of the earth's rotation). He had Aristarchus and Cleomedes, and Philo's *De mundo*, which, on account of its neo-Platonist leanings, had something of a vogue in the Renaissance. He

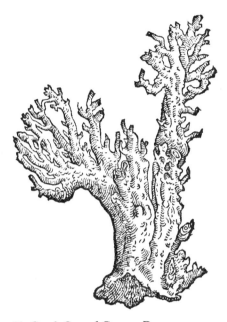

21. Coral. Conrad Gesner, *De rerum fossilium, lapidum et gemmarum* (Cat. 134).

63

had Ptolemy, and of the modern writers on cosmology he had Alessandro Piccolomini, whose own *Sphaera* followed Ptolemy closely. He had, too, a number of other scholarly treatises in the traditional mould, such as the work on comets by the famous scholar Joannes Ferrerius, who accepted the Aristotelian theory on comets, and who prefaced his work with a plea to James v of Scotland — Ferrerius spent much of his life at Kinloss — to give up the useless predictions of astrology and trust only in Jesus. Among the writers on particular problems in the physics, Drummond had Argenterius on sleeping and waking, and Simon Porta on pain. Both, again, were scholarly Aristotelians.

A major problem for the Renaissance — perhaps more severe than for the Middle Ages, since humanistic scholarship was establishing a new vision of historical perspective — was that of reconciling science with Christianity. The accepted system was Aristotelian, yet Aristotle was a pagan, and moreover his natural philosophy was based on teleological ideas which at certain points could not be easily married to Christian dogma. Even Person in his simplified summary 'Of the secrets of Nature' felt constrained to qualify his acceptance of Aristotle's law of the immutability of the heavens with the standard Christian qualification 'that at the last conflagration, it shall suffer a change and novation, but no dissolution, as the low elementarie world'.[1] With scholasticism the Middle Ages had for a time achieved a working synthesis between the Aristotelian cosmos and Christian beliefs, but now compromise was often out of reach. How acute the problem was can be seen by noticing its side effects: a poet could not assume (like Dante) that his description of God's world would be acceptable to both philosopher and theologian. Renaissance writers were forced to choose their own authorities, although the freedom with which they chose these authorities too often landed them in the middle of contradictions. Du Bartas, in his attempt to create a Christian epic, borrowed his cosmology from sources as varied as Lucretius and the Church Fathers, and as a Christian attacked Aristotle's principle of the world's eternity and Democritus' idea of infinite worlds — yet found himself using Aristotelian axioms to refute Copernican theories.[2] There was no other way for the layman to argue than by resource to alternative authority. Philippe de Mornay in his *De la vérité de la religion chrestienne* — a book which had a great vogue in Protestant countries — devoted four chapters to a refutation of the Aristotelian idea of the eternity of the world, and to do so quoted the authority of Plotinus and the Platonists against Aristotle.[3]

On the scholarly level this led to Draconian measures. Guillaume Postel, described as 'one of the most learned men of his age', spent much of his energy in his work on origins vindicating Aristotle from accusations of impiety. Aristotle, correctly read, did understand the providence of God and the immortality of the soul.[4] Here again we come to the point that exegesis of authority was more important than any attempt to grapple with the puzzles of nature unencumbered. Whatever seemed miraculous could be safely assumed to be miraculous; if the facts did not make sense there was still no problem,

1. *Varieties*, I, p. 8. The Renaissance problem of reconciling pagan and Christian philosophy can be seen in the treatment given to Lucretius. *De rerum natura*, in which Lucretius constructed a physics which showed a world functioning without divine intervention, was printed less than any other comparable Latin classic. Lucretius denied in passionate language the immortality of the soul; his Epicurean philosophy was especially hard for a Christian to stomach. See Cosmo A. Gordon *A bibliography of Lucretius* (London 1962) pp. 14–17.

2. Johnson, p. 187.

3. Johnson, pp. 149-50, n. 68.

4. Thorndike, VI, p. 343.

22. Logic systematized. Table from Gaspar Olevianus, *Fundamenta dialecticæ* (Cat. 161).

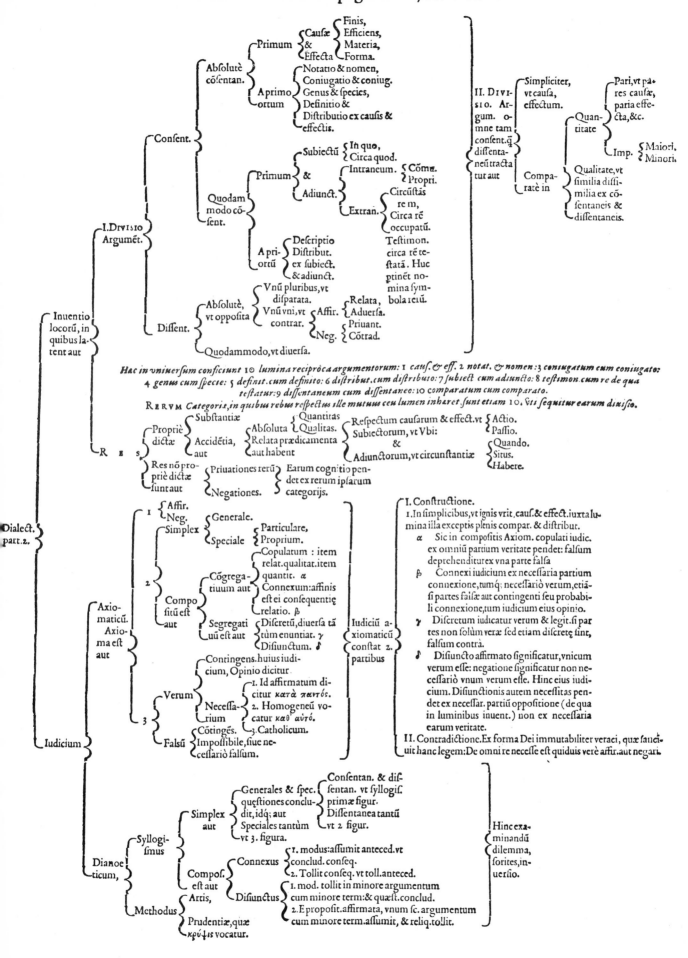

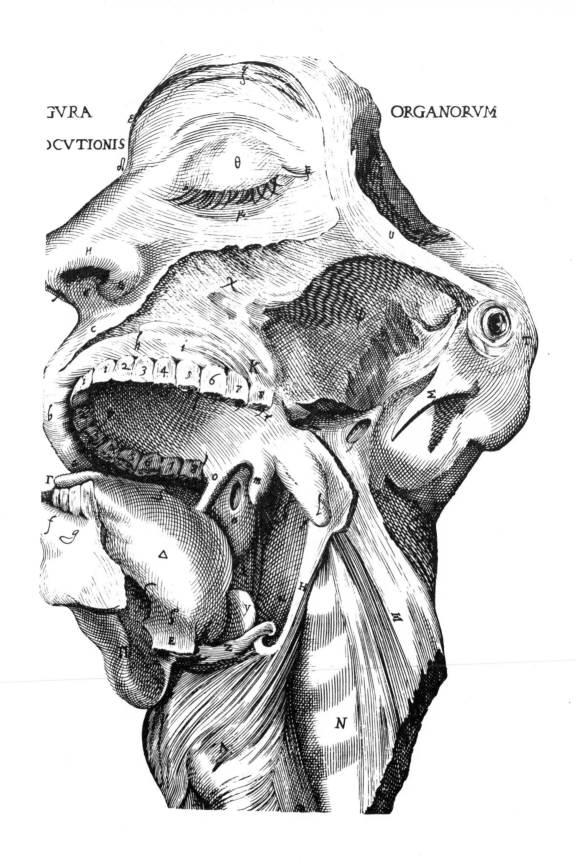

for God had arranged all in His wisdom. And the facts themselves were frequently fables. Postel, when faced with such oddities as springs on mountain tops or salt water ascending rivers, phenomena for which he could find no logical explanation, explained both as 'done by the will of the Lord Jesus'.[1] Daneau in his *Physica Christiana* carried the theological explanation to something of an extreme, and organized his view of nature quite for the benefit of the Bible. All genuine scientific knowledge, he held, was to be found not in Aristotle or Plato, but in the Holy Scriptures. The problems were practical. How did all the animals fit into the ark? The ark was large, and there were only thirty-five terrestrial genera. Why were metals unmentioned in the description of the creation? Metals were beneath the surface of the earth.[2]

Sometimes the arguments could be carried the other way, and Aristotelianism weigh heavier than Christianity. In his *De incantationibus* (*On the causes of natural effects*) the Aristotelian Pietro Pomponazzi discussed the problem of the supernatural—demons, spirits, miracles—and whether or not they could be regarded as existing in the light of Aristotle's remarks on the subject. Although he concluded piously that whatever canonical Scripture affirmed and whatever was decreed by the Catholic Church was so, he succeeded in casting doubt on many supernatural Christian beliefs—the canonization of saints, the adoration of relics and the miracles of the Bible. Significantly his reputation in Drummond's day was that of the doubter of the soul's immortality (though Pomponazzi had shown only that Aristotle himself did not accept the immortality of the human soul), as this epitaph implies:

> Trade softly, passenger, vpon this stone,
> For heere enclosed stayes,
> Debarrd of Mercies Rayes,
> A Soule, whose Bodye swore it had not one.[3]

If Pomponazzi was exceptional in his tacit opposition to the superstitions of the Church, it should be remembered that his 'scepticism' came from his ability as a scholar, and his success in finding out what Aristotle had really said on the supernatural.

These notes on Drummond's philosophy books have now covered the chief subjects of the Aristotelian canon, with the exception of ethics and metaphysics. Some ethics were taught in the universities, but very little metaphysics; both subjects overlapped with theology, and the problem always was to decide whether to rewrite Aristotle to suit Christian dogma, or to adapt Christian dogma to match Aristotle. At Edinburgh, students were introduced to Aristotle's ethics in their third year, but metaphysics was ignored, and this deficiency is echoed in Drummond's library: he had the usual texts on ethics, and only one or two books of metaphysics.

The standard university text for ethics was Aristotle's Nicomachean *Ethica*, although before hearing lectures on this students would probably have worked through some of Cicero's moral tracts, notably the *Paradoxa stoicorum* and the *De officiis*. Sometimes the categories of the *De partitione oratoria* were used.[4]

1. Thorndike, VI, p. 342.

2. Thorndike, VI, p. 347.

3. By Drummond; see Kastner, II, p. 245. Pomponazzi's attempt to apply peripatetic rather than theological explanations to the phenomena of nature cannot however be regarded as a triumph for commonsense over superstition, for as Thorndike shows his explanations were different rather than rational, and relied upon distinctions that he regarded as natural but that we would see as occult: Thorndike, V, p. 110.

4. See Fletcher's discussion of ethics, II, pp. 157-66.

23. The organs of speech. Hieronymus Fabricius, *De locutione* (Cat. 125).

Aristotle's doctrine of virtue as a mean between extremes was paraphrased in Christian terms, and Aristotle's (and Cicero's) list of opposites became the seven cardinal virtues and the seven deadly sins. Virtue was equated with Christian good, lack of virtue with evil.

The ancients could be accepted as writers of rational theology, as distinct from Christian revealed theology, and their moral propositions could be used to reinforce Christian ethics. The Christian virtues were supported by right reason—rational morality logically argued by the learned pagans, who though they had never known God, had come close to discovering His precepts through the exercise of mind alone.

Besides the twin authorities, Aristotle and Cicero, Drummond's other books of ethics are Renaissance commentaries on Aristotle. The most important of these is Jacques Le Fèvre's commentary on the *Magna moralia*. Le Fèvre was the great scholar of France's first humanist school, an editor who did much to reform the text of Aristotle to its original purity. For his contemporaries he was 'the restorer of philosophy.'[1] His own philosophy was composed of a compromise between Aristotelianism and Platonism: he was able to justify the compatibility of the two, though he never took the part of one against the other. His interpretation of Aristotle verged on the mystical, and indeed, he seems, by classing him as a transcendental, to have made him almost a Christian philosopher. This attitude of treating the two great Greeks as special cases almost within the Christian pale was common through the whole Renaissance. As late as 1635 Person in his *Varieties* made a point of noting 'how neer . . . they jumpe with our Christian Religion'.[2]

The science of metaphysics was the study of ultimate being, of the nature of the divine, that is, to Aristotle, the philosophy of theology. It inquired into the first principles of being, substance, essence, time, space, cause, identity, of spiritual and invisible things —what was their nature and how it was known. To the Christian it was distinguished from theology because its speculations were derived from logic: 'it treateth of most excellent matters, as of God and of the Angels, in so farre as they may be knowne, by the light of Nature: for as they are knowne to us by divine revelation, the consideration of them belongeth to Divinity.'[3] At Edinburgh, metaphysics was not taught until after 1625, but any student in the normal course of his instruction on theology, would be taught the rudiments according to the Aristotelian system.

Drummond had only one work that might be considered a textbook of metaphysics: that by James Martin. This attempted to cover the subject by raising and answering every likely metaphysical question, taking into consideration the views of other commentators (particularly Suarez and Timpler). Besides Martin's work Drummond had Giordano Bruno's metaphysics—an extreme contrast to the academic Aristotelian approach. Bruno, who was burned for heresy at Rome in 1600, developed his metaphysics from neo-Platonism, and moved towards a kind of pantheism. He was deeply influenced by Copernicus' theories, which encouraged his speculations towards free-thought.[4]

1. Arthur Tilley *The dawn of the French Renaissance* (Cambridge 1918) p. 233 et seq.

2. *Varieties*, v, p. 50.

3. Ibid. p. 92.

4. Copleston, III, pp. 258-63. For more detail see Frances A. Yates *Giordano Bruno and the Hermetic tradition* (London 1964).

With ethics and metaphysics we come to an end of the academic Aristotelian canon, though not to an end of the subjects embraced by Renaissance philosophy. Geography, mathematics, even medicine and the 'arts' of astrology and alchemy might all at times find a space under the ample wings of philosophy. And as Aristotle dominated formal scholastic philosophy, so other classical authorities were the chief guides to these sciences. To a great extent the whole of knowledge was merely a series of notes on the works of the classical authors, for the prevailing feeling was that if only enough could be discovered of Greek and Roman learning, then the remaining problems would be trivial. Renaissance scholars were continually offering compilations of the ancients: even the intellectually independent Conrad Gesner described his botanical work *Historia plantarum* as being compiled from Dioskorides, Paul of Aegina, Theophrastus, Pliny 'and more recent Greeks'[1]

Geography was studied from the writings of the classical cosmographers, Strabo, Ptolemy, and Pomponius Mela. The university student would learn a certain amount of physical geography while hearing lectures on the *Physica*, for physical phenomena like springs, rivers, mountains, earthquakes or metals were discussed in their place in the Aristotelian classification. From this he would go on to read a modern compilation of cosmography perhaps in verse (such as that of Honterus, used at Edinburgh). In spite of this being the age of discovery, of Columbus and Magellan, the ancients were still thought useful: Erasmus and Sir Thomas Elyot both recommended Mela's Latin geography as a grammar school text and Loritus Glareanus could write his metrical *Geographica poetica* with the addition of only two chapters on the regions outside Ptolemy.[2] Drummond's edition of the popular *Cosmographiæ introductio* was again based on Ptolemy, although it did carry a Latin translation of the account of Vespucci's four voyages.

By the beginning of the seventeenth century the discoverers of the New World and the Indies had transformed the Renaissance conception of geography by their heroic achievements, and relations of their voyages were an abundant form of popular literature. The Spanish and Portuguese had conquered Mexico, Peru and Brazil; the exploits of Cortez and Pizaro were known and vastly admired.[3] Captain John Smith urged Englishmen to emulate 'the worthinesse of their braue spirits' — 'it requires all the best parts of Art, Iudgement, Courage, Honesty, Constancy, Diligence and Industrie, to doe but neere well.'[4] The great lure was gold, but as the first pamphleteers were quick to explain, if gold itself could not be found there was gold in fish and furs. Smith's propaganda was typically both practical and idealistic: the New World needed men of adventure, and such as came would be well rewarded. 'And is it not pretty sport, to pull vp two pence, six pence, and twelue pence, as fast as you can hale and veare a line?... If a man worke but three dayes in seauen, he may get more then hee can spend....[5] Religion should move the clergy, honour the gentry, the hope for employment the artisan:

'Or be we so far inferior to other nations, or our spirits so far deiected, from our auncient predecessors, or our mindes so vpon

1. However, biology was one area of natural science where some advance was made on the Greeks. Scholars like Gesner and Leonard Fuchs successfully classified many plants not found in classical authorities. The needs of medicine for authoritative herbals was a spur to the botanists.

2. For Erasmus' and Elyot's opinions, see T. W. Baldwin *William Shakspere's Small Latine and Lesse Greeke* (Urbana 1944) II, p. 285 and I, p. 198.

3. Drummond had Cieza de Leon's *Chronica del Peru*, and Cortez' letters.

4. *A description of New England* (London 1616) pp. 6-7. Sir Robert Gordon's *Encouragements* has much the same.

5. Ibid. p. 38.

67

spoile, piracie, and such villany, as to serue the Portugall, Span-
yard, Dutch, French, or Turke (as to the cost of Europe, too
many dooe) rather then our God, our King, our Country, & our
selues? excusing our idlenesse, and our base complaints, by want of
imploiment; when heere is such choise of all sorts, and for all
degrees, in the planting and discouering these North parts of
America'.[1]

1. *A description of New England*
pp. 44-5.

MATHEMATICS

At Edinburgh as in other universities mathematics were studied only
in the most perfunctory manner. Arithmetic and geometry had
formed the first part of the medieval quadrivium (that is, the more
advanced section of the seven liberal arts), but by the Renaissance
the rigid divisions of trivium and quadrivium were ignored largely
to the cost of the subjects of mathematics and music. These were
still taught in the universities, but generally not to the undergraduate.
Milton, for instance, did learn some mathematics at Cambridge, for
he was fortunate in that some of his college tutors were interested in
the subject,[2] but he was the exception; while the ordinary, educated Englishman or Scotsman of the time might well leave his university without the least introduction to the art.

2. See Fletcher, I, p. 368 *et
passim.* Some time was allotted to
arithmetic in the second year at
Edinburgh.

This is not to say that mathematics were generally neglected, for as
in the other branches of learning the great discovery of the Renaissance was the supremacy of the ancients, and in this field particularly, the Greeks.[3] Euclid, Archimedes, and Ptolemy were known in
part of the Middle Ages (largely through Arabic sources) but with
the invention of printing and the rediscovery of more complete
Greek texts the full intricacies of their teaching could be appreciated.
Euclid alone went through numerous editions in both Greek and
Latin, and by the end of the sixteenth century had been translated
into Italian, German, French, English, Spanish, and Arabic. The most
important influence on Renaissance mathematics, however, was that
of Plato, for though he did not provide a textbook like Euclid he did
generate a philosophy. It is as well to qualify Plato's part in this
philosophy, for he can hardly be held responsible for all the developments of neo-Platonism. In particular the Platonic view that
mathematical truths could be applied to philosophical principles was
developed under neo-Platonism to the point where mathematics
were seen as the key to the whole of philosophy (a doctrine originally
Pythagorean). Plato had applied the mathematical discovery of the
existence of only five regular solids to a greater philosophical cosmological truth: they must be identified with the four elements,
while the fifth symbolized the whole universe. This sort of deduc-
tion was enthusiastically received by the Renaissance neo-Platonists
and under their direction mathematical philosophy became an
abstract science, whose truths, accessible, demonstrable and exact,
could now be turned to the greater questions of metaphysics.

3. For an account of the principal
mathematical authorities used in the
Renaissance, and the chief textbooks,
see George Sarton *The appreciation of
ancient and medieval during the
Renaissance* (Philadelphia 1955)
p. 133 et seq.

At its most extreme, this interest in the 'perfect' science led to an
excessive dabbling in numerology, where all kinds of significance,
even mystical, were found in the casual manifestation of numbers in
nature. Nicolas Contarini demonstrated the perfection of the uni-

verse from the perfect numbers six and nine, which relied for their innate perfection on the Trinity: 'As six, for example, is three plus or times two, plus or times one, so the universe proceeds from the Trinity, consists of matter designated by duality, and tends towards the divine unity, the *Summum bonum*.'[1] In common lore three had a magical importance, for it occurred again and again in the Scriptures — Faith, Hope and Charity, the Magi, even in David's choice of things for numbering his people; plague, sword and famine — and so as Person said, it 'should be held in greatest veneration'.[2] 'The Number of Seven by many learned hath beene held the most mysticall, and by some entituled the most sacred of Numbers',[3] for it supported the physical world: there were seven planets, seven metals, seven ages of man (and each planet governed an age).

Those that needed mathematics most were seamen, surveyors and astrologers, and many of the advances in mathematics came as a direct result of their particular problems. There are few books in Drummond's library that show this progress in navigation, apart from Edward Wright's *Description and use of the sphere*; Drummond as a landsman may be excused this omission. (However it is worth remembering that the easiest and often the quickest way of travelling from Edinburgh to London was by sea and Drummond like other wandering Scots had travelled this way.) The longer voyages of the sixteenth- and seventeenth-century navigators depended for their success on accurate sailing; more sophisticated navigational instruments were invented and advanced mathematics were increasingly used in taking observations and calculating position. Captain John Smith, sometime Governor of Virginia and Admiral of New England, told young seamen that they must use the new mathematics if they hoped to become proficient at their art, and to that end he recommended to them the works of Edward Wright.[4] He could have chosen from a wide variety of theoretical and practical works; from those by theorists like Dr John Dee and Thomas Digges to a mass of seaman's grammars, 'secrets' and calendars.

Drummond likewise had little in his library to illustrate the application of mathematics to the science of land measurement, though we should notice that both soldiers and architects began to appreciate such innovations as trigonometry. He did have a number of astrological works, which show quite clearly how closely mathematics was linked to this 'science'. In fact, the title mathematician was often thought a dirty word for astrologer, a synonym for one who dabbled in the occult arts. Judicial astrology — that part of the art concerned with the casting of personal horoscopes — depended for its success on accurate mathematical observation of the varying positions of the planets, which were charted in the annual *Ephemerides* or tables. The application of judicial astrology to medicine is referred to in the title of a work by Wolf Geuss, *Methodus curandorum morborum mathematica* — if only the arithmetic was accurate enough so that zodiacal observations were quite reliable, then astrology could not only predict but diagnose and even cure disease.

Against these extremes (and against the pedantry of Aristotelian methods) Peter Ramus in the middle of the sixteenth century was

1. As explained by Thorndike, VI, p. 350.

2. *Varieties*, v, p. 2.

3. Ibid. pp. 5, 9.

4. Wright was one of several authorities; see David W. Waters *The art of navigation in England in Elizabethan and early Stuart times* (London 1958) p. xxxiv. Waters documents in detail the navigational progress of the sea-faring nations, and the crucial part that mathematics played in this progress. The English particularly were successful: 'by the time of Captain John Smith's death, and in the space of seventy years, the English from being ignorant of the art of navigation had, almost entirely through their own efforts, largely transformed it into a science. Only the solutions to the mechanical and optical problems of measuring time and altitude accurately still eluded them', p. 500.

one of the first to campaign for a practical mathematics, the servant of the sciences (he felt, for instance, that astronomy should discard all hypotheses and rely solely upon observation developed by logic and mathematics). He was perhaps the greatest mathematical educator of his age; his textbooks on arithmetic were highly regarded, and stayed popular for half a century.[1] When Drummond graduated in 1605 he presented Ramus' arithmetic and geometry to Edinburgh—perhaps in the hope that it would be used on his successors.

Ramus, however, as a writer of textbooks was surpassed by the Dutchman Gemma Frisius, whose *Arithmeticæ practicæ methodus facilis* (written about 1536) was still holding its own as a popular textbook a century later. Besides Ramus and Gemma, Drummond had the arithmetics of Tunstall and Waserus. Of the latter little seems to be known. Tunstall, however, as an English bishop and a friend of Sir Thomas More (the book was dedicated to More) is a figure of some importance in the history of mathematics, if only for his attempt to write a textbook which could be used by the practical man and which would find its way into the counting house and workshop. Whether Latin was the best medium for this, and whether *De arte supputandi* itself (described by a modern scholar as 'a good book but very prolix')[2] was the best instrument for the purpose is not as important as the intention, which at the time (1522) was revolutionary.

Geometry in Drummond's library reflects, of course, the importance of Euclid as practically a synonym for the science, and of Ramus as one of Euclid's chief interpreters for the sixteenth century. Drummond owned Euclid as edited by the school of Ramus, Ryff's *Quæstiones geometricæ* (based on Ramus' text) and the geometry of Lens and Demerlierius (both obscure figures). In algebra his library was apparently deficient.

Drummond's small collection of mathematical works indicates an intelligent interest in the subject, but one that did not go very far. With one exception his books can all be described as textbooks; the exception—Henry Briggs' logarithms—might of course have been bought by Drummond for its interest as a new discovery, but may well have been added to his library merely for its associations. John Napier (whose discovery Briggs developed) was a fellow Scot whose estates were as close to Edinburgh as was Hawthornden: his work would have a local reputation. Napier's and Briggs' logarithms, with tables added by the Dutch printer, Adam Vlacq, were to be of the greatest help to all who used advanced mathematics, for they immensely shortened the labour involved in elaborate calculation. This Edward Wright realized when he at once translated Napier's work from Latin into English even before Briggs had his tables ready, for as he said it would be 'of very great use for Mariners . . . a booke of more than ordinary worth, especially for Sea-men'.[3] Few inventions can have been put to practical use so quickly.

1. See Smith, II, p. 263. An example of a practical arithmetic in Drummond's library is Jacques Chauvet *Les institutions de l'arithmetique*. Here problems are illustrated in terms of heirs dividing their land, paymasters paying their soldiers and lords of the manor calculating the size of their rooms. The sixteenth-century equivalent of our 'if 3 men dig a hole 5 feet deep in 1 day, how many men . . .' appears to be 'if a lieutenant has 15,864 horses to quarter in 7 villages, how many horses. . . .'

2. Sarton, p. 153.

3. Quoted by Waters, p. 404. Waters gives an excellent account of Napier's invention and its first appearances in print, pp. 402-10.

MEDICINE

In 1543 Andreas Vesalius published his great anatomical work *De humani corporis fabrica libri septem.* It was remarkable for its beauty as a book — Oporinus of Basle was the printer, and the wood-cuts were drawn by Titian's pupil, Johan von Calcar — and it at once raised the study of human anatomy to that of a systematic and pre-cise science. Before Vesalius, anatomy was taught from the writings of Galen, whose anatomical knowledge was drawn largely from the dissection of pigs and apes; Vesalius flayed, dissected and described human corpses himself (a great innovation, for the usual practice was for the anatomist to lecture from the text, while his barber assistants butchered the cadaver), and in so doing exposed the most blatant errors of traditional anatomy.

Vesalius' *Fabrica* prepared the way for the discovery of the circu-lation of the blood by William Harvey. Harvey brought his opinions to public notice in 1628, when the *Exervitatio anatomica de motu cordis et sanguinis* was printed, and, by the time of his death in 1657, his discovery was accepted, he himself honoured and the Galenic system was recognized as inadequate. Drummond was seven years Harvey's junior and as far as is known had neither the works of Vesalius or Harvey in his library; what he and most of his con-temporaries knew of medicine was traditional.

Drummond had about thirty books, both in Latin and the ver-naculars that might be (generously) classified as medical. The most important of these was the *Universa medicina* of Jean Fernel, which was considered the supreme medical textbook for the last half of the sixteenth century and for much of the seventeenth. It was from Fernel that human anatomy was taught at Edinburgh. With this exception Drummond's books are small or popular. Of the classical writers he had two treatises of Galen in French translation, a spur-ious work of Hippocrates, and the *De re medica* of Serenus Sammon-icus, a description of medical knowledge in verse. From the Middle Ages he had Albertus Magnus' *Secrets of women* and Michael Scot's *Secrets of nature,* both popular relations of medical and sexual lore. He had, too, a small piece on poisons by Arnauld of Villanova and a collection of plague pamphlets, and a compendium of the medical knowledge of Guy de Chauliac. The works of his own time range from the scientific anatomy of the vocal chords done by Fabricius — a follower of Vesalius — to the 'scientific' astrological method of curing diseases explained by its author Geuss as owing its success to its new mathematical approach. To these we may add a variety of popular works: the *Secrets of Alexis,* which was famous for its detailed recipes; *The schoole of Salerne;* and the handbooks of health by Sir Thomas Elyot and Thomas Cogan. On a higher level than these but still partially divorced from the academic world of medicine are the works by Champier and Chaumette, notable for their attempt to make medical learning available to a wider audience by taking it out of Latin and putting it in the vernacular — not, all in all, a remarkable collection of books but, from what one can judge by other private collections, a normal assortment for a cultivated layman.

24. Tobacco. Leonard Fuchs, *Histoire generale des plantes et herbes* (Cat. 1045).

Medical learning in the sixteenth and early seventeenth centuries was based on the works of Galen, interpreted and explained by the Arabic scholars. To Galen was added Hippocrates, and for herbal lore the text of Dioskorides; all three were known to the Middle Ages through Latin translations of Arab versions, and in the commentaries of great Arabic medical writers such as Avicenna and Rhazes. In the Renaissance some classical medical texts were recovered and the medical learning of the Greeks and Romans re-examined by humanist scholars. The results of this scholarship enabled Vesalius to replace 'Arabist' anatomical terms with others he found in Aristotle's zoological works, in Celsus' *De medicina* and in Julius Pollux's Greek *Vocabularium*, a work written in the second century but like that of Celsus, unknown to the Middle Ages. As in law or philosophy the aim of the humanist scholars was to find out what the classical authorities had really said, and to cut away the accretions of their Arab and medieval interpreters. Again it was thought enough to restore the text of the ancients. The great names of this movement were all men of learning: in Drummond's library Niccolo Leonicenus' edition of Aristotle's *De somno et vigilia*, Marsilio Ficino's *De triplica vita* and above all Jean Fernel's *Universa medicina* are advances in this respect—they are examples of erudite humanist scholarship expended upon classical learning though they contain little or no medical innovation.

At the centre of Renaissance medicine was the Galenic theory of humours.[1] The humours were the four fluids which governed the body: blood, phlegm, yellow bile and black bile. They corresponded to the four elements—air, water, fire and earth—they had comparable elemental qualities, and since one humour was bound to be dominant in the body, a man would thus have one of four temperaments or complexions. If blood dominated, he would be sanguine, with the qualities of hot and moist; if phlegm, phlegmatic, and so cold and moist; if yellow bile, choleric, and so hot and dry; if black bile, melancholic, thus cold and dry. If his body was in health then these four humours were in balance; if his body was diseased then the humours were abnormally out of balance, and the task of the physician was to correct that imbalance.

Drummond had the reputation of being melancholic. As *The regiment of health* (*The schoole of Salerne*) put it, the melancholic could be detected by seven signs: he would be shrewd and ill-mannered, sad, silent, studious, an insomniac suffering horrible dreams, steadfast in purpose but of good memory and hard to please, and finally, full of dread. In addition his colour would be earthy brown; he might be devout, a good faster and a great reader.[2]

When Melancholy in the body raignes,
It doth indanger many dreadfull paines.
It filles it with corrupting filthinesse,
Makes the skinne looke of blackish fulsomnesse.
The pulse beates hard, the vrine weake and thin,
Sollicitude, feare, sadnesse, sleepe it drowneth in,
It rayses bitter belches, breedes much Rheume,
And in the eares oft breedes a tingling tune.[3]

1. For a summary of the humoral theory see W.S.C. Copeland *Doctors and disease in Tudor times* (London 1960) pp. 87 et seq., though the information given in such handbooks as *The regiment of health* is quite straightforward. For a description of the state of medicine in the Renaissance, and the importance of the humanist scholars, see Sir Charles Sherrington *The endeavour of Jean Fernel* (Cambridge 1946). Drummond refers to the humoral theory in his *A cypresse grove* when he describes man's body as a 'Masse of discording humours'. Kastner, II, p. 74.

2. *Regimen sanitatis Salerni. The schoole of Salernes most learned and iuditious directorie, or methodicall instructions, for the guide and gouerning the health of man* (London 1617) p. 174. This description fits what is known of Drummond rather well.

3. Ibid. pp. 177-8.

The most popular method of treating a melancholic imbalance—or indeed any imbalance of the humours—was by bleeding. The theory behind this was that bleeding was a straightforward way of bringing the humours back to normal, for by drawing out one humour—blood —the balance of all would be restored, as they were all inter-connected.[1]

> Phlebothomie doth purge and clear the sight,
> Cleanseth the braine, and makes the marrow tight,
> The stomacke and the belly it doth cleare,
> And purge the entrailes throughly euery yeare.[2]

It was felt that it should be done even on the healthy at least twice annually, and it was important to do it at the right time under the moon and the planets, and in the right place on the body of the patient. Thus bleeding was usually done after reference to an 'an-atomie of mans bodie' showing the various veins which could be opened and after consulting a zodiacal table to indicate the most favourable influence.[3]

Since disease was caused either by imbalance of the four humours or of the 'natural spirits' (which controlled breathing or the beating of the heart), most medical treatment was founded on the Galenic doctrine of contraries; that is, the heats of fevers would be opposed by cooling medicines, dryness would be met with moisture, and so on. Physicians would prescribe drugs and herbs which would re-store the humours to their customary harmony. Thus lettuce or sorrel might be put upon inflammations.[4]

Diseases like the plague or leprosy were recognized as contagious, though they were still considered disturbances of the humours. The plague had four natural causes: 'the influence of sundry starres, great standing waters never refreshed, Carraine [carrion] lying long above ground, much people in small roome, living uncleanely and sluttishly.' A fifth and principal cause was 'the wrath of God for sinne'.[5] The plague began when venomous air drawn into a man's body 'inflameth the humours, especially where they bee superfluous, and bringeth them to a venemous temperature'. Such could happen to a man of any complexion. The remedies were to 'fly quickely from the place infected, abide farre off, and returne not soone againe'.[6] A change of air was imperative. All aromatic spices and herbs were good preservatives; one might chew cloves or cinnamon, inhale vinegar or drink wine spiced with saffron. 'A marvellous secret' recipe given in the *Secrets of Alexis* was a concoction made from 'Aloe Epaticum or Cicorrine, fine Cinamone, and Myrrhe', with 'Cloves, Mace, Lignum Aloe, Masticke, Bole Armenicke' ground down and taken in a little white wine and water every morning at dawn.[7]

A physician usually diagnosed disease not by looking at the patient closely—that was thought to be indecent, impractical and dangerous—but by cursorily establishing his predominant humour and questioning those around him about his illness. He could also use either of two other methods; taking the pulse (rediscovered in Galen's works)[8] or inspecting the urine. The latter was discouraged

1. See Copeland, pp. 144-5. The humours in women were naturally in better balance, for they were adjusted monthly: women's 'com-plexion is cold, and therefore commonly they are more temperate and chast, modest and patient, milde and mercifull, most constant and pitifull, and for the corruption that ariseth of grosse meates, and vnholesome fauoures, why they haue by nature a continuall euacuation of all superflous humoures, suche force hathe that which is pure, to expell the same that is vncleane'. Haly Heron *The Kayes of Counsaile* (Liverpool Reprints, Liverpool 1954) pp. 48-9.

2. *Regimen*, p. 178.

3. Added to Drummond's edition of Claude Dariot's *Astrologicall iudgement of the starres* is *A briefe treatise of mathematicall phisicke* by a certain George Coombe 'practicioner in physicke'. This has a plate showing the *anatomy* with the veins marked for bleeding, and beside it a table for determining the propitious moment by judicial astrology. According to Dariot the stars and the planets influenced the humours and the parts of the body, as well as men's actions. Under the zodiacial sign of virgo the melancholic humour tended to gain command, the belly, stones, bowels might be afflicted; it was a good time to send children to school, to seek the love of virgins, but 'euil to marrie for the woman then married, wil haue few or no children'; Sig. C2 recto.

4. But usually only after the usual bleeding and purging: see J. Fletcher *The differences, causes, and iudgements of vrine* (Cambridge 1598) pp. 130-2, where he discusses the treatment of the 'pissing euill'.

5. Thomas Cogan *The hauen of health* (London 1636) p. 297.

6. Ibid. p. 299.

7. Ibid. p. 311.

8. As Fletcher says in his preface.

1. Le Sage in *Gil Blas* satirizes this method of diagnosis.

by some writers like Fernel, but was still in common use even as late as the eighteenth century.[1]

J. Fletcher in a treatise on urine printed in 1598 thought it an easier science than pulse taking, and gave as his chief authorities Hippocrates, Galen, Aegidius, Actuarius and Avicenna. The expert physician should be able to detect from the state of the urine both the disease and the treatment, according to its colour, substance, quantity, salinity and smell, taking into account the patient's age, sex, condition and diet. The permutations and combinations of these qualities Fletcher listed with the normal logical precision, together with his deductions from the data, tied of course to the humoral theory. Melancholics were prone to thin watery urine.

What is interesting about Fletcher's book is that it shows the paradox of sixteenth-century medicine: though it was extremely logical after its (false) basic assumptions, at the same time it was always ready to accept lore or error. Fletcher did not even know the normal length of human gestation—when discussing methods of forecasting the sex of the unborn child (red urine denoted a boy, white a girl) he remarked that males were always carried for nine months, but females for ten, 'because the seeds of the male is hoter and liuelier then of the female, therefore all things in the male are sooner performed. . .'.[2]

2. Fletcher, p. 76.

In the 'spagiricall' or alchemical art of mixing medicines for the curing of gunshot wounds the gap between authority and practice was widest. The ancients had no remedies for the new wounds of war, and what recipes they had did not seem to work as well as the methods of the 'empericks'. A respectable surgeon might be in a quandary, for he could only justify the use of a drug or a treatment if he could find it recommended in Galen or some other classical writer, or if he could explain its action in terms of Galenic theories. Joseph Du Chesne in his *Scopularie* gave both methods, the old and the new, but felt he had to defend the new—since it evidently worked better—against the charge of magic.[3] The old way of treating wounds was to cauterize the wound, either by burning iron or boiling oil. The new method, which had been introduced by Ambroise Paré early in the sixteenth century, was to wash the wound in warm fresh water, then bathe it in oil and vinegar and bind it with tow. This treatment might be followed by others, such as linseed oil, or oil of worms or lilies, but the effect of these would be much less violent than the burning iron or the boiling oil. Even so the patient was probably lucky to recover, for in the name of restoring the humours to a normal balance he was likely to be purged and bled, while the surgeon awaited hopefully the formation of 'laudable' pus. One interesting thing about Du Chesne's book is that it classifies medicines by the patient's pocket: one 'for common souldiers approued', another 'for the richer sort'. Soldiers were laved with turpentine, honey of roses and lard, while rich men could afford essence of coral or essence of pearls.

3. Englished by John Hester. Du Chesne's discussion of treatment is on pp. 29-33. 'The which things', he says, talking of testing wounds that did not putrify by inserting apple pips into them before applying the new medicines, 'I haue spoken by the waye to proue, that manie were cured by medicines and not by enchantmentes as the common people iudge . . .'. Du Chesne mentions Paré as the inventor of the new treatment.

Although these remedies seem extraordinary to us now—there were others much worse: Fletcher advocated drinking urine for the plague or for ague, and applying it externally to itch, mange, ulcers and bee stings[1]—common medical lore on the whole seems sane. The watchword of such handbooks as *The schoole of Salerne*, Sir Thomas Elyot's *The castel of helth* or Thomas Cogan's *The hauen of health* was moderation. 'Hippocrates', says Cogan, 'in the sixt booke of his *Epidemies* setteth downe this sentence, Labor, Cibus, Potio, Somnus, Venus, omnia mediocria. . . . Every man therefore that hath a care of his health as much as hee may, must not onely use a measure in thos five things, that is to say, in labour, meate, drinke, sleepe, and venus, but also must use them in such order as Hippocrates hath proposed them.'[2] Three of the five things needed little comment. Work should be both mental and physical, the 'benefit of sleepe, or the necessity rather needeth no proofe . . .' and *Venus*, taken with all the others in moderation, was of equal value in preserving health, but used immoderately was just as damaging. Like the sparrows who 'through incontinency consume themselves' the profligate would die young. The value of moderation in these three being more or less self evident, the handbooks of health consequently became handbooks of diet. Thus, Cogan on venison:

> 'Venison, whether it bee or red deere or fallow, maketh ill juice, engendereth melancholy, and is hard of digestion, as Galen witnesseth. Wherefore it is no wholesome meate for students, no though it be drowned in wine, as the best manner is to eate it. Which way no doubt was first devised to amend the noysomnesse thereof, because wine is of contrary nature to that humour which venison most of all breedeth. For wine is hot and moist, and melancholy is cold and dry. A wonder it is to see how much this unwholesome flesh is desired of all folkes . . . And I could wish (saving the pleasure of honourable and worshipfull men) that there were no parkes nor forrests in England. For a good part of the best pasture in this Realme is consumed with deere, which might otherwise be better imployed for a common wealth.'[3]

The facts might be wrong, but they were justified by logic rather than experience. Venison was obviously eaten, perhaps even without provoking melancholy, as was hare, goat, pork and beef; Galen and his authorities before him had decided their effects on the digestion, and had given reasons to fit these effects into the medical logic. Venison was 'a pleasant meat: in great esteem with us', Burton noticed, yet he pronounced it 'melancholy', said it begat bad blood, was generally bad, and seldom to be used.[4]

Muddled amongst the logic of the humours were various bits of lore that were only justified by a logic of sympathies. Sea water was the best drink for those undertaking a sea voyage[5]; eels were not good for the voice (for they generated as Aristotle showed from the slime of the earth).[6] 'They that use filthy, standing, ill-coloured, thick, muddy water, must needs have muddy, ill-coloured, impure, and infirm bodies.'[7] As in the pharmacology of Paracelsus, this might be extended into a dominant theory, where by the doctrine of signatures every natural object would be found to betray God's intention for its proper use. 'Behold the Satyrion root,' wrote Paracelsus, 'is it not formed like the male privy parts?' Accordingly

1. Fletcher, p. 117 et seq.

2. Cogan, preface.

3. Cogan, pp. 137-8.

4. Robert Burton *The anatomy of melancholy* ed. Dell and Jordan-Smith (New York 1951) p. 190.

5. *Regimen*, p. 65.

6. Cogan, p. 165.

7. Burton, p. 196.

1. Quoted by Boas, p. 182.

magic discovered it and revealed that it can restore a man's virility and passion.[1]

But theory, fanciful or logical, was poor comfort to a sick man, and few can have had any illusions about the real state of medical knowledge. Certainly not Drummond: writing to Sir William Alexander in 1620 he told how 'for these eight weekes I haue beene languishing in sicknesse, and that more by the ignorance of physicians (which, being no where good, are heere naught), than any defect of nature: for my disease being a paine of the syde, they can not tell to what to adscriue the cause, nor how to help mee.'[2] This, added to the melancholy recital of infant mortality in the Memorials, makes a sobering epitaph on Renaissance medicine.

2. *Arch. Scot.* IV, 87.

ASTROLOGY AND ALCHEMY

Renaissance attitudes towards astrology and the experimental sciences were ambiguous. On the one hand the discovery of how much the Greeks had known of these things impressed scholars; on the other they were restrained by the traditional prohibitions of the Church. Astrology was opposed by official religion on the ground that God alone governed human fate, and any attempt to discover the future would be presuming on God's will. To an intelligent scholar like Ficino the difficulty could only be by-passed by creating the distinction that whereas the stars by no means governed man's life, they undoubtedly did influence it, and could thus be used to predict events in the future. The astrologer would not be pre-empting God but only discovering what God had already arranged. It was felt that if only enough astrological evidence could be gathered together then a comprehensive system could be worked out: what was needed was a mass of detail from which the general truths could be shown to follow.[3]

3. Paul Oskar Kristeller *The philosophy of Marsilio Ficino*, trs. Virginia Conant (New York 1943), pp. 310-11. For a more detailed discussion of Ficino's attitude to astrology and especially to magic, see D. P. Walker *Spiritual and demonic magic* (Studies of the Warburg Institute, London 1958).

During the Middle Ages astrology had been based on Arabic works; to these were now added those of the Greeks. The systematic completeness of Ptolemaic astrology came as a surprise to the Renaissance, and reinforced the conviction that there had been little but regression since. It was evident that the ancients had the answers, and all that was needed was to put their theories into practice. The respectability of the classics was thus lent to the theologically suspect sciences, and so during much of the sixteenth century some speculation was supported in them even by official institutions. Thus astrology was to be found in some universities, and even for a time, in the papal court. It held an official status at Bologna in the first half of the sixteenth century, and during the reign of Paul III (1534–49) it was encouraged at Rome.[4] Although attacked by men as different as Pico della Mirandola and Savonarola, and although the important university of Paris always remained hostile, on theological grounds, astrology kept above the surface, and its practice seems not to have involved a learned man in difficulties, at least before the second half of the sixteenth century.

4. Thorndike, V, p. 234 et seq.

The invention of printing ensured that more material was available to the curious than ever before, and in Drummond's library there is a selection ranging from the ancients through the Arabs to the commentaries of his own contemporaries.[1] In many of these works—particularly the classical, such as Seneca's *Naturales quæstiones* or Censorinus' *De die natali*—astrology forms only a section, but they were not ignored for this omission. Ptolemy's work on the courses of the stars was particularly influential in the Renaissance, and the remarks of Martianus Capella (in his *De nuptiis philogiae et septum artibus liberalibus*, a favourite of the Middle Ages) were still thought relevant. Enterprising printers revived the works of Arab astrologers: Alcabitius' introductory essay on judicial astrology (in the twelfth-century translation by John of Seville, with the fourteenth-century commentary by John of Saxony) was printed in Paris in 1521[2]; Messahala's ninth-century work, *On the elements and the celestial orbs*, was first printed by a certain Joachim Heller who was a friend of Philip Melanchthon, and its publication has been cited as good evidence of Melanchthon's sympathy with a public acceptance of Arabic astrology.[3]

Turning to the Renaissance authors in Drummond's library, they range from the greatest names—Ficino, Cardano, Pontanus—to the most obscure—Lemnius, Offusius. Notes on a few should indicate something of their pre-occupations. Joannes Mercurius' work acknowledges a debt to Melanchthon. It is a long-winded and dull, but Mercurius makes the interesting point that but for the fall of man astrology would be the perfect science, for man's sinfulness is the cause of astrology's flaws.[4] Another German, Jacob Koebel, takes in his treatise on the astrolabe the serious 'scientific' approach. By abandoning the old method of dividing the zodiac into twelve houses in favour of the new system devised by Peurbach and Regiomontanus, Koebel hoped to develop a new and more logical astrology that would allow a high degree of accurate prediction.[5] Jofrancus Offusius' work, *On the divine power of the stars, against a decadent astrology*, is in a way more significant, in that it represents an attempt to break away from classical Ptolemaic astrology in favour of a rational approach (or what seemed to Offusius a rational approach). Offusius, in search of reason, placed his trust in 'the symetry of the heavenly bodies and the mysteries of numbers'. This was more than the usual fascination with threes and sevens of this and that which his contemporaries enjoyed (Person found interest in trinities from that of the God-head to Rome's three-fold government). Offusius made complex calculations with perfect numbers, and by balancing these against the physical properties of the planets (whose influence was in proportion to these properties, Mars to burn, Mercury to dry) worked out a system so intricate that it seems a pity it failed.[6]

On the less ingenious side we can put Levinus Lemnius, whose treatise was *On the occult miracles of nature*. According to Thorndike this was a collection of little value, designed to entertain, and notable only for its frequent reference to the Latin poets.[7] More ambitious was Marsilio Ficino, who in his work on medicine *De triplica vita* put much astrological and even magical theory in his third book.[8] Such a typical renaissance man as Girolamo Cardano, with his wide interests in mathematics, medicine and other sciences, showed in his work on dreams his concern with omens and other

1. The libraries of the most curious and imaginative scientific thinkers were, of course, full of occult works: those belonging to the celebrated Dr Dee or the 'Wizard' Earl of Northumberland are good examples. For a description of Dee's library see E. R. Taylor *Tudor geography*; for Percy's see the article by G. R. Batho, 'The library of the "Wizard" Earl: Henry Percy Ninth Earl of Northumberland', in *The Library* xv, 246-61. Their interest in the occult has, as Johnson points out, tended to obscure thei genuine merit as scientists and patrons of science. Johnson, p. 135 et seq.

2. This is a reprint of the Lyons edition, c. 1520, which first contained the minor additions of Pierre Turrel the Lyonnese printer.

3. Thorndike, v, p. 395.

4. Thorndike, v, pp. 402-3.

5. Thorndike, v. p. 330.

6. Thorndike, vi, pp. 108-11.

7. Thorndike, vi, pp. 393.

8. The two subjects, for the Renaissance, were naturally linked. Ficino worked out a complex theory of astrological music, using the orphic hymns and the theurgic writings of Neoplatonists like Proclus, Iamblichus and Porphyry. See Walker, pp. 36-44.

portents of fate—all part of the stock-in-trade of the astrologer.[1] A century earlier Giovanni Pontano, who reorganized the Neapolitan Academus in the late fifteenth century, was also interested in astrology, and his contemporary Giovanni Bianchini became famous for his *Tables of directions*, which were an attempt to allow systematic prediction from observed movements of the stars. These names, of course, are taken from among Drummond's books, and are in themselves sufficient evidence that astrology and its sisters stayed above ground throughout the sixteenth century.

To these astrological works can be added the few treatises on another science of prediction, physiognomy. This art of forecasting men's fates from their faces had been popular in the Middle Ages; in the seventeenth century an educated man like Drummond was still taking notes on its secrets. In his library he had two treatises on physiognomy: one then attributed to Aristotle (Polemon has now been identified as its author), another by Peter of Abano, the Averroistic Aristotelian scholar of the thirteenth century, who discusses in great detail the relationship of this science with that of astrology.[2]

We are now able to distinguish confidently between the sciences and the pseudo-sciences, to set on the one side physics and chemistry, on the other astrology, alchemy, or physiognomy, to call the first respectable, and to dismiss the other as nonsense. This distinction was not possible in the Renaissance. The pseudo-sciences seem to us now to have offered a body of observations which could have been refuted with only a little trouble by any interested observer. Yet the sciences themselves purveyed a high proportion of the same lore—as long as a 'fact' had a respectable source it was not to be questioned but only explained. For example, consider the well-known phenomenum of the 'claick' or barnacle geese. These geese had a curious method of breeding, that is, they appeared rather than were seen to lay eggs and hatch them, and so were known (and described by such as the poet Du Bartas) as a rare work of nature.

> 'Their generation is beyond the ordinary course of nature, in so much that ordinarily one creature begetteth another; but so it is, that this fowle is engendred of certaine leaves of trees, out of which in a manner it buddeth, and ripeneth; Now, these trees growing upon the bankes of lakes, doe, at their due time, cast these leaves, which falling into the lake, doe there so putrifie, that of them is engendred a Worme, which by some secret fomentation & agitation of the waters, with the Suns helpe, groweth little and little to be a fowle somewhat bigger than a Mallard, or wild Duck; and in those waters, they live and feed, and are eaten by the inhabitants thereabouts.'[3]

This is David Person's version of the generation of the barnacle goose. To verify it he did not produce eye-witness accounts from his own Scotland, or even quote the respected historian Hector Boece, who said he had seen this generation with his own eyes, but instead Person went to the final authority—Aristotle. In the *De historia animalium* (lib. 1, cap. 1) Aristotle had discussed the spon-

[1]. Thorndike, v, p. 575. Drummond's own attitude to astrology, incidentally, was sceptical. In a letter 'to his Worthy Friend, M. A. G.' he claimed he 'never found any greater Folly in the Actions of Men than to see some busy themselves to understand the future Accidents of their lives.' He referred to 'those unlawful Curiosities', and advised M. A. G. to 'trust in the First Cause, God Almighty, and scorn vain Predictions.' *Works* (1711) pp. 147-8.

[2]. A part of Michael Scot's work, *The secrets of nature*, is also devoted to this art, and the work was sometimes known as the *Physiognomia*.

[3]. *Varieties*, I, p. 37-8.

taneous generation of 'wormes, froggs, snailes and the like' as the modern Scaliger had after him in his *Exercitatione*, and this should be sufficient explanation to convince the most doubtful. The facts were tailored to fit the theory: Person goes on to argue that the claick geese must be 'middle creatures', neither fowl nor fish but half way between, for they fell between the biological orders distinguished by the Greeks.[1]

This acceptance of the apparently miraculous in nature is surely relevant when we consider the sixteenth- and seventeenth-century craze of witchcraft, and the astonishing readiness of even the most sophisticated thinkers to believe in all the detailed, grotesque and often obscene tales of satanic practices. In the first place—as with the claick geese—if a fact had authority it should be fitted into the existing logical scheme of things rather than disputed. Witchcraft existed by papal bull, by texts of the Scriptures, by the *Malleus maleficarum*, and the scores of subsequent pamphlets and testimonies. Secondly, the supernatural was known to follow its own rules. The age was rational—holding firmly to a logical, all-comprehending Aristotelian system—and witchcraft, we might think, is the epitome of irrationalism. To the Renaissance mind this does not seem to have been so: theology was outside the natural system; knowledge of it was given to man by revealed truth, and he did not expect to understand it by reason alone. Coming within the province of theology, witchcraft had to be judged by different standards to other phenomena.

Drummond had only two books on witchcraft, but there is nothing in his library, his manuscripts or his life to hint that he was anything but a conformist, that is, a believer. The two works he did own are two of the most important of the time—James VI's *Daemonologie, in forme of a dialogue*, and Jean Bodin's *De la demonomanie des sorciers*. James has been accused of silliness, pedantry and superstition by historians; his contemporaries were readier to respect his intelligence and learning. A plot of witches had been discovered in the Lothians, James heard some of the confessions himself, and believed that his life was threatened. Jean Bodin too had listened to the evidence of self-confessed witches, and had been convinced by the impressive details of their foul league with Satan. And so the great legal authority, the philosopher and designer of a new methodology in historical research, was convinced. It was hardly a time for scepticism.

The fact that the miraculous could easily be dismissed as a rare work of nature, a mystery done by God, was one barrier to serious scepticism of known 'facts'; another was the belief that the secrets of nature were sacred, and it was not altogether meet for man to pry into them. Thus Person on the Philosopher's Stone (by which a man might make gold): 'O how great is the wisedome and power of the Creator of all, who reserveth the perfect knowledge of so high a secret to himselfe, and imparteth it but to very few, knowing the insatiablenesse of the heart of man. . . .'[2]

The 'elixir' or 'philosopher's stone' was a preparation which enabled the alchemist to transmute base metals into gold.[3] The theory

1. *Varieties*, I, pp. 38-40.

2. Ibid. v, p. 36. 'And to those who know not the value of gold, such as the West Indians, God in his wisdom gives it in abundance'.

3. There is a useful account of alchemical theory in Sir Charles Sherrington *The endeavour of Jean Fernel* (Cambridge 1946) pp. 45-52. The first authority on the subject is Thorndike. The problem for Renaissance scholars was that alchemy was not studied by the ancients, but was peculiarly a medieval pursuit. Hence the need for Hermes Trismegistus (see below).

1. As Timothy Willis put it, in his *The search of causes* (London 1616) p. 86.

2. The chief authorities of alchemy were Arnauld of Villanova, Raymond Lull, Rhazes, Albertus Magnus and Michael Scot, according to Pietro Antonio Boni, whose anthology of their treatises on the Philosopher's Stone was printed by the house of Aldus, Venice, in 1546.

3. According to Marsilio Ficino. Quoted by Sherrington, pp. 47-8. Hermes was thought to be an Egyptian priest. It was not until 1614, when Isaac Casaubon showed that the Hermetic writings were composed in post-Christian times, that his authority as the first and greatest of the mystical and magical philosophers was disturbed. See Yates, pp. 398-403.

4. *Azoth* was one of a number of works attributed to the mysterious Basilius Valentinus, who may or may not have been a fifteenth-century German monk. Basilius was the supposed inventor of antimony, and to him are attributed a variety of occult works, which were often printed in the seventeenth century. It is worth noticing that 'Basilius Valentinus' meant 'valiant king' in alchemy. For a general description of alchemy (including an explanation of some of the plates from *Azoth*) see Kurt Seligmann *The history of magic* (New York 1948) pp. 120-75. Some of the believers in alchemical allegory found it in the most unlikely places: Jacques Gohory believed that both the *Amadis* and the *Hyperotomachia* hid alchemical secrets. See Walker, p. 98.

5. *The search of causes* p. 73. This idea was in common currency: Fernel reasoned in the same way, and Person too named the *Elixir* 'the very true and just seed that engendereth and begetteth gold . . .' not out of brimstone or mercury but 'it is to be search't and found out of gold it selfe, and that most purified: for there is nothing in Nature which hath not of it, or rather in it the seede of its owne kinde, whereby it may be multiplied . . .' *Varieties*, v, p. 36.

6. *The search of causes*, pp. 86-7.

behind this transformation was logical, being based on Aristotelian physics, and followed from the observed transmutations of nature. The elements had elemental qualities: water, for instance, combined elemental moisture with elemental cold. Boiled (with fire) its cold turned to heat as it became steam — elemental air — and its qualities were transformed to elemental heat and elemental moisture. If the elements could be changed, why not the metals; they were all part of the 'Catholike unity'.[1]

Medieval alchemists had revealed in the most cryptic terms various recipes; in these transmutations began variously with salt, sulphur or mercury. Nothing was presented openly by such as Raymond Lull and Roger Bacon, for the secrets of nature were not to be divulged to the vulgar, but kept as mysterious for the initiated. Thus the sixteenth-century editor of Bacon's little book *De mirabili potestate artis et naturæ* in the section on the philosopher's stone — a stone which is not a stone — makes the marginal comment 'here are the enigmas'.[2]

A major source of the alchemical mysteries, both for Medieval and Renaissance alchemists, were the magical and allegorical writings of Hermes Trismegistus, who was supposed to have lived 'at the time when Moses was born'.[3] From such Hermetic scripts as the *Emerald table* they deduced pertinent truths — the scripts are vague enough to support a mystical, occult, or alchemical interpretation; they contain allegorical descriptions of the heavenly bodies and the elements, the sun is the father, the moon the mother, and so on. In conjunction with the alchemist's terms these phrases could be made meaningful, for the sun corresponded to gold, the moon to silver. As such treatises as the *Azoth* show, Hermes was thought to hold the key to the philosopher's stone.[4]

Short of experimenting in the laboratory (as Dr John Dee and the 'Wizard' Earl of Northumberland may have done) the alchemist could hope to discover the means of making gold by resort to logic. Man, the animals and plants generated by seed; did it then not follow that all parts of the hierarchy of nature from rocks to metals multiplied in like manner? As Timothy Willis explained in his 'theophysicall inuestigation of the possibilitie of transmutatorie alchemie', the seed was naturally nearest to first causes, and since in the breeding of animate matter — as the hen hatching her egg — one or all of the elemental qualities of heat, light and motion were necessary to success, so by employing these forces on the metals they might be transmuted upwards. From a little gold much gold might grow.[5] This was not interfering with God's creation, for there were two kinds of change, one to be found in nature, the other to be wrought by man. And in a rousing if vague conclusion Willis was thus able to claim that the secret of alchemy lay in the hierarchy of being, this, he said, is 'the wealth of Hermes his Smaragdine Table,' this 'is the ladder in nature of Angels ascending and decending between heauen and earth. This is the hoope of pure gold . . .'.[6]

25. Astrological figure: planetary positions. Franciscus Sarzozus, *In æquatorem planetarum libri duo* (Cat. 183).

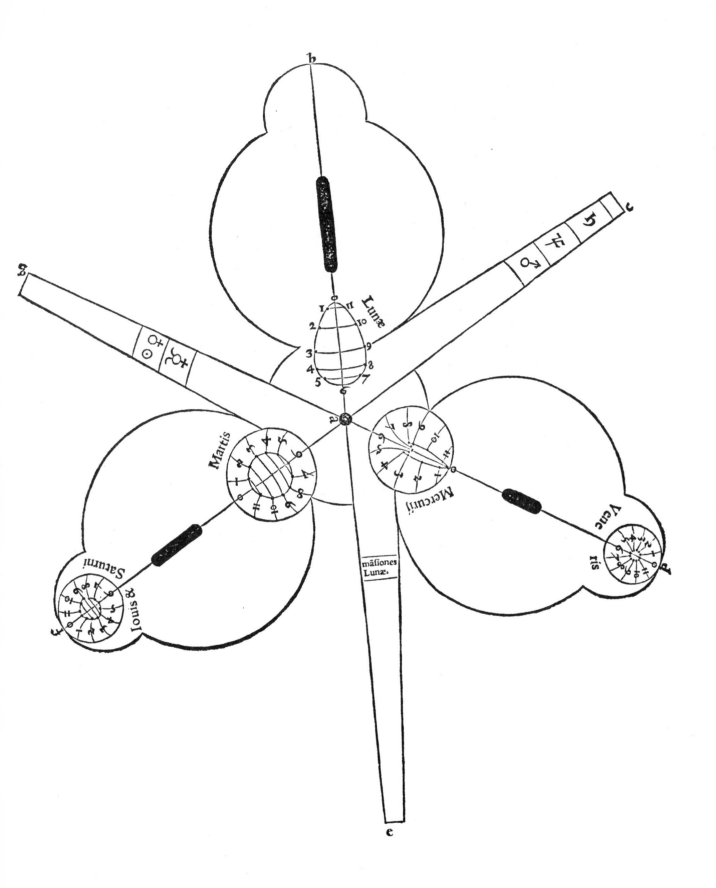

PLATONISM

We hardly need reminding of the importance of Platonism in the Renaissance, and even the details of its history will be familiar in some part to all readers. Preached and popularized by the Florentine Academy, taken up by a succession of writers, it had a most powerful effect on the Renaissance imagination. Founder of the Florentine school, Marsilio Ficino was the prime mover in the spread of Platonic ideas: as translator of Plato and his followers, as author of the *Theologia Platonica*, as philosopher in his own right.[1]

What the Renaissance understood by Platonism did not necessarily stem from Plato himself. The Middle Ages knew Plato only through the incomplete *Timaeus* in a Latin translation, and absorbed its Platonism from diluted sources: Apuleius, Macrobius, Martianus Capella and Boethius;[2] none the less Platonism was one of the great philosophical and theological forces of those centuries, particularly in its association with the teaching of St Augustine. The Renaissance was hardly less accommodating either in its ability to Christianize Platonism or to gather as many philosophers as possible into the Platonic fold. Plotinus, Porphyry, Iamblichus, Proclus —these were all translated and discussed in the first humanistic exploration of Platonism, and their development of Plato's thought, tending as it did towards the mystical, was even more acceptable than its reputed source. The mystical side of Renaissance Platonism stretched beyond the four Neo-platonist philosophers to include Hermes Trismegistus, the Sibyls and the hymns of Orpheus; Pico della Mirandola even took up and examined the allegories of the Jewish Cabbala. Each, in its way, was seen as adding something to the Platonic exploration of the soul's return to God, of immortality, of the ultimate good. The writings of the Pseudo-Dionysius were especially influential, for not only was Dionysius thought to be a contemporary of St Paul, and thus directly linked to divine revelation, but his particular kind of diffused and diluted Platonism had long been a spring of Christian mysticism.[3]

It is worth remembering that in the Renaissance Plato had especial esteem as one who nearly beheld the Christian light. Ficino was most anxious to place him in the line of those who had been given divine revelation, and to see Platonism adding to and fusing with Christian theology.[4] These beliefs were quite generally accepted in Drummond's time: as David Person in his *Varieties* claimed 'it was of old held for a truth, *Platonicos paucis mutatis fieri posse Christianos*', which, as he went on, was the reason that Plato was called divine.[5] Ficino wrote about the similarities in thought between Platonism and the Mosaic doctrines, and the agreement between Socratic and Christian morality.[6] To judge by Juan Huarte, who mentions as a well-known fact that 'Plato took from Holy Writ the best sententiae that we can find in his works',[7] it was even widely agreed that Plato had read the Pentateuch.

Plato was sometimes studied in the universities, but never to the extent that his works supplanted those of the Aristotelian curriculum; rather, Platonism permeated the Renaissance mind informally, in the first place, through literature. The Platonic doctrines of love

1. See Paul Oskar Kristeller *The philosophy of Marsilio Ficino* trs. Virginia Conant (New York 1943).

2. Ernst Robert Curtius *European literature and the Latin Middle Ages* trs. Willard R. Trask (London 1953) p. 108.

3. For a general summary of Platonism in the Renaissance see the still-useful chapter in Henry Osborn Taylor *Thought and expression in the sixteenth century* (New York 1920) II, pp. 271-84. For Ficino's exploration of Neoplatonic magic see Walker, *op. cit.* For the importance of the philosophical treatises of the *Corpus Hermeticum*—attributed to Hermes Trismegistus but not to be confused with the astrological, alchemical and magical literature also under his name—see Walker and especially, Yates, *op. cit.*

4. Kristeller, pp. 25-9.

5. *Varieties*, p. 230.

6. Kristeller, p. 27.

7. Otis H. Green *Spain and the Western tradition* (Madison 1965) III, p. 309.

26. Alchemical figure. Symbol of Hermetic transformation, showing allegories of the seven alchemical processes: *Azoth* (Cat. 97).

laid down in the *Symposium* and the *Phaedrus* were expounded by Ficino both in his own works and the commentaries to his translations — Ficino coined the term 'Platonic love' — and were taken up joyfully by those who were considering the ideals of courtly life. Love was supreme. Love was perfect, in its highest form a manifestation of the divine spirit. Love was the path towards God; through human love man might proceed to know first himself, then, if but dimly, God. Castiglione, Bembo, Marguerite de Navarre, all embraced this delightful form of Platonism, and a host of imitators followed.

The courtier ends with the famous examination of love (put in the mouth of Bembo) which is concluded as the dawn breaks over the hills of Urbino with a fervid evocation of the Platonic ideals. In Bembo's own *Asolani* love again is the honoured subject: condemned by its detractors on the first day as the cause of all trouble and sorrow, praised on the second as the source of all joy, and finally on the third, in a Platonic reconciliation of the two extremes, seen as the inspiration of both good and bad; bad in its lowest form as sensual desire, good in its highest as spiritual or Platonic love. This sort of dualism lent itself to dramatization: in the *Heptameron* of Marguerite de Navarre — which rivalled Boccaccio's *Decameron* in popularity in the late Renaissance — the opposing effects of sensual and spiritual love are shown in lively detail.

As one would expect, Drummond's library overflows with Renaissance Platonism in its literary form. Besides *The courtier* or the *Asolani* he could have found Platonism in a dozen places without leaving his Italian books: in Gelli's *Circe*, in Leone Hebraeo's *Dialoghi d'amore*, Mario Equicola's *Libro di natura d'amore*, or dramatized in Tasso's *Aminta*. From Italy Platonism spread to France, Spain and England; its effect varied, but was never negligible. It found a host in the pastoral romances: both Guarini's *Pastor fido* and Urfé's *L'Astrée* are filled with the sentimental glorification of love as the highest of human goals.

To return to the philosophy books themselves: Drummond had in both Latin and Greek several of the major Platonic writers, and a few of the minor; enough at least to furnish him with a sound knowledge of Platonic ideas. He had the works of Plato in Latin, translated by Ficino, and he seems to have been acquainted with their contents, for in one of his political essays — the one titled *Skiamachia* — he borrows an allegory from the *Republic*.[1] He had no Plotinus (though one of his editors suggests he had read Plotinus)[2] and his only work of Proclus' is an astronomical one. He had a Latin translation of Iamblichus' *De mysteriis Ægyptiorum*, a work which has been characterized as 'the loftiest and most moving defense of spiritual religion from the pen of any pagan,'[3] and a Greek edition of Hierocles' commentary on the *Golden verses* of Pythagoras. Of Christian works he had the Pseudo-Dionysius, Synesius *On Dreams*, a short piece by Psellus. Interestingly enough he had the main medieval sources of Platonism: Macrobius' commentary on the *Somnium Scipionis*, Martianus Capella's *De nuptiis philogiæ et septum artibus liberalibus* and Boethius' *De consolatione philosophiæ*, books which remained popular and read.

1. This is the allegory of the cave from the seventh book of the *Republic*, where the state of mankind is compared to that of captives in a cave, having behind them a great light, but only able to see the shadows cast by this light; these shadows they take to be the real objects, the only reality. Drummond's title means fighting about shadows.

2. See William C. Ward's edition of Drummond's *Poetical works* (London 1894) ii, pp. 263-4.

3. Moses Hadas *A history of Greek literature* (New York 1950) p. 263.

Drummond's own Platonism was absorbed from these varied sources. In his best and most well-known essay, *A cypresse grove*, he contemplates death, man's present misery on earth and his consolations in the world to come: a common enough theme, but elevated by Drummond's high style and his solemn, philosophical rhapsodies. This essay is a synthesis of Renaissance mystical thought. Platonism is uppermost—that is, Christian Platonism with a strong Augustinian flavour—as Drummond finds relief from the fears of death and the unhappiness of life in contemplation of the return of the soul to its source, to union with the essence Divine. The soul being the image of the 'Good', seeks union with its superior form when freed by death; earth is but an 'infected and leprous Inne', an unpleasant but temporary halt:

> 'Bedded & bathed in these earthlie ordures, thou [my Soule] canst not come neare this soueraigne Good, nor haue any glimpse of the farre-off dawning of his vn-accessible Brightnesse, no, not so much as the eyes of the Birds of the night haue of the Sunne. Thinke then by Death, that thy Shell is broken, and thou then but euen hatched; that thou art a Pearle, raised from thy Mother to bee enchaced in Gold, and that the death-day of thy bodie, is thy birthday to Eternitie.'[1]

1. Kastner, II, p. 92.

And as the soul has its higher image, so the body is a reflection of the form of the soul, and so the body, seeking reunion will ultimately achieve its own resurrection:

> 'If the Soule bee the Forme of the Bodie, and the Forme seperated from the Matter of it, can not euer so continue, but is inclined and disposed to bee reunited thereinto; What can let and hinder this desire, but that some time it bee accomplished, and obtaining the expected end, rejoyne it selfe againe vnto the Bodie?'[2]

2. Kastner, II, p. 93.

And if the body does not rise again, 'how can the onelie and Soueraigne Good bee perfectlie and infinitlie good?' For, says Drummond descending to the lower ground of Christian dogma, if God does not reward the righteous and punish sinners in the hereafter how then can He be just? (This is an unfortunate fall from the heights, but, one might add, not untypical of Drummond. He gathered his thoughts from all sides, and he could not always sustain his good taste.)

Law

In law, humanism had one of its most brilliant yet practical successes, for under its impetus a revolution took place in the sixteenth century that completely transformed legal study, teaching and practice in every country where Roman law remained in use. The centre of this movement was France; the great humanistic civilians were almost all French, and they taught the new law at a few progressive French universities, notably Bourges, Toulouse and Poitiers. From 1607 to 1609 Drummond studied law at Bourges while Bourges was still at its height as a school of the new legal teaching: Cujas and Hotman had died in 1590 but their influence was well established, as we can see from Drummond's library of law books. His collection was not large, but it was eminently useful, and more than any other section of his library it was up to date, with little lumber from the past. In fact, it seems a list that might well have been recommended by his Bourges professor, for it encompasses in a small way the whole history of the humanistic reformation of law.[1]

Civil law was founded on the codification of Roman law that was made to the Emperor Justinian's directions during the years A.D. 533–65.[2] The chief editor was Tribonius, and the work was issued in three main parts: the *Digest*, the *Institutes* and the *Novels*. The whole is now known as the *Corpus Iuris Civilis*, and so it was to Drummond, but it is worth noting that this title dates only from 1583. In the Middle Ages Justinian's code was taught, and, so far as it did not directly interfere with local strongholds of feudal and canon law, it was practised, the great preoccupation of the civilian jurists being their effort to explain Roman law in such a way that this might be done as consistently as possible. Thus, around Roman law there grew up a great body of commentary or glosses, which in time also took on the sanctity of the actual text. The last and yet the greatest among these glossators was Accursius (1182–1260), whose *Glossa ordinaria* (which revised and superseded the work of his predecessors) earned him the name of the great father or regenerator of the glosses. For the lawyers of the Middle Ages, Justinian was regarded in much the same way as Aristotle or the Bible—a sacred text, immediately valid, quite perfect, needing only explanation and commentary to resolve its apparent contradictions. There was no attempt made to understand the historical conditions that

1. Edward Henryson, a Scot, was Professor of Civil Law at Bourges in the 1590s, and may have survived till Drummond's time; David Baird Smith 'Roman Law' in *Sources and literature of Scots Law* (Stair Society, Edinburgh 1936) p. 178.

2. The information in the following section is taken from the relevant articles in A.A. Roberts *A South African legal bibliography* (Pretoria 1942).

Roman law had sprung from, nor was it realized that several different periods in Rome's development were haphazardly entombed in the *Corpus*, nor that society had radically changed in the thousand years since the codification, and that many of the terms, titles and judgements had no medieval equivalent.

What in fact kept the Justinian code in being as the supreme authority was that it was increasingly freely adapted, especially from the fourteenth century onwards, when the influence of the great jurist Bartolus of Sassoferrato and his school made itself felt. The glossators had done the main work in explaining Justinian, now the post-glossators could concentrate on the refinements of the law. With Bartolus the *mos docendi Italicus*, or Italian way of teaching, was developed in which the jurist no longer need expound the letter of the *Corpus Juris*, but only call upon it at a late stage in his argument as an authoritative illustration of his point. The *mos Italicus* thus freed the jurist from the necessity of applying every point of the Justinian code to the medieval context, and indeed this was its strength, for it meant that the jurists could easily adapt the *Corpus Iuris* to everyday needs, while retaining its supreme authority. This, however, was the only freedom that the *mos Italicus* allowed, for it was based upon seven fixed processes, and employed finally a dialectic 'so subtle and refined as to make it seem that any opinion could be wrung from traditional authority'.[1]

At the beginning of the sixteenth century the study and practice of civil law had hardly changed; Bartolism still enjoyed a wide acceptance, and the scholastic method still ruled in the law schools. Two chief assumptions still obtained: one, that Roman law was essentially perfect; two, that Roman law as it was taught was the law as it was understood by Justinian. These two premises now for the first time came under attack, and by the end of the sixteenth century both had been quite discredited — such was the force of the humanistic revolution.[2]

The first blow of the humanists is usually reckoned to have been struck by Guillaume Budé (Budaeus) when in 1508 he published his *Annotationes in Pandectas*. In this seminal book Budé examined the Justinian *Digest* and the mass of medieval scholarship with which it was encrusted, and by bringing to bear his great knowledge of Roman history and philology he exposed for the first time the errors of the medievalists. These errors as Budé showed were based on ignorance of good Latin, on a complete lack of historical perspective, on corruptions in the text, and on a readiness to explain away all contradictions in the *Corpus Iuris* itself. Accursius, Budé claimed, had taken 'note of neither histories or annals; and such questions as when did jurisconsults, legislators, or emperors live, or who among these were contemporaries, were of no concern to him'.[3] Budé tried to examine the *Corpus Iuris* in its historical context, to ask himself for whom was it written and when, and what the titles and terms it used actually meant to Justinian's editors. Where Accursius had stated that no two statements in the law were ever contradictory, Budé was prepared to show how they often were, and to explain such antinomies as due to the failure of the editors of the *Corpus Iuris* to distinguish be-

1. Julian H. Franklin *Jean Bodin and the sixteenth-century revolution in the methodology of law and history* (New York 1963) pp. 13-14.

2. Franklin, p. 17.

3. Franklin, p. 22.

tween laws gathered from different periods of Rome's history. Budé's *Annotationes* was but the beginning of the attack on authority, but it was crucial since it showed the means whereby the whole scholastic system could be undermined. Budé himself though not primarily a lawyer, was soon recognized by other humanists as the progenitor of this new approach to law: in Erasmus' words, together with Ulrich Zasius and Andreas Alciatus he was one of the *triumviratus constituendae rei pandectariae*.[1]

The last member of this triumvirate, Alciatus, was the man most responsible for introducing the humanistic teaching to the universities and especially to Bourges, where he founded the law school in 1529. Under his leadership the *Corpus Iuris* was examined afresh with all the weapons of the new humanistic learning. Alciatus himself, it has been said, was 'the first who united the study of the law with polite literature and a knowledge of the antiquities'.[2] His writing, as with most of his humanist successors, took the form of commentaries on particular problems of the law, rather than any definitive study of the whole *Corpus Iuris*, and this emphasis can be seen in the titles of his main works: *Paradoxa, Dispunctiones, Annotationes,* (the first of which was probably among Drummond's books). Drummond certainly owned his treatise on single combat and duelling, a piece in which Alciatus displayed all his considerable skill not only as a lawyer but also as a historian, a classicist and a writer—in short, as a very perfect humanist.

Alciatus died in 1550, but even by 1561 Étienne Pasquier, in *Les recherches de la France*, was able to distinguish a new school of jurists, who had generated 'une nouvelle estude de Loix, qui fut de faire un mariage de l'estude du Droict aveques les Lettres Humaines, par un language latin net et poly'. This marriage was between the 'Docteurs de droict' (the Glossators) and the 'Humanistes' and was the practical application of the principles of legal reformation set out by Budé and Alciatus. The centre of the new teaching was Bourges, and the greatest of the new teachers was Jacques Cujas— 'le grand Cujas'.[3] Cujas continued the movement begun by Budé and Alciatus whereby the *Corpus Iuris* was scrutinized in its historical perspective, but he progressed beyond the Justinian code itself and attempted to examine its sources. He was a learned historian and philologist, and his knowledge of these two subjects allowed him to explore the work of several of the Roman jurists from whom the *Corpus Iuris* was compiled, and to estimate to what extent Justinian's editors had corrupted their sources. Cujas was also an assiduous collector of medieval and classical manuscripts, many of which he edited and prepared with commentaries for publication (Paulus' *Sententiae* is a fine example of this side of Cujas' achievement in Drummond's library). Above all Cujas is important for his establishment of the historical approach, for his teaching marks the final overthrow of the Bartolist faction (which had still defended itself until it was overcome in the second half of the sixteenth century). Cujas insisted that his students went to the source, not to the exegesis of some glossator, or yet worse, to the involved scholastic jargon of the Bartolists, who seldom bothered to examine the text.

1. *Great jurists of the world* (London 1913) p. 71. And by Étienne Pasquier the 'trois premiers entrepreneurs de ce nouueau mesnage'; *Les recherches de la France* (Paris 1643) (Book 9), p. 901. (Drummond only owned books one and two.) Ulrich Zasius (1461-1535) was professor of law in the university of Freiburg, and did much to spread Alciatus' ideas in Germany.

2. Quoted Roberts, p. 32. In spite of his interest in the subject Drummond did not own a copy of what was Alciatus' most influential non-legal work: the *Emblemata*.

3. Pasquier, p. 901.

How could such teaching be improved, we might ask: it seems intelligent, scholarly and practical, the very antithesis of scholastic jurisprudence. Yet to a large body of Cujas' fellow civilians, it was not practical enough, it was too idealistic, it was not capable of being put to everyday use. The leader of this rival school (again, for a while a professor at Bourges) was François Hotman, and his teaching proved to be extremely influential. He did not deny the importance of the work of his predecessors, nor that their battle with the ignorance of the Bartolists and the corruptions of the *Corpus Iuris* had been eminently necessary. Indeed Hotman advised his son never to be without Cujas' *Paratitla* on the *Digest*, and in his own *Antitribonianus* he went over in greater detail than ever before all the many sins committed by the glossators and their inheritors.[1] Hotman's main concern, however, as it developed in his writing, was that Cujas' teaching was too bound up with the value of historical perspective to the detriment of the law in practice. French law in practice was a muddle of customary, feudal and canon law, on top of which civilians had traditionally tried to justify their arguments from the body of the Justinian code. Hotman saw that it was little good exposing the errors of the code and leaving the other elements of the law in confusion. He wanted to break free from Roman law, and to build up a national law by rationalizing local and traditional law, so that France would have a legal system free from anachronism, based on a philosophy of taking the best that custom and experience could provide, and adapting all to suit present needs.

1. Franklin, p. 46 et seq.

It is not possible here to go in any detail into this controversy between the rival teachings of Cujas and his school and Hotman[2]; at this distance of time their differences narrow, and we are inclined to see them as fighters for the same cause—the reformation of the civil law. But their more important contemporaries should be mentioned, particularly since many of them are represented in Drummond's library. From among those who have been grouped with Cujas, Barnabé Brisson is notable (typically, in humanistic fashion, he had a high reputation as a philologist) as is Charles Du Moulin, whose great lifework was the rationalization of the customary laws of the country. Douaren and the Godefrois, *père et fils*, are usually also classed as members of the French school sympathetic to Cujas; Drummond did not own their works. On the other side was Doneau (again, unrepresented) and Jean Bodin (only present in his works on witchcraft). Among other jurists whose reputation was higher in other countries under Roman law, such as the Netherlands, two can be named from the first half of the sixteenth century: Andrèa Tiraquellus and Jacob Raevardus.

2. In the fashion of the time much of the discussion was conducted through the publication of abusive polemics (cf. the Ramist controversies). An example from Drummond's library is Cujas' *Notata Antonii Mercatoris*.

What was the result of the humanistic revolution in law? A recent work has placed the climax of this revolution in Jean Bodin's philosophy of law as the fruit of universal history, a synthesis of the juristic wisdom of the ages. Bodin's work was a response to the historical Pyrrhonism argued first by Cornelius Agrippa (1486–1535) and then Francesco Patrizzi (1529–97), who had both challenged the first principles of historical belief. Their sceptical philosophy denied that any certain historical knowledge was possible: historians were ignorant, partisan, deceived, or alive and writing long after the events they attempted to describe. Bodin's task was to exploit their spirit of criticism and objectivity, but to transform their negative approach into a contructive methodology. Clearly the humanistic revolution had two stages: the first, the debunking of the old method of exegesis of authority, the second, the rebuilding of the law by incorporating all its parts into a consistent and cohesive whole. Bodin's theories (put forward in his *Methodus* and his *Six livres de la république*) were the crystallization of this second stage, and they carried the earlier realization of historical particularity forward to a view of historical development. Thus, where Budé had pointed out the historical conditions under which the *Corpus Iuris* was compiled, Bodin attempted to show the historical growth of customs, peoples, and nations. A modern philosophy of law could only be evolved that used the comparative view of history.[1]

The effect of the humanistic revolution in practice was quite undramatic, as could be expected in a well entrenched and traditionally conservative profession like law. In France the greatest changes were made as the customary laws were codified and rationalized (a process which had already begun in the later Middle Ages) and these innovations had their echo in other countries where the high reputation of the French civilians and the predominant position of the French law schools made France the natural source of legal inspiration. Such was the case with Scotland, and indeed Scotland provides an excellent example of how the humanistic revolution could be applied in practice.

In Drummond's day law in Scotland was still in a somewhat rudimentary state, largely unsystematized, without any major codification or collection of precedents. The foundation of the College of Justice in 1534–5 can be seen as the first step towards receiving Roman law into the Scottish system, but this introduction was gradual. Customary law, feudal law and canon law were all still important sources of inspiration, while Roman law, besides providing the basic training for the Scots lawyer, was chiefly a guide which could be appealed to when there were gaps or contradictions in the older jurisprudence. For the want of a body of reference which clearly recorded the precedents of special cases (Balfour's *Practicks* was not published till the middle of the eighteenth century) the Scottish advocate had to turn to France, and in place of local authority often cited French courts and French decisions. Collections and codifications of French customary law were also used, chiefly the decisions of the *parlements*, but frequently the collections of local and provincial decisions. It is probable that this practice, necessary as it may have been, retarded the native development of Scots law, although there is no doubt that Scottish lawyers were well aware of the more theoretical and idealistic humanistic teaching. Thus, Sir Robert Spottiswood in his *Practicks* (written in 1633) has as many as eleven references to Cujas, though he also frequently cites men of the older schools, such as Guy Papon (who died in 1477).[2]

The chief means whereby the humanistic revolution was taken to

1. Franklin, *op. cit.*

2. David Baird Smith, articles on 'Roman Law' and 'Canon Law' in *Sources and literature of Scots Law.*

Scotland was undoubtedly the lawyers themselves, who went to France for their training in large numbers during the last decades of the sixteenth century and the first of the seventeenth. Holland was to be the place for legal teaching thereafter (having the advantage of the right religion) but in Drummond's day the universities of Poitiers, Bourges and Toulouse were the most popular, for Scotland had no law school of its own and if a man wanted academic legal training, he had to go abroad.[1] He could be admitted as an advocate without attending a university, though this involved a long apprenticeship and, as a means of joining their ranks, seems to have been regarded without much favour by the officials of the College of Justice. The most usual method for the Scots lawyer was to attend university at home and become a master of arts, then to go abroad and study law for two years (as Drummond did). On his return the 'expectant' lawyer, probably attaching himself to some senior member of the profession, would then try to gain practical experience, acting as an 'auditor' of cases, before putting himself up for admission as advocate.[2]

It is clear that even in Protestant Scotland, canon law was by no means dead, for almost all the petitioners for advocate make a point of their knowledge of the subject (the first to state he had read only civil law did not present himself till 1598).[3] Though the reformers might refer to 'the dunghill of the Canon Law',[4] the lawyers themselves found it harder to dispense with it, chiefly since many matrimonial and land titles had been drawn up under the old system, and needed a canonist's attention and skill. Drummond, it should be noted, owned a handsome edition of Gratian's *Decretals*.

Although Scottish law was still so largely undeveloped in the early seventeenth century, and its organization suffered so much from the religious and political upheavals of the time, Scotland was a fertile field for the ideas of the French humanistic revolution in law.[5] The great Scots lawyers later in the century, such as Stair and Mackenzie, were profoundly influenced by it, and their attempt to provide Scotland with a national system of law owes much to this French inspiration. By the eighteenth century the battle seem to have been won, and in Lord Gardenstone's dicta on the sources of Scots law we can see the echoes of Hotman's and Bodin's philosophy: after naming usages and established consuetude, feudal law, and civil law, Gardenstone claims finally that the law is based on 'every apparent principle of justice which has been received by the other civilized nations of Europe'.[6]

It is thus by no means an accident that Drummond's law books are a choice selection of the best of sixteenth-century law. Scotsmen learned their law in Drummond's time from the men who were revolutionizing Europe's legal teaching and, particularly since Scotland had no system of her own to oppose the new, the lessons were well learned. English lawyers had the strength of the common law behind them, Italian lawyers the tradition of Bartolism,[7] but the Scots, studying under the humanist civilians at Bourges, Poiters and Toulouse were in a position, with the paucity of their native theorists, to put French teaching into practice. Whereas Drummond's

1. Chairs of law were abolished at the *Nova Erectio*. There were abortive schemes to introduce the teaching of law at both Glasgow and Edinburgh at the end of the sixteenth century. At Aberdeen the canonist's office was re-appointed in 1619, and only in 1639 limited to the teaching of matrimonials, wills and teinds. This office, however, cannot have been much more than nominal, since its holder was presumably one of the regents, and thus responsible for conducting ordinary classes. Alexander Morgan *Scottish University Studies* pp. 102-3. *Fasti Aberdonenses*, p. 278.

2. Robert Kerr Hannay *The College of Justice* (Edinburgh 1933) pp. 135 et seq. Unfortunately there is a gap in the records after 1608 — just before the very years in which Drummond might have petitioned for advocate. Though it is almost certain he never practised, we cannot tell what stage he actually reached.

3. Hannay, p. 147. Even today canon law provides the fundamentals for some parts of Scots law, especially, for instance, marriage law.

4. Quoted Smith, in *Sources and literature of Scots Law*, p. 188.

5. Italy, for instance, seems to have been slower to accept the French lead. The mainly conservative nature of sixteenth- and seventeenth-century Italian law can be seen in its literature: c.f. *A catalogue of a collection of civil and canon law books in the University of Glasgow* (Glasgow 1949) — 262 commentaries, mainly Italian.

6. Smith, in *Sources*, p. 173.

7. Cf. footnote 17.

philosophy books represent very much the *status quo* of accepted learning and are rather scholastic in tone, his law books show humanism in practice, as it reached the student lawyer. From among only a modest number of titles nearly every name of the humanist revolution in law is represented—and usually by his most important work. Budé, Alciatus, Cujas, and Hotman—the four great civilians of the sixteenth century—are there, and while we might have asked for more of Alciat, and, for instance, Hotman's *Antitribonianus*, we cannot really complain that the selection is thin. Bodin's works may well have been thought too theoretical for the student lawyer, who would after all be more concerned with the law in practice, and for whom Hortensius or Hopper might make better reading. But taken together, this is a most up-to-date collection of law books.

ΠΡΟΘΕΩΡΙΑ
SIVE DISPOSITIO TI
TVLORVM PANDECTARVM IV-
RIS CIVILIS, EX CLARISSIMI IV-
risconf.D. Ioachimi Hopperi Phri-
fii prælectionibus collecta,
nunc primum in ta-
bulas digesta,
PER
OTTONEM AB
Hoeuel.

COLONIÆ AGRIPPINÆ
Apud hæredes Arnoldi Birckmanni,
Anno 1 5 6 4.

*Cum Gratia & Priuilegio Cæsaræ Maieftatis
ad decennium.*

27. Title-page, with Drummond's note of purchase while at law school Bourges 1608. Joachim Hopper, Προθεωρια (Cat. 216).

Theology

One sixth of all Drummond's books were theological: some seventy-five being in Latin, Greek or Hebrew, the remainder in the vernaculars. Nowadays this would seem a generous proportion in a private library, but for the seventeenth century it was much less than usual. About a third of all books printed then were theological — depending on where one drew the line, for to include popular religious matter such as sermons, devotional works, controversial tracts and pamphlets would put the proportion even higher.[1] The printed catalogues of the time reflect this balance. Draud's theology section of the *Bibliotheca classica* covers the first 652 of 1,654 pages (Latin works only); Thomas James' 1605 catalogue of the Bodley Library shows *libri theologici* filling 162 pages, while *libri medici*, *libri juris* and *libri artium* take only 37, 55 and 140 pages respectively.

This taste for the printed word of theology should really be no surprise to us when we remember that in contemporary eyes the Reformation was still hardly won. Religion was not just a matter for social Sunday observance; it was enmeshed in political, social and personal life. Drummond was born in 1585, when the Scots Kirk was established in its Calvinist attachment, but had still to settle its organization and its forms of worship. In his lifetime he saw the ministers of the kirk engage in an endless series of debates and quarrels both with the king and the state and between themselves: bishop or presbyter, kneeling or standing, prayer-book or psalm-book. Drummond lived as a child in a Scotland governed by a king who was able to keep Church and State apart, but he died in a country without a king, in a theocracy whose armies had won by force the desires of their most extreme Calvinist ministers. To face such change, such strife, such argument, a man needed to be prepared, for there was no withdrawing from the controversy.

Religious training was part of the curriculum of the school and the university. As it was taught in the Protestant countries it became part of the general system, that is, it was treated like other academic subjects, being ordered and organized around logical principles so that any student trained in Ramist or Aristotelian methods would have little trouble acquiring the given truths. Calvinism, with its intrinsic systematic theological structure, lent itself especially to this kind of treatment, and a textbook such as Keckermann's (used at

1. See H. S. Bennett *English books and readers, 1558 to 1603* p. 112.

91

1. Harris Francis Fletcher *The intellectual development of John Milton* II, pp. 195-200.

2. *University of Edinburgh: Charters*, pp. 110-15.

3. Clyde Leonard Manschreck *Melanchthon: the Quiet Reformer* (New York 1958) p. 82.

4. Don Cameron Allen *Francis Mere's Treatise 'Poetrie'* University of Illinois Studies in Language and Literature, XVI (Urbana 1933) 20. Roger Ascham thought 'bookes of common places be very necessary, to induce a man, into an orderly generall knowledge, how to referre orderly all that he readeth, *ad certa rerum Capita* and not wander in study'. He thought Melanchthon's collection 'notable'; *The Scholemaster* (London 1571) f. 43r.

Cambridge) was able to present theology in a 'thoroughly Aristotelian' manner.[1] No textbook is mentioned in the Edinburgh curriculum (though that of Ramus, which Drummond owned, would be a likely choice), but it seems probable that the teaching of theology followed the usual practice: the students were started on Buchanan's *Psalms*, proceeded to the catechism and spent the last two years on the Common Places and controversies of religion.[2]

Catechism, Common Places and controversies: from the first, the youth would learn the principles of his religion; from the second, moral truths pointed from the sacred texts; from the third, the proper defence for the common debates on dogma. All three were based on the ultimate Protestant authority—the Bible. The catechism presented the fundamental beliefs of the Church in a simplified and popular way. The most important were at the beginning, the most complex at the end, and even the dullest child would not escape the schoolroom without knowing the chief end of man (man's chief end, as the Presbyterian catechism has it, is to worship God and to glorify Him forever). Catechisms abounded in the Reformation, being rewritten as dogma was modified, and being written for all manner of men. Drummond had several, Calvinist and Catholic, from the simple *Preguntas y respuestas sobre la importancia del acto de contricion*—'muy prouechoses para todo genero de gente'—to the longwinded, breast-beating *Modell of divinitie*.

Loci Communes, or Common Places, were also popular, particularly in the Protestant countries. Essentially they were systems of doctrine drawn from the Scriptures, arranged under topics, but frequently their authors enlarged them to include comments, sententiæ and explanation from the Fathers and the Schoolmen. Melanchthon in 1521 in his *Loci Communes* directed the attention of theologians back to the Bible[3]; by the end of the century most of the major reformers had adopted his or written their own, and they were answered by a considerable number of Catholic interpretations. Common Places and compendia became so popular that they threatened their own sources: James I, for instance, in 1616 ordered the Cambridge divinity students to give up such books and devote themselves instead to the study of the Fathers, the Councils, Schoolmen, controversies and histories.[4]

The third of the subjects taught in the Edinburgh curriculum—the controversies—was the most advanced, but equally essential for the student, who, going out into a world where theological opinions varied from country to country, even from parish to parish, needed a good understanding of the main matters of dissent. Transubstantiation, predestination, the sacraments, trinitarianism: these were the subjects of the chief controversies, these were the questions that separated not only Protestants from Catholics, but also divided Lutheran from Calvinist, Anglican from Arminian. The bulk of Drummond's books in the vernacular are on the controversies: these we shall return to later; first let us finish looking at the formal religious education that a man like Drummond would normally have had.

Instructed in the university in the catechism, the Common Places and the controversies, the student would scarcely have been allowed to lose sight for one moment of the foundation of all three, indeed the foundation of the Protestant Church—the Bible. Protestantism, of course, rested on affirmation of the supreme authority of the Scriptures, and therefore the correct goal of theological study for the Protestant was study of the Bible. It is probable, however, that at this date university students were considered as yet unprepared for this: instead the aim of their theological education was to drill them in the dogma and beliefs of the Church, then to give them the means whereby they might eventually become scholars. Thus the *tongues* were taught; Greek, Hebrew and even sometimes Chaldean! This must have been at best rudimentary learning, a bow to the ideals of true Calvinist scholarship. Very few indeed would leave the Scottish university prepared to be their own exegete.

In practice what happened was that many ministers from inclination, inability or poverty, fell short of the mark. In 1602 the Kirk felt obliged to devise a questionnaire for the use of the Kirk Visitors, that in its second part, after asking 'with quhat fidelitie, prudence, and impartialitie, he [the minister] discharges himselfe in doctrine and discipline, and in his life and conversation', went on to try him 'by the opening up of some place of Scripture prescryved to him' and by the examination of his library. A minister should own 'for the advancement of his studies' the following books: the text of Scriptures in the original languages (and he should be 'fein in the tongues'), Tremellius' translation of the Old Testament (that is, into Latin), Beza's of the New Testament, the vulgar English translation, the Common Places, some ecclesiastical history, commentaries on the Scriptures, the acts of the Council of Trent, and some controversies of religion.[1]

This—what was evidently considered the basic library for the Presbyterian minister—makes a useful comparison with Drummond's main theology books, for it describes them quite accurately —in particular as they are in his catalogue of 1611. He, too, had the Scriptures in the tongues: a Hebrew Bible, and a Greek Bible. Tremellius does not appear, but Drummond had Beza's translation of the New Testament (both of these were Protestant versions, of course). He had besides two Greek New Testaments, Crespin's and Henri Estienne's. He must have owned an English Bible (probably the Genevan version, for that was in common use until long after the Authorized Version appeared in 1611)[2]; he had the Bible in Jerome's Latin Vulgate, as well as in French and Spanish. He had the *Psalms* again in Latin, French and Spanish (like his Spanish Bible, in Protestant translation) and various books of the Old Testament in Hebrew. If he ever owned a book of Common Places, it is now long lost, and his only compendium—that of Albertus Magnus—is a survival from the medieval Catholic Church. It was necessary to have a copy of the Acts of the Council of Trent the better to refute them, for these were the acts which set down the Catholic position on the important controversies. Drummond had these, and also Gentillet's virulent and provocative Protestant examination of the Council's work. In short, together with some commentaries (written, like

1. William Row's *Additional illustrations* to John Row, *The historie of the Kirk of Scotland* (Maitland Club, Edinburgh 1842) II, pp. 462-4. Things may not have been as bad as the Kirk Visitors made out—it being in the nature of Kirk Visitors occasionally to exaggerate the enormity of their appointed task.

2. G. D. Henderson *Religious life in seventeenth-century Scotland* (Cambridge 1937) p. 2.

93

that on Genesis, by Protestant scholars), some works of Protestant martyrology (for example, Crespin's) and a few controversies (Perkin's), Drummond's theological books in Latin are only what a good Calvinist who took an informed interest in the subject should have had. There are not many, but what are there are the right ones.

It is when we look at the other books in the theology section that questions arise. If Drummond had the main Calvinist works, even to refinements like Calvin's own *Institutes* in French, Calvin's *Catechism* in Greek, and again in Hebrew, or the *Psalms* in Italian, he also had much that may at first sight seem to us unusual for a Protestant library: works of the Fathers and the Doctors, catechisms and liturgies of the Catholic Church, controversies by its chief apologists.

Let us consider first the Greek Fathers, the Doctors and the writers of the Church—all those whose commentary and interpretation served to define Catholic dogma, and upon whom the Catholic Church placed as much reliance as upon the Scriptures themselves. The Reformers were by no means willing to cast all such authority away. While insisting in the first instance upon the proper scholarly interpretations of the Scriptural texts, they clearly felt the need for outside help, and they brought in whenever possible the interpretations of the Fathers, the Doctors and the Schoolmen.[1] The 'auncient martyres and fathers of the primitive kirk' were the common ground between Catholic and Protestant: accepted by both, they could be called upon to document the case of either side. Thus Ninian Winzet writing to John Knox ('To the Caluiniane Precheouris') refers to the early Fathers as to a referee,[2] and on the Protestant side John Craig in 1581 calls no less confidently upon 'the iudgement of the ancient and godlie Fatheris' to support his case for the final authority of the Bible.[3] Drummond was hardly a serious theological scholar, but he did have a number of the ancient writers: Primasius, Gregory of Nazianzus, Clement of Alexandria, John of Damascus, Theodoret, St Augustine, St Thomas Aquinas—they are all represented, but compared with the stock of men really interested in the subject (Clement Litel, for example) they are but a handful. And we hardly need to refer to them to illustrate the Protestant taste for such authority, for the margins of the Protestant commentaries are cluttered with their names, with Tertullian, Damascus, Bernard, with Chrysostom, Origen or Basil, as well as with the 'Neotericks'—Calvin, Beza, Peter Martyr and all their fellow Reformers.

Yet, for the Protestant, scholarship was always less important than the Bible itself. William Fowler, Drummond's uncle, is typical in the way he comes back finally to the firmest grounds of Calvinist belief. 'For in stead of all thais learned fathers', he writes, having just cited several, 'or rather aboue them al, cums vnto my minde the scripteur of God, quhairin is an exclusue [*sic*] sentence pronuncit, na man cummeth to the Father but by me. To it I appele from all maner of wrytaris that thinkes vther waies. For the docteurs of the Kirk, as men are oft deceaued'.[4] From here it is not far to the call to read the scriptures less critically, to accept them humbly, to

1. Even in literary composition it was as fashionable to refer to the Fathers in theology as to Aristotle in philosophy, Galen in medicine or Justinian in law; Thomas Lodge wrote his *Prosopopeia*: 'in imitation of no lesse than five & twenty ancient, holy, and Catholique Fathers of the Church. . . .' And into the bargain he threw Aristotle and Albumazar, for these, too, are among the authorities he quotes.

2. Ninian Winzet *Certain tractates* (Scottish Text Society, Edinburgh 1888) I, p. 89.

3. John Craig *A shorte summe of the whole catechisme* (Edinburgh 1581) f. G2v.

4. *An answer to the calumnious letter of an apostat named M. Jo. Hammiltoun* (Edinburgh 1581) f. G2.

receive them with the heart and not the mind. Balnaves in his *Confession of faith* has this evangelical appeal: 'submit you to god and his holy spirit, who is Schoolemaister of his scriptures . . .', do not read them as you would a profane history such as Hector or Alexander, nor as the 'manly science of Plato, Aristotle, the bishop of Romes lawe', for these are the sciences of men and 'may be judged by the reason of man'. This belief that theology was governed by its own laws set a limit upon Biblical scholarship. Protestant interpreters did not probe too deeply into textual problems; they looked first for plain meanings and accurate translations. They were not particularly interested in questions of authorship, for the whole Bible was regarded as a unity, the word of God revealing Christ. Christ was everywhere; Christ was the treasure to be found in the Old as well as the New Testament. The purpose of exegesis was to make His presence clear, by way of explaining the intention or purpose of the Scriptural passage. Although not altogether divorced from traditional Catholic scholarship, especially in the use of the ancients, this was quite different from scholastic theology, and as such was regarded as worthless by the Catholic Church. Heretical Protestants examined the Scriptures without the proper apprenticeship or training, for as John Colville put it 'thai interprit, disput, distinguish conclud, prech and pen before thai can veill reid the rudimentes of vther inferior sciences much les attentit vnto any perfection in this science of sciences'.[1]

1. *The parænese or admonition of Io. Coluille* (Paris 1602) p. 11.

Of course by this time (the end of the sixteenth century) the attitudes and opinions, the very first principles of both sides were quite irreconcilable. If Protestants insisted upon going back to the Scriptures, Catholics equally stood firm upon the traditions of the Church, and regarded their theology as an historical synthesis revealed by God to the Church over the centuries. Although both used the ancients, they did so in different ways: the Protestant theologians as convenient buttresses for their arguments from Scripture, the Catholic writers as the vessels of revealed truth. And though the Protestant commentators preferred the plain interpretations of the Bible, they had behind them the spirit of humanistic scholarship. Had not Erasmus himself attacked the scholastic framework of theology? Were not Luther and Calvin both humanists, their writing plain, simple yet vigorous? Were they not with their chief followers learned men, and did not their academies teach the tongues and their presses put out Hebrew dictionaries?

Humanism came to theology as it had come to the other sciences. The same principles that were applied so successfully to the texts of the classical writers, or to the Justinian code, were used on the texts of Scripture. Even before the Reformation itself—and humanistic scholarship was an integral part of the Reformation—the new scholarship had had some notable triumphs. Laurentius Valla, for instance, had exposed the falsity of the Donation of Constantine, the (interpolated) passage of canon law which alleged that the Emperor Constantine had presented Pope Sylvester I with his own diadem, and thus given him temporal power over Rome, Italy and the West: a matter of obvious importance to papal ambitions. By examining the text critically, Valla was able to prove the passage spurious, for on several grounds — legal, linguistic, political and historical — it denied its supposed provenance. Valla, again, was one of the scholars who doubted the authenticity of Dionysius the Areopagite, and, again, his arguments were based upon a critical examination of the text. Dionysius was held to have been a contemporary of St Paul, and his mystical writings thus took on added meaning for the Church: here was another voice from apostolic times. Translated into Latin by Johannes Scotus Erigena in the Middle Ages Dionysius became a favourite guide to mystical theology, and influenced such as Albertus Magnus, St Thomas Aquinas, and later, Dionysius the Carthusian. Valla and his fellow humanists like Erasmus argued that Dionysius' writings could hardly have been composed in St Paul's time, for not only had his Greek the mark of later Greek (being rather pompous in style), but also several anachronistic references to church institutions, and to other writers such as Clement pointed to a date of composition several centuries later. The humanists argued thus, but they did not convince the orthodox. The Dionysius controversy continued throughout the next century, and was hardly settled in the seventeenth; it became entangled in the battles of the Reformation, for the Catholic Church chose for a time to defend Dionysius. It became attached even to politics, for Dionysius was traditionally identified with St Denis of France — a claim that Abelard had challenged, although he was forced to recant — and so those who defamed Dionysius defamed France, as well as proving their own unorthodoxy.[1]

1. Drummond's edition of Dionysius was an orthodox one, and includes a preface defending the orthodox position (see Cat. 29).

But not every scholar was a Valla and, although the reformers laid claims to humanist scholarship, the Protestant cause was not always allied to reason and light. The reformers' anti-scholasticism often strayed into iconoclasm and anti-intellectualism — Luther himself referred to Aristotle as a 'damnable heathen' and to human reason as 'the Devil's harlot'. The study of the classics was unprofitable unless it served God; education was the tool of theology. In the early years of the Reformation, humanist scholars, such as Erasmus, Melanchthon, and Reuchlin, had been sympathetic to the principles of reform and had furthered them in their writings, but after the Council of Trent the lines hardened, and their kind of compromise became virtually impossible. The humanistic sciences of philology and history became the instruments of partisan controversy.

But what of the controversies themselves? What were the main arguments about? Drummond's books provide a little history of the Reformation. They contain the propaganda of both sides, the defences, propositions, apologies, refutations, retractions, discourses, and in them we can see at once the complexity of the issues and the multiplication of sects and opinions — facts that are not often brought out in the usual codification of our history books.

The best place to begin describing the controversies is with the Council of Trent. By its decrees, which were issued over the eighteen years (1545–63) of its intermittent existence, the Council set down positive statements of Roman dogma on the main controversies raised by the reformers. For Catholics the official orthodoxy and the

28. Paradise and district. John Hopkinson. *Synopsis Paradisi* (Cat.514),

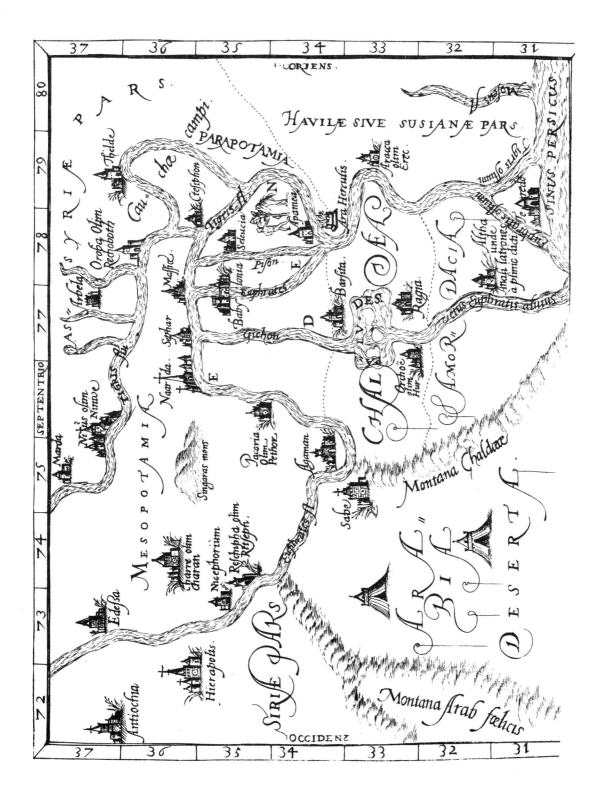

A briefe Map of Gods Election.

In the salua- tion of all the Elect.

originally to effect all

to repaire all

to finish all

vntill we haue our perfect saluation

hath by the coun- sell of his will de- creed by his om- nipotencie and efficacie

hath by the price of Redemption obtained, and still by his intercessi- on doth obtaine

hath & doth apply by testimony seale and gouernment the fathers electiõ & sonnes redemptiõ

And by which we are both ingraf- ted into Christ, and made to grow vp with him

Who for the first man- ner of working

Who for the second man- ner of working

Who for the third man- ner of working

Which receiues all, as most freely graced of God.

From the Father

In the Sonne

By the holy Ghost

The inchoation and beginning whereof is

The dispensation, or progresse

The consummation, or ending

And for conclusion, all 3 apply the same to faith.

Election

chief heresies were now distinguished, while the Protestants were condemned to damnation by Mother Church. For both sides the Council marked the end of any real hopes that reconciliations or compromises were possible: the Protestant heresies were all condemned with the refrain 'Anathema sit'. The Council decided that the Scriptures and the traditions of the Church were to continue to be held as equally important sources of divine revelation, the Vulgate (St Jerome's translation) was taken as the authoritative text,[1] and the apocrypha was put on a par with the other books of the canon. The seven sacraments remained dogma; the doctrines of transubstantiation and justification by faith and works were likewise confirmed.

1. Valla challenged some of the Vulgate's readings; Bellarmine succeeded in having some amended.

The Council marks a convenient crystallization of doctrine on the Catholic side, but it cannot be said that it lessened controversy. It at once became a target for both Catholic and Protestant polemic: Paolo Sarpi's famous history of the Council was hardly less scathing in its castigation of the Papacy than the Protestant Gentillet's. But whereas Catholics could in the controversies attack all heretics, the Protestant sects were forced to fight on two fronts: one, against Rome, the other, against their fellow reformers. In the uncharitable terms of the time all Protestant sects were equally heretical to each other, and these divisions were exploited by the Catholic writers, who, like John Colville, rejoiced in the unity of their Church: 'Behold Martin Luther hes most satirikly scharpit his pen agans the Anabaptists, Zuinglius, Carolostadius ad Æcolympadius: and thai vho vill be callit no Lutherains both protestants vrit bitterly agans Luthers doctrin: Agane Ioachimus Vestphalus, Hessutius, Castalio Casanouius, Molineus, Morellus vex Io. Caluin most mychtely, and the same Castalio, Brentius, Smedelinus and Sindry vthers Inuad Theodor de Beza.'[2] All true: one has only to refer to the pages of Draud's catalogue to be impressed by the enormous amount of Protestant controversy.

2. Colville, p. 51. There were several important writers who advocated some kind of religious toleration such as Jean Bodin or Philippe Du Plessis-Mornay. The unorthodox sects were however regarded as politically unreliable by the state, and hence dangerous; toleration was at best spasmodic and capricious. See Joseph Lecler's major work *Toleration and the Reformation*, trs. T. L. Westow (London 1960) 2 vols.

Transubstantiation: did the bread and wine used in the sacrament of Mass become the body and blood of Christ or were they but tokens of remembrance—what did Christ's words 'This is my body' really mean? Was the Trinity Three-in-One, or was Christ but a prophet of God? Were God's elect really predestined for heaven; who were God's elect? Was baptism a sacrament? Such were some of the doctrinal disputes; but, as the century wore on, pettier quarrels became almost as important, and the scene of controversy shifted to more local and political issues. Was the Kirk of Scotland a presbyterian church? How else should it be governed? Should its ministers wear vestments? Should the congregation kneel? What about a prayerbook? All was entangled with politics—were there two states in the land, kirk and king, or only one, ruled by James and his bishops? Who should have supremacy?

In Scotland the episcopacy controversy was so bestuck with political and national thorns that a man loyal to his king and his kirk might well wonder what obedience he owed to whom. The minister William Cowper, for instance, joined in signing the protest against episcopacy in 1606, but later he went over to the side of the

29. God's election. John Yates, *A modell of diuinitie* (Cat. 953).

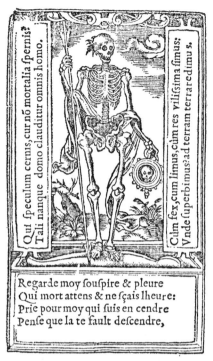

30. Death. *Heures de Nostre Dame*
(Cat. 1090).

1. George H. Williams *The
radical Reformation* (London 1962)
pp. 657-8.

king and was rewarded with a bishopric in 1612. David Calderwood on the other hand resisted prelacy constantly, argued his case against obedience with James himself, was imprisoned and later fled to Flanders. The king's position was clear: he should be head of the church, and receive the obedience of its members, while his bishops governed in his name. The Calvinist ministers, too, were resolved: the king as a man owed obedience to them in matters religious, and they with their presbyteries would govern themselves. All that was imposed upon them by James and his bishops, all that was intended to bring them in line with English practice, was anathema to them. Kneeling at communion, observance of holidays, episcopal confirmation, vestments, prayerbooks — these stank of Rome, and were foul threats to the true Kirk, to be resisted by the Calvinist orthodoxy.

By the number of books on these questions one can readily see how much they interested Drummond: it is less easy to explain the pieces of religious history, the relics of quarrels long past, now settled, and one would have thought, forgotten. Why would Drummond want to read seventy years after the event about the *Confutation of the XIII articles whereunto N. Shaxton subscribed*? (In 1546, Shaxton, an English bishop, was suspected of Lutheran heresies, and sentenced to be burned. He recanted and tried unsuccessfully to persuade his fellow prisoner, Anne Askew, to do likewise. She was burned, and the Lutheran printer Robert Crowley wrote attacking Shaxton's recantation.) Was the *Augsburg Interim* —the attempt of the Emperor Charles v in 1548 to draft some kind of compromise between the German princes at the end of the Schmalkaldic war—still interesting reading in the Scotland of 1611? Or more strangely, what of the funeral oration of John Laski, and the letters intended to discredit Stancaro? (These were both débris from an internal dispute of the Polish reformed church: Stancaro had advanced ideas on the Trinity; Laski and the conservative group opposed him. On Laski's death Stancaro's faction put it about that Laski had so defamed God's word, that God striking him dead, had sealed his lips. Laski's followers opened the coffin, and to their joy found that the rumour was false).[1] One can only suppose that these are examples of the curiosities that find their way into any library, perhaps bought on a whim, inherited or picked up—the printed flotsam of the age.

This is but a sketchy summary of the controversies: the printed evidence of their course lies in the books themselves. There, in a work like *Issachar's asse*, we can see what the opinions were of a man caught between kirk and king, and there, free from the bias of Presbyterian historians (like Calderwood himself), we can find the royal point of view in Hayward's tract: *Of supremacie in affairs of religion*. There, too, we can see the occasional deviousness of the pamphleteers, when, for instance, in the piece *Calderwood's recantation* John Scott, with hopes of winning the king's favour, exploited the rumour of Calderwood's death and composed a recantation in his name. Here Calderwood was supposed to abandon his objections to episcopacy, to praise the king for his judiciousness, and to condemn the writings of Beza, Knox, and the Geneva reformers. Scott claimed that James himself had had a hand in the writing of this piece.[1]

It is perhaps more interesting to us to look at the manner in which the controversies were written, rather than the matter they were made of, for the issues have now only an historical relevance. The Latin controversialists organized their disputations on rhetorical lines; that is, they used the methods and tricks of academic rhetoric taught in the schools and universities, and they framed their arguments in formal rhetorical sequence. Any man who had been learned the rhetorical rules of Aphthonius, who had had rhetoric explained to him according to the basic precepts of Aristotle and Cicero, who had read Quintilian or Talon, would be familiar with such organization, and would have no difficulty in following all the stages of the controversy. He would look first for the exordium, then find the narration and the division, and he would identify as they followed in order the proof, the refutation, and the conclusion. This was the arrangement used for sermons or disputations by both Catholics and Protestants, in both the *Controversiae* of the renowned Cardinal Bellarmine or the answers signed by his royal protagonist, James VI and I.

We have discussed already the employment of authority: few arguments could be conducted without the solid buttresses of scholarship. The pages of John Bale's famous *Actes of English votaries* are liberally sprinkled with 'learning': speaking of the coming of the Antichrist (the Pope, of course) he says 'than fyrst began the papacye at Rome vnder the false Emperour phocas, as witnesseth Abbas yrspergensis, Hermannus Contractus, Singebertus, Ranulphus, Matheus Palmarius, christianus Masseus, Archilles Pirminius Ioannes Carion, et Martinus Lutherus In Mundi suppatacione'—a string of names, recited gratuitously, probably gathered out of the last two quoted authors, that one may be sure served only to impress the ignorant.[2] Such works catered in the manner of popular journalism for the prejudices of their readers. The margins of John Bale, for instance, are sprinkled with titillating phrases like the worst gutter newsprint: 'The Deuils commissioner', 'Maryage condempned', 'Whores rule all', 'A monks bastard', 'Spiritual knauerye', 'with lies', 'craftye scyence', 'Roma et Babylon, 'Merlyne Balaam', 'A carnall synagogue'—all pointing the curious reader's way to the most salacious gossip served up hodge-podge, authenticated by a display of for the most part quite spurious scholarship.

If Bale is bad, he was by no means alone in his crudity. Both the Protestant and the Catholic polemicists gloried in the middens of abuse; no sin was too horrid to be paraded before readers already convinced of the heretics' awfulness and only too willing to read about the details of their crimes. Both sides, of course, accused each other of theological errors, and of sins like simony, pride and ignorance which were failings of the Church in general. Over and above these the favourite targets were the personal sins, and in particular, the failings of the flesh. For the Protestants the Pope and his court were initiates in all that was most foul: Rome itself was 'City supream and seate of Sodomie' and had been for a long time.

1. Of James' certain works Drummond had only the *Declaration against Vorstius*, in which the king attacked the Arminian Vorstius and vindicated his own orthodoxy. Of the major royal pieces—the *Apology*, the *Premonition* and *A remonstrance for the right of kings*—there is no trace, and only echoes of the mass of controversial material produced at James' instigation on the question of the oath of allegiance (which he claimed English Catholics owed to him, and which Pope Paul V forbade them to take). One such echo is Gordon's *Antitortobellarminus*, against the opinions of Cardinal Bellarmine ('refutatio calumniarum, mendaciotum, et imposturarum Laico-Cardinalis Bellarmini, contra iura omnium regum . . .'), the great Catholic controversialist who was James' chief opponent. Drummond had read the *Apology* [see Appendix I].

2. John Bale *The first part of the actes of English votaries* (London 1560) f. 34v.

1. John Napier *A plaine discouery of the whole Reuelation* (Edinburgh 1645) p. 38.

2. Robert Burton *The anatomy of melancholy* ed. Dell and Jordan-Smith (New York 1951) p. 811. Estienne in his work reprinted a part of Bale's *Acta Romanorum Pontoficum,* namely the report printed by Bale of the visitation of monasteries under Henry VIII. See Jesse W. Harris *John Bale* University of Illinois Studies in Language and Literature (Urbana 1940) pp. 122-3.

3. Jean Chassanion *De la secte des Iesuites* (Geneva? 1592) p. 35.

4. Nicol Burne *The disputation concerning the controversit headdis of religion* (Paris 1581) pp. 102-4.

5. John Hamilton *A facile traictise* ed. Thomas Law (Scottish Text Society, Edinburgh 1901) p. 242. Hamilton goes on to repeat a libellous story about John Craig, who, he says, married at eighty a girl of fifteen, 'of what sacriligious mariage sprang out a cursit generation, as the inhabitants, and ane of the cheif ministers of Edinbrocht can beare witnes'.

6. These speculations were often quite imaginative: Burne, for instance, writing of the kingdom of the Antichrist then come to Scotland, claimed that as the true kirk had its bishops, so the false kirk promoted 'not onlie Bairnis, and Idiotis bot Vemen also in place of bischopis and hie preistis'. Burne, pp. 135-6.

7. Napier used the word Latinus which he said signified Rome; Burne used Martin Luther, which he conveniently spelled *Lauter*. Both names if juggled against their appropriate values in Latin numerals totalled the mystic number 666. The first beast of the Antichrist was agreed to be Mahomet; Napier, p. 44; Burne, p. 140.

8. The *Alcoran des Cordeliers* was written to refute the 'maudit & execrable liure ' *Conformité de la vie S. Francois à la vie de Iesus Christ* by Bartholomaeus of Piza, a Franciscan monk, which had something of a vogue in the fifteenth and sixteenth centuries. The *Alcoran's* method is interesting, for it is an example of a technique frequently used at the time—that of reprinting the work refuted, the better to refute it passage by passage. Thus the *Alcoran* counters the first sentence of the *Coformitez* 'Sainct François, qui es le Iesus typique & adombré . . .' with "Christ est la propre image de la substance de Dieu. Heb. 1.' Here are two sides of Renaissance religion— Catholic reverence for saints, Protestant reliance upon the Bible.

'Of Popes', according to Napier, '13 were adulterers, three were common brothellers, four were incestuous harlots, eleven were impoysoned with vile Sodomy, seven were whore-mongers, and erecters of brothel-houses. Finally, one was a whore, and dyed of child in open Procession....'[1] The Popes did well from their sins; one from his brothels alone made 40,000 ducats in a good year. With such examples from Rome, what sins might not the ordinary monk be expected to commit? In the ranks the unnatural papist practice of continence did nothing but encourage lesser abominations: '... mastupration, satyriasis, priapiasm, melancholy, madness, fornication, adultery, buggery, sodomy, theft, murder, and all manner of mischiefs' —as Robert Burton pointed out (his authorities being two of our books, Bale and Henri Estienne's *Apology for Herodotus*).[2] Even the Jesuits were supposedly guilty, their vows of chastity empty vows, 'pur monstre de leur continance ont rempli de monde de leur batardaille, & infecte l'air de leurs puantes ordures'.[3]

The Catholic writers were scarcely less inventive. They too concentrated their attacks upon the leaders of the opposing churches, upon Protestant monarchs and whenever possible, upon individual ministers. Thus Nicol Burne in his *Disputation concerning the controversit headdis of religion* took the chance of reproducing an epigram of Beza's together with his own free translation into Scots, the better to show the 'practeise of bourgrie and sodomitical syn' committed by 'Beze the neu Pseudoprophet and pretendit reformator of the varld . . . vith the zoung man Audebertus' which he, Beza, preferred to his 'adultery with Candida, ane vther manis vyf . . .'. Calvin, too, enjoyed the same vice, while Knox was accused of witchcraft.[4] Protestants (according to Catholic polemicists) only attacked clerical chastity out of cupidity. They used the verse 'better to marry than to burn' as a mere excuse, thus 'be this fleschlie libertie thay alluret volupteous religious personnes to thair Epicurian Euangile, to accomplis thair insatiable lustis of the flesche, be adulterous and sacrilegious mariage of Channons, monkis, Nunnes, freres, and all vther sortis of renegat priests . . .'.[5]

In addition to this kind of abuse, both sides frequently gave over a part of their tracts to a proof of God's knowledge of their opponents' sin, and His forecast of its consequences. Using chiefly the Book of Revelation, they spent much ingenuity in deducing the true identities of the Whore of Babylon, the Beast with seven heads and ten horns, the Antichrist himself.[6] The chief concern of the propagandists was to name names: for Catholics Martin Luther was the Antichrist, for Protestants the Pope, since both with some contrivance could be made to express the number of the Beast, 666.[7]

One of the great merits of Drummond's whole library is that it gives a tolerably accurate reflection of the questions of the day; it is not marred as a sample of taste by any particular eccentric bias. In some respects this is odd, and it is perhaps most so among the theology books, where we might be quite ready to allow a certain partisan choice. Drummond certainly had his share of Protestant books, from the Heidelberg catechism to the *Alcoran des Cordeliers*[8]; important and well-known tracts like Philippe Du Plessis-Mornay's *De la verité*

de la religion chrétien, the famous *Satyre Menippée*,[1] Du Bartas'
Christian poems, Ochino's works, Zanchius' *De operibus Dei* — the
catalogue is full of titles that would be well received by any Presbyterian librarian.[2] But Drummond also had many Catholic books,
many more than one might expect. He had an ordinary, a breviary,
two books of hours, works on the sacraments, confession, and the
Passion of Christ. These are all Catholic books for Catholics. Most
of them date from the first half of the sixteenth century, and may
have been inherited by Drummond. Others he bought. He had also
many Catholic books already referred to earlier, tracts and pamphlets on the controversies by authors such as James Gordon or
Cardinal Du Perron, John Hay and John Hamilton. These one might
explain by their nature — what would be the attraction of reading
only one side of a controversy? There are other books that are not
controversial, but straightforward explanations of the Catholic
religion, written to win back the strayed sheep: *The parænese of Io.
Coluille (laitly returnit to the Catholique Romane ... religion)*,
Warford's *Briefe instruction* or Adam King's translation into Scots of
St Peter Canisius' *Summa*. Again, there is St Ignatius Loyola's
Spiritual Exercises: what was a Calvinist doing with this in his
library?

In Drummond's day Catholic books were seditious, and were
forbidden by law to be bought, sold or even owned. The official
records of both Scotland and England contain repeated enactments
on seditious books, and many instances of their enforcement. 'All
manner of persons' according to the English act of 1569, were 'to
forbeare vtterly from the vse or dealing with any such seditious
books', and private persons could be searched and punished if
suspected of so doing.[3] When the Douay version of the Scriptures
was published in 1582 and imported into England 'every corner of
the realme was searched for those bookes ... Colleges, chambers,
studies, closets, coffers, and deskes, were ramsackt for them ...
auncient men and students of Divinitie were imprisoned for having
of them'.[4] In Scotland such persecution if more spasmodic was at
least as severe. Acts such as those of 1600 and 1612 forbade Jesuits,
seminary priests, their gear and their books to enter the country, and
as late as 1628 were still advising moderators and brethren of the
presbyteries to seek them out in their parishes.[5] Booksellers were
forbidden 'to utter ony wrettin be ony popishe or suspect wreater,
without license obtenit of the Bishop'.[6] The matter needed the
constant vigilance of the Kirk, whose ministers found themselves
having to make complaints against 'the impunitie of skipers trans-
porting hither Jesuits, Preists, etc., vnder the name of passingers;
bringing hither their coffers and bookes; and the impunitie of those
that conveyes and scatters their bookes through the countrey'.[7]
When found such books were burned and their owners punished.
On 5 November 1596, for instance, there is an entry in Edinburgh
burgh records that forty-eight papist books belonging to the minister, Mr Robert Bruce, were seized and ordered to be burned.[8]
Again, 'Patrick Cone, sone to the goodman of Auchrie, servitour
to the Earle of Erroll, was apprehendit in Leith' on his return from

1. The *Satyre Menippée* ridiculed
the Catholic League (set up to
combat the Huguenots) whose
autocratic claims by 1592 were a
threat to Henry IV of France. The
Satyre was anti-Spanish, and
denounced the efforts of Philip II
to make political capital under the
banner of religion. It was said to be
remarkably effective at the time, and
it remained popular years later.

2. These books, of course, appear
not under theology but in the vernacular sections of the catalogue.

3. A. C. Southern *Elizabethan
recusant prose : 1559-1582*
(London 1950) pp. 38-9.

4. William Rainolds, quoted by
Southern, p. 235.

5. *R.P.C.S.* VI, 185. *R.P.C.S.*, 2nd
ser., II, 358.

6. *R.P.C.S.* IX, 400.

7. Row, II, p. 455.

8. *Extracts from the Records of the
Royal Burgh of Edinburgh 1589-1603*,
p. 166.

France, and when asked to open his 'chist', refused. On forcing it open customs officers found in it 'sundrie Popishe treatises and works, and diverse missive directed to sundrie noblemen. . . .'[1]

On first sight then it seems that Catholic books as contraband would necessarily be scarce in England and Scotland—but the evidence needs to be read most carefully. In the first place most of the persons harried for owning Catholic books were themselves Catholics, or like Patrick Cone, servants to known Catholic families. As such they would be particularly watched by the authorities. Secondly, it seems that Catholic books were thought to be not dangerous in the right hands; on the contrary, they were considered valuable: when Archbishop Spottiswood arranged for the seizure of the goods of the Abbot of New Abbey, Gilbert Brown, in 1609, James I made him a present of the books by way of reward.[2] The sort of books that were disseminated throughout the country by the Catholic missionaries were usually devotional or controversial (the books taken at Newcastle in 1626 included for example breviaries, Jesus psalters, Thomas à Kempis and Parsons' *Christian directory*)[3]; in contrast to these, serious theological works were acceptable since they would be needed and used by theologians and scholars. Napier wrote his tract on the Book of Revelation in Scotland, yet he was able to consult all the Catholic authorities he wanted, for as he says 'concerning my citation of ancient and unexpected writers, I have chosen the same out of the most old and faithfull copies, chiefly those that be found in old Popish Libraries, and Imprinted by Popish Printers. . . .'[4] And in such mainly theological collections as Clement Litel's, Catholic books were saved with Protestant in the Tounis College library, for they were considered not dangerous but useful if read with understanding.[5]

We cannot know surely (when faced with such conflicting evidence) but it does seem likely that Catholic books were kept in private libraries by respectable Protestant gentlemen without any fear that they were committing a crime against their church and state. It is known that there was a great demand even for the controversial Catholic books.[6] Over 250 editions of controversial Catholic works were printed abroad or secretly at home between the years 1558 and 1603,[7] and considering the number of answers the Catholic writers provoked it is plain that their books were read, even read eagerly. Yet it is still odd that Drummond should have owned so many Catholic books. He laid himself open to the suspicion of the Kirk, whose ministers frequently remarked that youths such as he who went to France Protestants, returned as Papists.[8]

By concentrating upon the problems of Drummond's theological library (and they are the more interesting side of it) it would be a pity to lose sight of its ordinariness. Most of his books fit in smoothly with the facts of his education, travels and religion: some serious works of theology such as he would be encouraged to study during and after university, controversies in French and Italian bought abroad, controversies and devotional works collected throughout his whole life.[9] The devotional books particularly we should not neglect, for these, if now forgotten, were most popular in the six-

1. David Calderwood *The history of the Kirk of Scotland*, ed. Thomson (Wodrow Society, Edinburgh 1842-9) VII, p. 426.

2. *R.P.C.S.* VIII, 301.

3. *State Papers: Domestic, Charles I,* XXIV, no. 23 III.

4. Napier, sig. A3.

5. In the formal academic subjects the universities in Scotland and England had to rely upon textbooks written by Catholic authors; in philosophy, for instance, by Zabarella or Toletus.

6. See Southern, pp. 30-43.

7. Bennett, p. 126, n. 3.

8. Row, II, 455, 456.

9. Drummond's motives for buying books may not always have been governed by his taste, instead, they may have been ruled by his pocket. If he had a desire to build up a collection of solid theological reading, Biblical commentary, exegesis and such, he would have found it expensive. Drummond's books are chiefly quartos, octavos and less, while the usual theological book would be folio, as heavy in fact as in scholarship.

teenth and seventeenth centuries. Man was closer to death and sickness then. A child born as likely as not died, and there was no sure cure for most sicknesses. Drummond's own Memorials bring home these ugly facts with a jolt: his wife would give birth, and again and again the baby would live a little while, then sicken and die. Adult lives were punctuated by mysterious agues and fevers for which all the many known drugs were too often ineffectual. A man's best hope, then, was not the physician but God, his surest comfort not medicine but the certain knowledge of his own salvation.

The devotional books, strictly speaking, were not controversial, in fact many of them were directly translated from Catholic works — such writers as Luis de Granada were popular, and St Thomas à Kempis' *De imitatione Christi* alone went through numerous printings in Protestant England.[1] Others were translated from Huguenot writers: Drummond for instance, had Du Vair's *Holy loue of heauenly wisdom*. English divines such as Joseph Hall, and Samuel Hieron and Robert Hill varied their controversial productions and sermons with devotional pieces, and these were the most popular of their works. Sir John Hayward's *Sanctuarie of a troubled soul* went through at least seven editions before 1640, Philip Stubbes' *A christal glasse for christian women* some fifteen or so, and Hieron's *A helpe vnto deuotion* at least twenty. The matter of these works is by and large unremarkable, being exhortations to piety, clean living, a proper respect for the Christian virtues, and constant reminders of man's uncertain fate, God's grace, and the transitory nature of life's pleasures.

In style these pieces are more interesting, for sometimes their writers are master craftsmen, and one is forcibly reminded of the beauties and strength of English prose at its best. The spare and balanced phrases familiar to all reared on the Authorized Version are echoed in Feltham's *Resolues* (1623): 'Prosperities are strong pleaders for sinne: Troubles be the surest Tutors of Goodnesse'. And again: 'Death to a righteous man, whether it commeth soone, or late, is the beginning of ioy, and the end of sorrow.' Hayward's more elaborate prose has much in common with Lyly's high style; he had a liking for hyperbole and a rather grotesque kind of imagery; a kind of sensationalism which in an apostrophe like 'Haile, holy wound of my Sauiors side; the entrance to his heart, the issue of his love' suggests a French or Italian source.[2]

Even going outside the strictly devotional works the prose style is often remarkable. Richard Hooker's defence of the Church of England and its episcopal government, *Of the laws of ecclesiastical politie*, was as important for the effect its lucid, forceful style had on English, as for its elevation of the theory that government rested ultimately on the 'original contract' and the consent of society. At the less ambitious end of the scale a popular guide to good living like *Keepe within compasse* is still good reading, full of pithy saws and devices, with a kind of hearty prose half rustic, half Biblical: 'Religion is that absolute cleane beast, which cheweth the cud, and diuides the hoofe: for it makes a man ruminate and chaw holy meditations till they give diuine nourishment: and the one claw

1. See STC 23955-24000.

2. As pointed out by Helen C. White *English devotional literature* 1931) p. 238.

103

pointeth man to the feare of God, the other to the loue of his neigh-bour'. And in the handbooks of the Puritans there is a passion that prompts the wildest imagery, a wordy, ranting, self-confident lectur-ing that seems particularly a part of Calvinism:

> 'And yet (O Lord) what a world of blindnesse is there in con-ceiving, and vnderstanding of thee? O muckworms of the world, which like the Gentiles breede of putrefaction, and Beetles fed in the dung, relishing nothing els but earthly things: thinking there is no other godlinesse but gaine; no happiness but to scrape and gather, to haue and to hold. Let them know that the treasures of wickednesse and wrath will goe together: and that they that make casting Nets for all fish that come, will in the end get the Deuill and all . . .'[1]

1. John Yates A *modell of divinitie* (London 1623) p. 53.

Men like Yates and Yarrow described sin with joy and zest; they seemed to relish horrifying their readers with visions of punishment to come. Reassured by the certain knowledge of his own election (Yates even prints a diagram of it) the Calvinist could face the worst, shudder, and take comfort from the fact that though he himself might be bad, others who knew not the depths of their degradation nor God's remedies were ten times worse:

> 'Seest thou not how they suck up sinne like water, and how wan-tonly they sport and pastime themselves, in swallowing the poisonfull Henbane of their own confusion? Doest thou not see how many, most wickedly doe pastime themselves, in Gluttony, Drun-kennesse, Witchcrafts, Sorceries, Adulteries, Periuries, Murthers, Rapines, Thefts, and such like filthy and damnable abominations, without any *sense* or feeling of the horrour of so great a sinne? How farre more happy then is thine estate, to whom God hath giuen a feare and dread of sinne, a sorrowing heart euen before-hand, to consider, that *thou* shouldest be thus intised to such a grieuous wickednesse. Thou *tremblest* to commit it, thou *quakest* to think upon it, and art *amazed*, at the very motion of such an horrible and fearefull fact . . . *Oh happy soule!* that is thus dis-quieted at the vgly shape of such an hideous Monster, namely sinne'.[2]

2. Robert Yarrow *Soveraigne comforts for a troubled conscience* (London 1619) pp. 35-6.

Such a sentiment would have been well received by Drummond's Calvinist fellow Scots. They would have applauded Yarrow and his fellow Puritans—but they would not have founded their theological libraries wholly upon their books. That honour instead would have gone to Tremellius and Beza, to Peter Martyr, Calvin and Oecolam-padius; to St Augustine and Origen, and even, in a well-balanced library, to Suarez, Bellarmine and St Ignatius Loyola himself.

Latin Poetry

If we look at the Latin poetry printed in the sixteenth century — and this is after all the century in which the classical poets were first offered to the reading public in small, relatively cheap editions — the most surprising fact is that the bulk of the verse was written not by the Romans, nor by the monks of the Middle Ages, but by the humanists of the Renaissance. The library of a man like Thomas Reid, who was Latin secretary to James VI, and whose books, naturally enough, were nearly all Latin and mostly literary, is perhaps the best illustration of this; for Reid's catalogue, while recording that he owned practically every classical author then printed — and by the beginning of the seventeenth century nearly every Latin author had been rediscovered and printed[1] — shows clearly the quantity of the Renaissance productions.[2] Drummond's much smaller collection of Latin poets reflects the same fact: less than a quarter of his poets are classical. Of course, as Drummond's catalogue shows, much of the Renaissance verse was ephemera; short pieces celebrating a wedding, a voyage, or a funeral of the king's son or wife. Yet even allowing for this trivia the neo-Latin verse far outweighs the classical, in quantity if not quality, and since it is so largely forgotten today its presence, profusion and evident popularity clearly needs something of an explanation for the modern reader.[3] Before this can be given it would be as well to look at Drummond's list of classical poets, considering in brief the main points of Renaissance taste.

It is worth remembering that in the Renaissance Roman poets were read not only for their own sake, but also as models. Schoolboys have been trained even till today to produce their own Latin verse; in the sixteenth century it was hoped — and frequently with cause — that they would continue to do so throughout their life.[4] Whereas in prose Cicero was the humanists' favourite model, in poetry Virgil was usually thought most suitable; the two for the same reasons: purity of language, high moral tone, and a patriotic glorification of Rome that itself agreed well enough with the humanistic conception of the golden age. Virgil stood supreme for his _Æneid_, for the epic above all was admired by the Renaissance, whose poets, from Petrarch to Vida, when they attempted the greatest of all forms invariably turned to Virgil as master. Scaliger the Elder, glorified by

1. See the table of first editions of Latin authors in John E. Sandys _A history of classical scholarship_ (Cambridge 1908) II, p. 103.

2. Reid's catalogue is preserved at Aberdeen University Library.

3. There are very few scholarly books on the subject. Henry Hallam, _Introduction to the literature of Europe_ (London 1839) 2 vols., is sometimes useful, though brief, since Hallam does give his opinion of the works he discusses and does mention whether he has read the book or not. F. A. Wright and T. A. Sinclair, _A history of later Latin literature_ (London 1931), give a survey of the field, but they confine themselves to the major authors. Leicester Bradner, _Musae Anglicanae_ (Menasha, Wisconsin 1940), is very detailed, and especially good on the Scottish poets, but of course is limited to only a small part of the subject, and he does not often venture critical opinions. The most comprehensive study of neo-Latin prose and poetry is Paul Van Tieghem, _La litterature latine de la Renaissance_ (Paris 1944), in _Bibliothèque d'humanisme et Renaissance_, IV, for he discusses in detail classical models, the various forms of verse written, giving critical opinions on the quality of the poetry.

4. T. W. Baldwin _William Shakspere's Small Latine and Lesse Greeke_ (Urbana 1944). Baldwin is used throughout this next section for Elizabethan critical opinions and the curriculum of the grammar school.

Henry Peacham as 'the Prince of all learning and iudge of iudgements, the divine Iul. Cæs. Saliger', was speaking for all when he named Virgil 'the King of Latine Poets', whose prime virtues, not to be found elsewhere, were 'Prudence, Efficacie, Varietie, and Sweetnesse'.[1] Virgil also attracted the translators: the *Short-title Catalogue* lists no less than six English, one Scots and one Greek translation of the *Æneid* or its parts printed before 1640.[2] Richard Stanyhurst explained the reasons for Virgil's supremacy in the dedication to his version in 1583:

> 'But our *Virgil* . . . doth labour in tylling, as it were a Cantorburie tale, to ferret out the secretes of *Nature*, with wordes so fitly couchte, with verses so smoothly slickte, with sentences so featly ordered, with orations so neatly burnisht, with similitudes so aptly applyed, with eche *decorum* so duely obserued, as in truth he hath in right purchases too himselfe the name of a surpassing Poët, the fame of an odde oratour, and the admiration of a profound philosopher'.[3]

There is an emphasis here, quite true to the age, on the mechanics of the poetry: indeed, we might almost think it was not poetry but rhetoric, such is Stanyhurst's praise of decorum, of keeping true quantities, and of the burnished phrase. Though these were much admired qualities, Virgil's lofty tone and his inspiring subject were also attractions. Again and again sixteenth- and seventeenth-century critics emphasize the moral value of his work, and its suitability as a model, furnishing ethical precepts for the schoolboy and poetical inspiration for the poet and scholar.[4] Virgil, too, provided the supreme example of the utility of imitation, for was not his *Æneid* drawn after Homer?

Next to Virgil stood Ovid. The Renaissance schoolboy might expect to read him even more than Virgil, because his master saw that Ovid provided more for discussion and imitation: a wider technical range, a fuller use of rhetorical devices, a language that since it was more colourful was more of a problem for the student. The surprising thing is that Ovid too was regarded as a moral poet; at least, his works were seen by man as being capable of providing moral example. In a way this was nothing new, for Ovid, moralized, had been popular at intervals since the twelfth century,[5] and the claim by an Elizabethan critic, William Webbe, that if 'the trueth of euery tale be discouered, it is a worke of exceeding wysedome and sounde iudgement', was following in a long tradition. But Webbe, too, names Ovid as 'a most learned, and exquisite Poet',[6] and it is in the first adjective that we discern the humanistic attitude, for Ovid was much admired as a source of classical lore, and as Peacham put it, his style was seen to be 'seasoned with profound and antique learning'.[7] Ovid had his critics—those apparently who found it hardest to moralize him 'according to his meaning'. Sir Thomas Elyot, recommending the *Metamorphoses* and the *Fasti* to Prince Edward in 1531, did so since he felt that they were both 'right necessary for the vnderstandynge of other poets', but he proposed that not too much time be spent 'which might be better employed on

1. The order in which the virtues are listed is probably significant. Peacham *The compleat gentleman* (London 1634) p. 82 (1st ed. 1622). Virgil was not altogether uncriticized: Sir William Alexander thought that Scaliger over-praised him, and he objected to Virgil's handling of Æneas' defeat of Turnus, which, he thought, made Æneas look ridiculous, for Turnus was made to 'die like a Dastard', unworthily, 'burdening the Gods with his cowardice'; Alexander, 'Anacrises: or, a Censure of some Poets Ancient and Modern' in Drummond, *Works*, 1711, pp. 159-62. Baldwin discusses the views of his chosen Elizabethan critics who put Virgil at the head; Baldwin, II, pp. 380-90.

2. For other translations of the classics into the vernacular (before 1600) see R.R. Bolgar *The classical heritage and its beneficiaries* (Cambridge 1954) Appendix II, pp. 508-41.

3. *The first foure bookes of Virgils Æneis* (London 1583) sig. A2v.

4. See those discussed by Baldwin, II, pp. 380-90.

5. See Peter Berchorius' *Metamorphosis Ovidiana moraliter explanata* (c. 1340), written to meet an obvious need and itself based on earlier mythological handbooks, and the fourteenth-century French poem *Ovide moralisé*, which tried to give Ovid an allegorical and ultimately Christian meaning.

6. *A discourse of English poetrie*, 1586 (Arber, Eng. Repr. 26) p. 29.

7. Peacham, pp. 87-8.

suche autors that do minister both eloquence, ciule policie, and exhortation to vertue'.[1] Yet Elyot was writing for a prince, and Webbe and his fellow were theorists; perhaps Peacham's judgement is a more everyday one: instructing gentlemen, he remarks of Ovid's *Amores* and *Ars amatoria* that 'the wit will . . . beare out the wantonnesse'.[2]

The poet whom the critics had no difficulty defending as a furnisher of moral precepts—and whom Elyot in fact named as ministering eloquence, civil policy and exhortation to virtue—was Horace. Horace rivalled Ovid as a text in the grammar schools, and served the gentleman and scholar with quotable tags in his maturity. Horace was 'ripe, pythye, excellent for moral precepts full of pretye speaches, full of Iudgement',[3] suitable both as a model for the students to imitate and for the gentleman to read and profit from in his maturity.

Turning to Drummond's library it is perhaps surprising to find that the only poems of Horace that Drummond seems to have owned are the *Carmen saeculare*, the least personal and most official of all his works, written at the command of Augustus for the celebrations of the inauguration of a new century in 17 B.C. Of the *Odes*, the *Satires* or the *Ars poetica* there is no trace, although Drummond may well have studied all three in his year in the humanity class at the university when he was sixteen.[4] His books of Virgil and Ovid, however, are what we would expect. He owned the complete works of Virgil in an Aldine edition of 1545, together with the *Georgics* and translations in English and Scots. Of Ovid he had again the complete works, but in the Lyonnese pirate 'Aldine' edition of about 1506, in addition to separate copies of the *Heroides*, the *Epistolae* and a Spanish translation of the *Metamorphoses*.

To turn again to the question of Renaissance taste; it is clear that one criterion that guided the critic—and particularly the sixteenth-century critic—above others was that of moral intention. Poetry should delight, certainly, but it must instruct.[5] Thus we frequently find those we now consider good poets being recommended not for their poetry itself but for what could be learned from it, and bad poets being excused their dullness for the sake of their good intentions. Thus Lucan and Silius Italicus were both equally admired for their high seriousness by Ludovicus Vives in his most influential treatise on education, while their literary qualities pass without comment.[6] Critics today join in praising Lucan's *Civil war* as an epic triumph, and point out his rejection of the conventional usages of learned allusion, divine interposition and mythological epigrams, in fact all the Homeric machinery used so skilfully by Virgil and often abused by his successors. As Moses Hadas comments, Lucan writes 'almost as if he had never read Virgil'.[7] Silius Italicus, on the other hand, clearly had read Virgil, for 'there is hardly an episode or a simile in the entire *Æneid* which [he] does not borrow—and spoil'.[8] It is hard to understand how an Elizabethan critic like Sir Thomas Elyot could readily couple Lucan and Silius,[9] Silius of whom there is now a general critical agreement that his *Punica* is not only the longest poem in classical Latin but also the worst.

1. From the *Gouernour* (London 1531) f. 34r.

2. Peacham, p. 88.

3. Lambinus, as quoted by the Elizabethan critic Drant, quoted Baldwin, II, p. 525.

4. See the curriculum for the 'Classe of Humanitie', *University of Edinburgh : Charters, Statutes, and Acts of the Town Council and the Senatus* (Edinburgh 1937) p. 114: 'The classe of Humanitie is taught be thair Regent in Latine authors poettis and orators, such as Horas, Juvenall, Plautus, Cicero his Orationnes, and such uther the whole yeir.' See also Drummond's verse to John Ray, where he mentions being taught Plautus, Martiall and Virgil. Kastner, II, p. 249.

5. As in Sidney's dictum, derived from Horace's *Ars poetica*.

6. Baldwin, I, p. 192.

7. Moses Hadas A *history of Latin literature* (New York 1952) p. 263.

8. Hadas, p. 269.
9. Baldwin, II p. 550.

1. See H. A. Mason *Humanism and poetry in the early Tudor period* (London 1959), for a revaluation of humanist taste.

2. Baldwin, I, p. 108.

3. See Cosmo Gordon *A bibliography of Lucretius* (London 1962) pp. 14-17.

4. *Charters*, p. 114.

5. Plautus and Terence Drummond listed among his poets. He had a few neo-Latin plays, such as *Vertumnus* (see Cat. 297).

6. Baldwin, I, p. 109.

7. Besides, schoolroom tastes were at times quite catholic: Plautus, Terence and Martial were all occasionally used, although as Roger Ascham warned, a schoolmaster needed to 'make wise and ware choice . . . chieflie in choice of honestie of matter. . . .' Ascham *English works* (Cambridge English Classics 1904) pp. 286-7.

8. Cf. Mason's position, that the humanists approach to the classics was essentially trivial, in their preoccupation with moral instruction; Mason, p. 66 and throughout.

In explanation of this difficulty it can only be repeated again that the Renaissance critics were not looking for the qualities we now seek in poetry, and above aesthetic pleasures came moral instruction.[1] Statius, another imitator of Virgil, and now regarded as a poor poet, was approved of by Erasmus and placed in the company of Virgil, Ovid and Horace,[2] while Lucretius, whose fatalistic and pessimistic views were generally regarded with suspicion, was never popular, and compared to his fellow Latins, sparsely printed.[3] Juvenal was thought a fit text for schoolboys (and recommended at Edinburgh),[4] in spite of the bitter and personal nature of much of his satire.

It might be as well here to distinguish between the two poles of taste: public and personal. What was recommended for the schoolboy was not necessarily what was preferred by the courtier, and it would be a mistake to take the textbook as necessarily the favourite of the gentleman. Yet taste to an extent must have been formed in the classroom, and poets especially well thought of for their moral values, in an age which respected both Christian moral teaching and the wisdom of the ancients, would hardly be excluded from a gentleman's library. Drummond owned editions of the poets of the grammar school and university curriculum, but the gaps in his collection are, for the most part, of those outside the pale. Thus, although he had Plautus and Terence,[5] and Seneca's *Medea*, he had no Martial, Catullus, Tibullus, or Propertius—the very poets that Thomas Bacon in 1560 declared to be 'wanton and unhonest'.

'From the reading of these and such-like filthy writers, is convenient that the youth do abstain; lest by the reading of them they make shipwreck both of their faith and manners, and in their tender years drink in such corruption as shall be noisome unto them all their life after.'[6]

This is not to condemn Drummond to schoolroom tastes, but just to notice that he does seem conformist here.[7] If we were to look for 'filthy writers' in his library we would notice at once Petronius Arbiter's *Satyricon*, whose splendid realism and racy description is decorated by the grossest pornography. Against Petronius we can set Boethius' *Consolation of philosophy*, which though also a Menippean satire (and thus included by Drummond in his poetry and not his prose) is altogether set on a loftier plane. It is perhaps invidious to weigh invividual books one against the other: does Ausonius' presence here, we might wonder, condemn the taste of Plantin for printing the book, and Drummond for buying it? The answer must be that any piece of Latin literature that survived was thought by the Renaissance printer to be worth publishing: printers were in a competitive trade and there was a good market for the classics. The first edition of Ausonius' works was printed in Venice as early as 1472, and the British Museum lists seventeen more between then and 1595, so Plantin as a shrewd and successful printer must have felt there would be a market for another. We must also assume that what was bought was read.[8]

To echo Gibbon: it would seem sensible to condemn the taste of an age which supported such quantities of pedestrian verse as that which was produced in the Renaissance, for a first impression of the mass of neo-Latin poetry is that it is routine, trivial, and dull. The huge amounts of dedicatory, commendatory and commemorative stuff do nothing to dispel this feeling; *epithalamia, elegia* and *epicedia* abound; not a king or a prince was married or buried without receiving an outpouring of Latin verse. Universities outdid each other in the speed with which they would gather together a collection of Latin (and Greek and even Hebrew) verse to mark each royal occasion, and the solitary poets were never far behind.[1] When Henry Prince of Wales died in 1612 the versifiers excelled themselves, for the subject of a promising youth cut down in his prime offered for once a chance to display some sincerity and honest grief.[2]

It would, however, be a mistake to scorn all Renaissance Latin verse, and to judge it by its excesses; to understand its popularity we must understand the accepted conventions of the time. What inspired the Renaissance Latin poets was the humanistic reverence of the classics, and almost all neo-Latin verse was written in direct imitation of one or other classical model. The neo-Latin poet of the Renaissance believed that Latin was not an alternative to his vernacular, but a better language, a language with nobility, a language which would endure, a language in which sweetness, melodiousness and all the sounds of true poetry could best be displayed. Above all the neo-Latin poet knew that imitation itself was a commendable thing. He felt none of our present prejudice towards the copy, nor did he share our longing for originality. For him the greatest work of art was that which approached most closely the greatest that Rome or Greece had produced, and so, by employing the same conventions, by using the same language, by celebrating the same subjects, he would create new works in the same mould, and moreover he would be congratulated for doing so.[3] Imitation was a means to an end. The humanists wished to write well, and the way to write well, as they saw it, was to write as the ancients had written.

As early as the fourteenth century, Petrarch epitomizes this attitude. Now we remember him for his 'canzone', for the 'Petrarchan' sonnet, for his poetic history of love for Laura—and these, after all, were extolled and imitated by poets in the next two centuries, Italian, French, Spanish and English.[4] But Petrarch thought his Italian verse unworthy of him. It was the stuff of youth, and it could only hinder his reputation as a Latin poet. When he was crowned poet-laureate upon the Capital at Rome in 1341 it was not for his Italian sonnets, but for his Latin epic, the *Africa*. The *Africa* now is regarded as a failure, 'a weak dilution of Livy and Virgil'[5] (Livy provided the historical subject, which was Scipio Africanus' struggle with Hannibal), but for Petrarch, as the first Renaissance humanist, it represented the highest achievement possible: the greatest poetic form in the most suitable language; an imitation in subject, metre and imagery of the Virgilian masterpiece.

The writer of the Latin epic achieved immortality at one stroke, yet admired as this form was in the Renaissance, only a few poets

1. Political events, too, inspired the university poets. Thus, four volumes of Latin verse were produced at Oxford to commemorate the revelation of the Parry plot against Queen Elizabeth, and the murder of the Duke of Guise in 1589 was the subject of another; Bradner, p. 60.

2. See the titles listed in Bradner's appendix for the years 1612 and 1613.

3. Franceso Pico gave a reasoned defence of the convention. He explained that literary excellence is the result of a combination of separate effects—like pebbles in a mosaic—which the artist could choose from the classic genius and reassemble in his own pattern as he saw fit. Bolgar, pp. 271-3.

4. Drummond himself rather after the fashion had changed wrote verses on his own love in the Petrarchan manner, celebrating his Auristella in life and in death.

5. Wright and Sinclair, p. 339.

attempted it. Perhaps this was because this greatest of classical forms demanded the greatest of subjects; beside themes from Roman history (which had a second-hand relevance) there was only the Christian story. Vida's *Christiados* and Sannazzaro's *De partu Virginis* are two of the better known sixteenth-century examples of the Christian epic, but although they contain passages of good poetry, they are, it is generally thought, failures. As Paul Van Tieghem explains, although the writer of the epic in the vernacular (such as Camoens) drew his knowledge of the form from Virgil, he was free to explore the richness of his own language, and he had the inspirations of a new-felt nationalism.[1] The neo-Latin poet on the other hand was always directly competing with his model in the same language, with Virgil, as it were, looking over his shoulder. It is little wonder then that the epic imagination of the Renaissance was freer to flower in the vernacular.

In the love lyric the neo-Latin poets were more successful. Here the classical models were those not generally recommended for the schoolroom: Catullus, Tibullus, Propertius and Ovid — Ovid that is, not of the *Fasti* and the *Metamorphoses*, but of the *Amores* and the *Ars amatoria*. Where Catullus had his Lesbia, Tibullus his Delia, Propertius his Cynthia, and Ovid his Corinna, so the Renaissance lyricists extolled their mistresses, frequently giving them these very names so that they might come closer to the true classical spirit. The personal nature of this poetry kept it for the most part simple in language, and following the Romans much of it was sensuous and erotic. Thus Joannes Pontanus in his *Hymn to night*, to Fannia, described the joys of kissing, and all, according to Van Tieghem, in a Latin that is easy, supple, without archaism or studied elegance.[2]

Much of the best of this poetry is represented in Drummond's library, from lyricists of the fifteenth century like Marullus, who hymned Næra, to Beroaldus, whose love was Panthia, to Joannes Secundus, with his Julia, who himself inspired a generation of imitators. Of these, Secundus is undoubtedly the greatest, both for his own achievements and for the following he created. Born at The Hague in 1511, he studied law under Alciatus at Bourges, moved to Spain as secretary of the Archbishop of Toledo and, before falling ill and returning to the Low Countries, was recruited by the Emperor Charles V as an amanuensis for an expedition to Africa. (This career seems less extraordinary when it is explained that Secundus came from an important Dutch family high in the service of the Habsburg Emperor, who of course possessed the Netherlands.) In the short time Secundus lived — he died before he was twenty-five — he wrote an enormous amount of Latin verse; some of it epigrams, odes and obituary poems, but the most part love lyrics. He was influenced by his immediate predecessors, particularly Marullus and Beroaldus, but in his most famous groups of poems, the *Basia* ('The kisses') he turned for a model to Catullus. The *Basia* are addressed to his lover in Madrid, whom he calls Næra — for Secundus, like Ovid before him and many poets after him, paid attention to more than one woman — and to her these nineteen Kisses go, full of joy,

1. Van Tieghem, p. 123.

2. Van Tieghem, p. 64.

wit and passion, telling of the pleasures of fondling, of love bites, of tasting, watching and sparring with his mistress, and always with a little hymn to the god of love for contriving such bliss.[1]

Secundus' love lyrics are marked by an attitude of raillery never designed to hurt but always to charm, that keeps his passion clear and far from sentiment. This attitude, more than the form itself, was his legacy to his many imitators, and can be traced right down to the Caroline and Restoration poets, to such as Suckling or Carew, in whom wit and tenderness keep a delicate balance.[2] Of his more immediate followers throughout the sixteenth century there were as many writing in the vernacular as in Latin: Ronsard, Belleau and Baïf were all in his debt, as were scores of Latin poets now no longer remembered. In Drummond's library writers such as Muret and Jean Dousa the Younger, and especially Daniel Heinsius, were all influenced by Secundus, as was Jean Bonnefons (whose *Pancharis* was translated and imitated by Gilles Durant). Bonnefons has been described—admittedly by a nineteenth-century critic—as a writer of verse in the worst possible taste, vastly inferior to his model Secundus.[3]

If Virgil and Catullus had their Renaissance imitators, so too did Horace, though his seem to have been less attracted to his *Satires* than his *Odes*. Joannes Salmonius (who called himself Macrinus) succeeded in maintaining an Horatian detachment amid the political and religious confusion of sixteenth-century life, and his urbane yet Christian verse was infused with the best of humanism. While Macrinus had to his contemporaries the reputation of the French Horace, his countryman Nicolaus Borbonius was equally acclaimed, favoured by such as Erasmus and Sainte-Marthe, and according to Étienne Pasquier was 'un des premiers poètes latins de notre temps et de la France'.[4] In his *Nugae* (Bagatelles) he records the small adventures of his life, his journeys, his accidents—his horse falling into the river Rhône—his patriotism, his criticism of the follies of the age. It is typical of the spirit of humanism that such criticism should be given with such concern yet with such detachment, conveyed in the body of elegant Latin verse. Incidentally, Borbonius was the first humanist to use the phrase 'litterae renascentes'.[5]

There is, happily, no need to discuss all the neo-Latin poets of the Renaissance, or even all the ones Drummond bought and presumably read, for many are now sunk into what we can only regard as a deserved obscurity. Nor can we even do justice to all the forms of neo-Latin poetry—poems of cities, of nature and of art, poems congratulatory,[6] poems of grief or poems funereal—beyond noticing that they were popular and that poems were written, printed and bought, and by existing so bountifully tell us something of the taste of the time for occasional verse. Drummond's catalogue is crowded with such works. Many he must have bought because they were written by friends or fellow-countrymen, such as those by John Leech or John Johnston,[7] but many more for the sake of their authors' contemporary reputation: the names of Marc Antoine Muret (for his *Juvenilia*), Michel de l'Hospital, and Vulteius (for his *Xenia*) were only three of the many famous in Drummond's day.

1. Wright and Sinclair, pp. 374-81.

2. This point is made by Wright and Sinclair, p. 380.

3. Hallam, II, p. 340.

4. Quoted by Van Tieghem, p. 90.

5. Van Tieghem, p. 90.

6. The popularity of such verse was mocked by Owen the epigrammatist:
   'The latest product of the tuneful lyre
   Is called 'In praise of Thomas Jones Esquire'.
   Quoted and translated by Wright and Sinclair, p. 391.

7. Summaries of the work of these and many other poets can be found in detail in Bradner's *Musae Anglicanae*. The Scots particularly seem to have produced quantities of occasional verse, but to give space to them here would be invidious. The wealth (if this is the right word) of verse written by Scots between 1570 and 1637 is more of a comment on the culture of the country than an indication of a neo-Latin Renaissance. Rollock, Dempster, Hegate, Boyd, Andrew Melville, John Johnston, Arthur Johnston, David Hume, John Leech, Sir Robert Ayton, John Barclay, George Chalmers all figure in Drummond's library; Buchanan does not.

Three kinds of poetry, however, should be distinguished from the ruck: pastoral, epigrammatic, and religious. All three were popular, and each in its way shows up a different side of Renaissance taste. Pastoral poetry — and we need only to look at England to remind us of this, and at such a work as Spenser's *Shepherds calendar* — was a favourite and highly respectable form throughout the Renaissance, having a pedigree through Virgil to Theocritus. The convention was well enough understood, and the pastoral deemed sound and moral, as well as pleasantly entertaining. This explains the esteem with which Mantuanus' *Bucolica* (composed around the year 1485) was held in the sixteenth century, for Mantuanus sat almost as high as Virgil himself, and his work was widely used as a textbook in the grammar school.[1] It is odd not to find it in Drummond's library (for he himself wrote much pastoral verse, and would have known of Mantuanus), although two other pastoral poets are there: Vida and Euricius Cordus. The former is interesting since his *Bucolica*, while employing the Virgilian form and phrase, is inspired by Christian themes. Cordus was a disciple of Mantuanus, and is evidence of his popularity with German poets.[2]

Epigrammatic and satiric poetry, usually styled on Martial, had a considerable vogue in the Renaissance, and poets like Vulteius, and again, Cordus, were among the better writers of epigrams. The best of these was John Owen, a Welshman (1560–1622), whose epigrams became so popular in the seventeenth century that they were translated into English, German, Spanish and French, and from their first printing in 1607 went through at least six more editions in England alone before 1635.[3] Owen's epigrams are usually quite different in tone from his classical model, Martial, for whereas Martial described characters, manners, and the stuff of everday life, Owen contented himself with the niceties of morality, mankind and womankind in general, and with the accidents of life and death. Martial can make pungent comment on the incongruities of everyday life — the country estate, with vegetables fresh from the city; the draughty guest room; men who try to conceal their baldness — his wit gloried in realism, and the sordidness of much Roman life induced grossness in his verse.[4] Owen's satire, is much gentler, and never offensive, although his wit is sharp, and this saves his epigrams from sentimentality. He was a confirmed misogynist, and some of his best epigrams were directed against women:

> The sage who said he needed naught in life
> Save what he carried on him had no wife.[5]

Owen is worth attention because of his popularity, a popularity that must in some measure be due to his tone as well as his mastery of an admired medium, His ironies foreshadow the cynicism of La Rochefoucauld's *Maxims*, but they are wise, never harsh.

In an age of religious strife and frequent political confusion, invective was more usual than considered satire, and what satire there was, when not modelled directly on the classical — and so restrained — showed much bitterness. George Buchanan's *Franciscanus* is notable for little but its virulence, and a pre-Reformation

1. At least six editions of Mantuanus were printed in England between 1569 and 1600. Drayton's phrase, 'honest Mantuanus' is a typical epithet for the time.

2. Van Tieghem, pp. 116-22.

3. According to the *STC*. This is counting separate printings of individual books. Bradner gives a list of the complete editions, and beginning with the London one of 1622 numbers eighteen English and Continental editions printed before 1700. Harvard evidently has a first edition of the epigrams dated 1606; Bradner, p. 355. Ben Jonson gave an ill-natured characterization of Owen as 'a pure Pedantique Schoolmaster sweeping his living from the Posteriors of little children, and hath no thinge good in him, his Epigrames being bare narrations'; Herford and Simpson, I, p. 138.

4. Hadas, pp. 292-3.

5. Quoted and translated by Wright and Sinclair, p. 389.

31. Title-page, with Drummond's note of donation to the University of Edinburgh. Raphael Thorius, *Hymnus tabaci* (Cat. 385).

HYMNVS
TABACI
autore·
Raphaële Thori
Lugd. Bat.
TYPIS
Isaaci Elseviri.

Academiæ Edinb: Gulielmus Drummond D·D·Q.

In obitum Sereniss. Reginæ Annæ
ænigmata quædam Cabalistica.

Cadit Sol quoque.   **Regina Anna.**

Anagramma.

הֶן חַמָּה כַּלָּה   חַנָּה הַמִּלְכָּה

Qui seminârunt cum lacrymis, cum cantu metent.

Natus peccator, per Christum liberatur.

Left column (Hebrew): החופֵץ · נָחוּם · חָכַם · מָצָא · הוֹן · נפר · לכפות · הַתְּלָאוֹת

Right column (Hebrew): חוֹטֵא · נֶפֶשׁ · הָאָדָם · הַמָּשִׁיחַ · מחסרו · לָנוּ · בָּבוֹר · הַגָּדֹל

NAscimur hæredes Epimetheos, omnibus vnâ
 Dos ex Pandoræ pyxide nostra venit.
Nulla mora est, miseri quin demergamur in illis
 Mors vbi Tartareis sæua triumphat aquis;
Ni in læuum Samij tendamus protinùs, illic
 Currit vbi læua stans Μετανόια manu.
Hæc iter ad dextrum deducet tramite Christum,
 Qui Styga, qui solus vi Phlegetonta domat.
Vescere tunc pomis, ô Fœlix, vescere! Christus
 Quæ tibi perpetuo vere virere facit:
Non velut antè, Mali quæ tristis præbuit Arbor;
 Nunc comedas Vitæ qualia ramus habet.
His stans à dextra cum Christo vescitur Anna,
 Ambrosiam fœlix hanc habet Anna nouam.

ה ל כ מ ה   ה נ ח
5 20 30 40 5   5 50 8

163   Ἴσαζων ἀριθμῷ.

ה י ל כ א ד   ז ט ס ס
5 10 30 10 20 1   4 3 40 40

Vescitur cœli pomis.

Nathanael Flick, Collegy Corp. Christ.

poet like the German Jacob Locher (1471–1528), in a work like *The death of Pluto and his demons*, can be exceedingly harsh with the servants of the Church.[1] Drummond counted Locher's translation of that most popular poem of the sixteenth century — Sebastian Brant's *Narrenschiff* (The ship of fools) — among his Latin verse writers, and we may number it among the satirical works. It is worth noticing that the success of the *Narrenschiff* was on a popular level: Brant was no humanist, nor did he decorate his poem with classical allusion, but rather stayed within the native tradition of past centuries, employing the allegory.[2]

In writing religious poetry the Christian humanists found themselves in something of a dilemma. Their themes of course were Christian, but while paying due attention to these, at the same time they felt bound to acknowledge their classical predecessors. Where the medieval poet could write (and even imitate an Horatian ode) without invoking Jupiter and Venus,[3] Renaissance humanists often cheerfully mingled the whole Olympian pantheon in their recitations of the Christian story. Classical models must be imitated to the full, even if this meant incorporating pagan deities, and claiming Roman mythology as a kind of unenlightened but equivalent sainthood. Thus Joannes Pontanus in his *Divine odes* equated the Virgin Mary with Venus, mother of mankind, queen of the world.[4] Vida, too, in his hymns, made the same attempt to reconcile the two mythologies, as did Sannazaro in his epic *De partu Virginis*; but perhaps the best example of all in Drummond's library is the edition of Giovanni Francesco Pico della Mirandola's *Hymnes*, where the scholarly commentary discussing the classical and Biblical allusions quite drowns the text itself.[5] It should not be thought that this passed without criticism. It was a convention practised for the most part by the Italian humanists of the fifteenth and early sixteenth centuries, but outside the circle of extreme enthusiasts there were some who saw and ridiculed its excesses. The *Epistolae obscurorum virorum* — the collection of mock-serious letters by Crotus Rubianus and Ulrich von Hutten, written in 1515 in support of the scholar Reuchlin against the stupidities of his opponents — has this confusion of pagan lore and Christian scriptures as one of its prime targets. Friar Dollenkopf, for example, quotes from a book by 'Doctor Thomas of Wales' (Thomas Wallis), which examines Ovid's *Metamorphoses* in the allegorical light, most seriously and profoundly:

> 'Concerning Actæon, who beheld Diana naked, Ezekiel prophesied, saying, "Thou wast bare and full of confusion, and I passed by thee and saw thee"'.[6]

But as the Reformation and Counter-Reformation increasingly undermined the spirit of detachment that had characterized early humanism, and that had at times almost approached free-thought, so the writers of the religious lyric withdrew from pagan contamination. There is, for example, a marked contrast between the freedom of the earlier lyricists and the more literal and serious matter of the later hymnists. Thus Fabricius, who was one of the first Lutherans

---

1. Van Tieghem, p. 138.

2. Van Tieghem, p. 137.

3. The Latin poets of the Middle Ages also used classical models; for example, Hildebert, Marbod and Baudry all wrote their elegies and love poems in imitation of Ovid. Bolgar, p. 189.

4. Van Tieghem, p. 53.

5. The author of the *Hymns* was the nephew of *the* Pico della Mirandola. The index of the *Hymns* is itself revealing, for it runs from Argonautici to Zeus, through Peloponnesus and Thessalia. The *Hymns* are addressed to the Trinity, to Christ and to the Virgin Mary. Figures from Greek and Roman mythology had been introduced before in Christian literature and (especially) art. Panofsky cites an instance of figures from Virgil's *Eclogues* used to decorate a liturgical fan of the Carolingian period, and notes that pagan images were used even to decorate the Passion of Christ. In the twelfth and thirteenth centuries classical imagery was often used alongside religious; the allegorical significance of pagan mythology was highly developed. But Panofsky points out that the Italian Renaissance 'reintegrated the separated elements'. Erwin Panofsky *Renaissance and renascences in Western art* (Uppsala 1960) pp. 51-101.

6. Wright and Sinclair, p. 373.

---

32. 'Cabalistic' anagrammatic obituary verse.
Lacrymæ cantabrigienses (Cat. 265).

1. Such as Spangenberg. 'Of Latine Poets of our times in the judgement of Beza and the best learned, Buchanan is esteemed the chiefe . . . as appeareth by that master-peece his Psalmes; Peacham, p. 91. The desire to grace religious poetry with classical dress did not die out: Alexander Ross, for instance, produced in 1634 his *Virgilius evangelizans*, a strange hybrid piece, in which he related the life of Christ in an hundred passages excised from Virgil's works; Bradner, p. 196. This is perhaps excused by the long-lived tradition that Virgil should be read sympathetically by Christians, since he had foreknowledge of Christ's coming (Eclogue 4 being known as the 'Messianic' eclogue).

2. *Delitiæ poetarum Scotorum hujus ævi illustrium* (Amsterdam 1637). Arthur Johnston is sometimes credited with editing this collection, though Bradner feels that Sir John Scot himself was responsible. It is reasonable to suppose that Drummond would have owned a copy of this, though he had most of the authors represented (see footnote 42).

3. It 'would have done honour to any nation'. *Works* (London 1787) X, p. 344.

4. According to Bradner, Raphael Thorius' *Hymnus tabaci* was the most popular Latin poem of the seventeenth century in England. A long work, it tells of the discovery of tobacco by Bacchus, and is remarkable chiefly for several 'brutally nauseous' passages describing Bacchus' visit to a cannibal king; Bradner, p. 73.

5. Baldwin, I, pp. 642-4.

6. This point is made by Wright and Sinclair, p. 335.

7. The first printed edition of Abelard's works recorded in Brunet and the BM catalogue is dated 1616; the earliest edition of St Thomas Aquinas' *Lauda Sion* in the BM is dated 1618, and the earliest of Joannes Peckham's *Philomena*, 1924. For details of what actually was printed of medieval Latin poetry, see E. Ph. Goldschmidt *Medieval texts and their first appearance in print* (Bibliographical Society, London 1943).

to write Protestant hymns, felt quite free to go to Ovid's *Amores* for inspiration, and turn those sensual pieces into Christian moralities—no small feat in its way. Later in the century typical productions were George Buchanan's and Theodore Beza's metrical versions of the *Psalms* (Buchanan's particularly being highly praised)—an exercise that attracted countless pious poets, most of whom have now been forgotten.[1]

No survey of neo-Latin poetry would be complete without noticing the collections of verse, usually by poets of one nation. Drummond owned the most famous, the *Carmina illustrium poetarum Italorum* in the Paris edition of 1576, but he does not seem to have had any of the collections, edited by Gruterus and printed between the years 1608 and 1612, of the poets of Italy, France, the Low Countries and Germany. The size alone of these productions is evidence enough of the profusion of Latin verse, for in the volumes of French poets alone there are over 100,000 lines. The collection of Scots poets is also missing. This was a project encouraged by Drummond's cousin Sir John Scot of Scotstarvet[2]; its excellence was in the next century commended by Samuel Johnson.[3]

With such a wealth to choose from we can hardly expect to find Drummond with a complete list of Renaissance poets; as in other sections of his library the remarkable thing is that so many of the most notable names are numbered. The gaps (besides those already mentioned) include such as Fracastorius—whose *Syphilis*, a highly admired poem, named the disease—Lotichius, Conrad Celtes, and Vossius. But against these can be set others not yet mentioned, such as the two Scaligers, Passerat, Thorius,[4] or Teofilo Folengo, who under the name of Merlinus Cocaius created macaronic poetry. There is no copy of Mancinus, whose *De quatuor virtutibus*, a celebration of the four Ciceronian virtues, was highly approved of for use in the schools[5]; but Palingenius is present, with his philosophical poem the *Zodiacus vitae*, and he was equally at home in the normal curriculum.

Finally, it must be emphasized that an appreciation of the classics did not spring full-fledged into being with the first Renaissance humanists. Virgil, Ovid, Horace and Martial were all known, read and imitated in the Middle Ages, and the scholars and poets of that time were far from ignorant of the classical heritage. The humanists did see themselves as bringing in a new age of classicism, rediscovering lost glories, and restoring purity and grace to the Latin language, but it is a mistake to think that all was darkness before Petrarch. In Latin poetry the innovations of the humanists were to some extent retrograde, for they abandoned such developments of the Middle Ages as rhyme and free rhythm in favour of a faithful imitation of classical metre,[6] although by insisting that all be judged by the best of Rome and Greece critical standards were undoubtedly raised. As a final comment it is worth pointing out that whereas in fields like philosophy or theology the writings of such as Albertus Magnus, William of Occam or St Thomas Aquinas were printed in the Renaissance, the medieval lyricists were neglected, for the taste of the age was for the classics.[7]

Latin Prose

The last section of Drummond's Latin books is also the largest, and
at first sight it appears to be a collection of titles he could not very
well classify under philosophy, theology, law or poetry, and so just
flung together at the end in a miscellaneous gathering. Indeed, some
books that escaped his first lists are here, like Juvenal, Persius and
Ovid from the poets; but besides these strays, there are dictionaries,
collections of letters, orations, histories, grammars, treatises on
rhetoric and works on philology, political philosophy, literary
criticism, antiquities, and much more, even some fiction — all surely
too various to put together under one heading. Yet for Drummond
and his contemporaries — though it was not the fashion then to be
concerned with the business of classification — these works did form
a rational whole. They were all necessary for that less formal part
of a man's education in which he learned to write well, and in which
he studied history and oratory as models to this end. Peacham calls
his chapter on the subject 'Of stile in speaking and writing, and of
History', and tells his reader (the Compleat Gentleman) to 'imitate
the best Authors as well in Oratory as History'.[1] No gentlemen could
consider himself educated unless he had a good style in both Latin
and English, for style was but the reflection of the man.

Richard Holdsworth, in his 'Directions for a Student in the Uni-
versitie', gives a programme for the Cambridge student of Milton's
time (1625–32) in which this humanistic attention to style and the
classical model is laid down in detail. The Cambridge student was to
spend his afternoons (according to the *Studia Pomeridiana*) reading
history, oratory and poetry in the Greek and Latin tongues, for
these were

> if 'Studies not less necessary than the first [logic, physics, etc.,]
> if not more useful, especialy Latine, & Oratory, without w:ch all
> the other Learning though never so eminent, is in a manner voide
> & useless, without those you will be bafeld in your disputes,
> disgraced, & vilified in Publicke examinations, laught at in speeches,
> & Declamations.'[2]

And of the books that Holdsworth recommends, many are in
Drummond's list.

Style then is the real subject of these miscellaneous prose works:

1. Peacham, pp. 42, 44.

2. Fletcher, II, p. 637.

115

oratory for the formal, rhetorical style, letters for the familiar, and history for the descriptive and expository styles. As in poetry the classical authors provided the models. Grammars and dictionaries were the scholar's tools, and works on the classical antiquities, philology and politics were useful additions to the gentlemen's store of knowledge. Again, as in the poetry, the classical authors are out-numbered by the writers of the Renaissance.

Whereas Virgil, for the Renaissance, was the supreme classical poet, Cicero was the prose writer that stood above all. To Peacham, he was 'Pater Romani eloquii[1]; to Gabriel Harvey 'the eldest son and indeed heir of Eloquence'.[2] Whatever the relationship Cicero was without rivals. He was used in the schools and the universities as an authority on oratory and a model of style; he became (as we shall see later) a cult to such an extent that we can confidently divide the Renaissance Latin writers into Ciceronians and anti-Ciceronians.

Yet there is less of Cicero in Drummond's library than we might expect. Among what can be loosely described as Cicero's philo-sophical works, Drummond had the *Paradoxa stoicorum*, the *Somnium Scipionis*, the short *De fato*, and a collection of philo-sophical pieces which would probably include the *Academia*, the *Tusculanæ disputationes*, and the *De natura deorum*; he also had a Greek edition of the essay on old age, *De Senectute*. His copy of *Sententiæ* must have been a relic from the schoolroom, for it was almost certainly one of the many collections designed for the novice[3]; a choice selection of moral thoughts on which the schoolboy could both practise his translation and improve his mind. Another school text would be the *Partitiones oratoriæ*—known in England as the 'partition of rhetorike'—which was recommended, adapted and explained by many sixteenth-century writers on rhetoric, from Melanchthon to Sturm and the Ramist Omer Talon.[4] Of the orations Drummond had only three: Ramus' edition of the three speeches *De lege agraria contra Rullum*, in which Cicero successfully attacked Rullus' agrarian bill before the Senate and the people. (The bill was ostensibly designed to help the poor and unemployed, but according to Cicero, Rullus' motives were political, and the bill impractical; a mere demagogic device.'[5]) Cicero's letters are more complete, for here Drummond owned the sixteen books *Ad Atticum*, and twelve of the sixteen books *Ad familiares*, lacking only the smaller collections *Ad Quintum fratrem* and *Ad Brutum*. But, as Peacham said, it mattered little what Cicero a man had: 'you cannot make your choice amiss.'[6]

At the Tounis College in Edinburgh, Drummond would have learned his formal rhetoric according to Ramist principles, that is, in the simplification and reorganization of Cicero's categories by Omer Talon. Talon's work is listed among the philosophy books, pre-sumably because Drummond associated it with formal instruction, while other works on rhetoric or style—such as the *Partitiones oratoriæ* (even though it was used as a text)—are with the prose. So, too, is that much greater work on rhetoric: the *Institutio oratoria* of Quintilian. In the Renaissance Quintilian was the supreme auth-ority, *the* Rhetorician,[7] for the discovery of a complete manuscript

1. Peacham, p. 45. Peacham's title is repeated on the title-page of the French translation of the *Epistolæ familiares.*

2. Gabriel Harvey *Ciceronianus,* ed. Harold S. Wilson, trs. Clarence A. Forbes (Lincoln, Nebraska 1945) p. 57.

3. These collections were evidently so much in use that English and Scottish printers found it worth while to print their own editions: Vautrollier, for instance, put out a *Sententiæ Ciceronis* in 12⁰ in 1584.

4. Baldwin, II, pp. 21-2, 24, 66.

5. See Hadas, pp. 113-14 for a summary.

6. Peacham, p. 45.

7. Baldwin, II, p. 197. Rhetoric as formally taught in the Renaissance was divorced from Aristotelian theory, particularly after Ramus' reforms, and Aristotle's *Art of rhetoric* gave way to Talon's *Rhetorica.* This was a great simpli-fication of the complicated Aristotelian system: it insisted on practical rather than theoretical rhetoric, and though rule books like Aphthonius were still important for teaching the terms, the study of Cicero's orations provided prac-tical classical models. Significantly, Talon's *Rhetorica* was printed with his lectures on Cicero's works.

116

of his work in the fifteenth century coincided with the new humanistic emphasis on the purity of style, and especially, the new appreciation of Quintilian's own model orator, Cicero. His book was a
source of wisdom not only on the finer points of rhetoric, but also
on the larger subjects of education and literary criticism, for he
covered the whole education of the orator, proceeding from grammar and language, through the technical points of oratory, the formal
structure of speech, to the orator's reading, bearing and dress. In
Book 10 (discussing reading) he provided concise criticism of the
important Greek and Latin authors: all useful information for the
Renaissance man seeking classical authority.[1] Despite the respect
he was given, Quintilian was somewhat abused, especially by the
pedagogues, often being milked for his technical information, and
used as an advanced textbook in addition to such rule books as
Aphthonius. Even Holdsworth seems to have told his students to
read Quintilian for his terms, and mark down technical expressions
in their commonplace books.[2]

'Quintilian's 6.7.8. bookes were not only to be read',[3] Ben Jonson
told Drummond in 1619, 'but altogither digested.' 'Petronius,
Plinius Secundus, Tacitus, spoke best Latine',[4] he said, and perhaps this rather offhand opinion impressed Drummond, for he
provided himself with a new Pliny at about that time.[5] Quintilian
had shaped his orator after Cicero; Pliny the Younger, his pupil in
rhetoric, took Cicero as his model in letter-writing. Cicero does not
seem to have intended his letters for publication—indeed, it has
been claimed that they are so revealing only his enemies could have
wanted them published—but Pliny wrote or at least revised each
letter with the public in mind. The reader is given a portrait of an
upright citizen, kindly, moral, highly respectable; a good example
to the Renaissance schoolboy and an inspiration to the gentleman.
Thus, together with Cicero and Seneca (whose *Epistolæ morales* are
really moral homilies, not true letters), Pliny was most commonly
recommended 'for Epistles'.[6]

We have noticed before that the critics of the Renaissance often
praised classical authors for reasons we now disregard: to Erasmus
and many educational writers morality often outweighed all else,
and they thus promoted such a poet as Statius; for the Italian
humanists the poetic vocabulary, the figures of speech, the devices
sometimes became more important than the poem itself.[7] Prose
authors tended to be read not so much for their matter as their
style, historians as well as letter writers. And in addition to style,
history was an entertainment, yet it taught moral lessons:

> 'historie is the mixture of profite and delight, the seasoning of
> more serious studies, the reporter of cases adiudged by euent, the
> interlude of our haps, the image of our present fortune, the com-
> pendiary director of our affaires by which valor is quicked,
> iudgement ripened, and resolution entertained. Here are the
> reasons, why some estates liue quietlie, others turmouled in con-
> tinuall disturbances, some flourish by the delights of peace, others
> by continuing warre, some spend lauishlie without profite, others

1. Fletcher, II, p. 206.

2. Fletcher, II, pp. 644-5.

3. That is, the theory of rhetoric.
Books 3-9 contain the whole technical analysis of oratory.

4. *Conversations*, in *Arch. Scot.*,
IV, 249.

5. Drummond's copy of Pliny's
Letters was printed in 1611.

6. See, for example, Hoole's *New
discovery* (1560), quoted Baldwin,
II, p. 566.

7. H. A. Mason's opinion is
relevant here:'. . . the Humanists'
impasse was that they could find no
justification for literature other than
its moral instructiveness, that is, the
only valuable thing they could find in
literature was the boiled-down,
abstracted statement, the moral of
the poem, or the lifted statement
taken from the poem, the wise
saying or adage'. *Humanism and
poetry in the early Tudor period*
(London 1950) p. 66. Mason's
essays are valuable correctives to the
common over-estimation of
humanist taste.

sparinglie with honor. Here we may see ruines without feare, daungerous warres without perill, the customes of all nations without expence'.[1]

Caesar's *Commentaries* had a yet more utilitarian use, for from them the soldier could learn tactics and strategy. Clement Edmundes could expect a sympathetic audience to agree, when in his *Observationes* on his translation of the *Commentaries* he insisted that 'Reading and Discourse are requisite to make a soldier perfect in the Art militarie,'[2] and what better study for the soldier than the greatest Roman of them all. Thus Shakespeare had Fluellen call the 'true disciplines of the wars' the 'Roman disciplines', and Sidney explained that Palladius Musidorus 'was acquainted with strategems . . . by some experience, but especially by reading Histories'.[3]

Style, however, was usually the chief reason for reading Caesar. Roger Ascham in the *Scholemaster* pronounced him supreme in his chosen style, for his books were written

> 'so wiselie for the matter, so eloquentlie for the tong, that neither his greatest enemies could euer finde the least note of parcialitie in him (a meruelous wisedome of a man, namely writyng of his own doynges) nor yet the best iudegers of the *Latin* tong, nor the most enuious lookers vpon other mēs writynges, can say any other, but all things be most perfitelie done by him.'[4]

His forthright, masculine prose made him ideal for the schoolroom, although as Peacham noted, the abundance of technical military terms always posed a difficulty. The gentleman could turn to his learned commentator—Lipsius or Ramus—or indeed could read the English translation and commentary by Peacham's 'worthy friend' Sir Clement Edmundes.[5]

Besides Caesar and Cicero, the style of Sallust and Tacitus was generally admired. Sallust was praised for brevity—Milton preferred him to all the other historians for 'the dispatch of much in few words'[6]—though many, such as Sir John Cheke, detected contrivance: 'more Arte than nature, and more labor than Arte.'[7] Sallust, who had followed Thucydides' theory that general truths may be demonstrated from the exposition of particular events, is now regarded as the first Roman to write true history (that is, history that does not, to any great extent, distort events to make a moral or chauvinistic point). Tacitus was termed 'the Prince of Historians' by Peacham (who was fond of epithets; he referred to Sallust as *Historiae pater*),[8] and praised for being 'so copious in pleasing brevity, each Sentence carrying with it a kind of lofty State and Majestie, such as should (me thinks) proceed from the mouth of Greatnesse and Command. . .'.[9] Tacitus was more popular in the northern countries than in Italy, for the High Renaissance preferred Livy. Tacitus was of course especially read in Germany (for his *Germania*), and in England after a late start (1591) was Englished by three translators, whose most popular collection went through six editions before 1640. The only translation of Livy, on the other hand, was not reprinted after its first appearance in 1600.[10]

1. Robert Johnson *Essaies, or rather imperfect offers* (London 1601) Sig. C8v, Dlr.

2. Clement Edmundes *Observations*, p. 1.

3. Although for Sir Thomas Kellie the 'best Masters of the Arte Militarie' were 'Aelian and Leo' (Aelianus *Tacticus* and Leo VI, Emperor of the East), for he thought that the Grecians excelled the Romans in both 'Mars and the Muses'. See his preface to his *Pallas armata*.

4. Ascham, *English works* (Cambridge English Classics, 1904) p. 301.

5. Peacham, p. 46.

6. In a letter dated 1657. Fletcher, II, p. 329.

7. '. . . and in his labour also, to mock Toyle, as it were, with an vncontented care to write better than he could, a fault common to very many men.' According to Ascham, p. 297.

8. Peacham, pp. 46, 48.

9. Peacham, pp. 46-7.

10. Englished by Philemon Holland.

We should not, however, attach too much importance to the scanty showing Livy makes in the *Short-title Catalogue*—one Latin edition, one English—for this is only evidence of the inability of the English printers to compete with their continental rivals. Livy was widely read and much admired throughout the Renaissance,[1] for his great work was so rich, it had 'such banquet-like variety', that the reader's taste was nearly spoiled for any other author.[2] 'Livie triumpheth in the conquests of virtue, and in every page erecteth trophees unto valour', said Edmundes,[3] pointing to another great merit in Livy for the Renaissance: his glorification of Rome. Livy wrote his history to show the divine destiny of the Roman people, a destiny that was readily applauded fifteen hundred years later, and all action he engineered to demonstrate his thesis. For the gentleman and the scholar the great presses of Europe produced many editions in folio with full critical apparatus, and for the schoolboy octavos were printed in abundance. Livy was a popular choice for the school-master, for not only could he be read for his stories of ancient Rome, but also his model orations were a handy size for study and trans-lation.[4]

Drummond's copy of Livy has not survived. He must have owned one, for his own *History of Scotland* is quite imitative of Livy. While he was writing this history he must have kept a library of history books about him; his excuse to the Marquis of Douglas in 1639 when refusing an invitation to travel to study a history of the Douglases was probably genuine: 'being nearer manye historyes in diuerse languages in myne own studye, I can more conuientlie peruse them than in your L. Castell, where I will be but like an artizan without tooles.'[5]

If we feel able to commend the popularity of the histories of Caesar, Sallust, Tacitus and Livy in the Renaissance, we may also wish to condemn the high regard in which some of the lesser names were held. We can explain this regard if we remember that historical factuality was not the chief criterion by which they were measured— if indeed it was ever a consideration—so what we now dismiss as bad history because it is unscientific and inaccurate, let alone deriva-tive, would have been judged in most cases on quite different standards in the sixteenth century. In the Middle Ages the 'Trojan' version of the fall of Troy, purporting to be an eye-witness account, was a principal source (along with the equally suspect Dictys) of classical information.[6] It was still popular in the Renaissance. Similarly, Quintus Curtius' history of Alexander the Great survived for the appeal of the subject as much as anything else; much read in the Middle Ages,[7] it was still recommended by such as Peacham for its author's eloquence and sound judgement. In it, Peacham said, the gentleman might see 'the patterne of a braue Prince.'[8] Pompeius Trogus' universal history, preserved in a synopsis and abridgement by Justin, was another favourite,[9] and although the Latin was difficult the reader might feel rewarded by the quantity of informa-tion. Holdsworth in the 1620s was still advising his students at Cambridge to read it.[10] Florus—now disregarded as a none too accurate compiler—was admired for his elegant style, graced by much rhetoric, and his Livian attempt to present history as a Roman

1. Fletcher, II, p. 328.

2. Peacham, p. 47.

3. Edmundes, p. 3.

4. Collections of these orations from Livy, Sallust and others were specially printed for school use. Baldwin, II, p. 567.

5. *Arch. Scot.*, IV, 96. He could have seen John Bellenden's trans-lation of Livy (1533) in MS.

6. For their popularity in the Renaissance, see the numerous editions printed, e.g. the list in the BM catalogue.

7. Hadas, p. 238.

8. Peacham, p. 48.

9. Fletcher, II, p. 597.

10. Fletcher, II, p. 627.

1. Fletcher, II, p. 327. One merit of Florus was that the work was short.

2. Fletcher, II, p. 329.

3. Hadas, pp. 330-3.

4. Hadas, p. 371.

5. Peacham, p. 52. Most gentlemen, like Drummond, would know their Plutarch in Latin translation: Montaigne, for instance, quoted Plutarch 398 times, and mentioned him 68 times by name in his *Essaies*, according to P. Villey *Les sources et l'évolution de essais de Montaigne* (Paris 1908).

6. Hadas, p. 280.

7. Fletcher, II, p. 647.

8. Hadas, p. 351.

hagiography. Florus was taken up by the Renaissance, and was in vogue as a textbook.[1] Suetonius, too, was used in the classroom;[2] his lives of the *Twelve Caesars*, though full of gossip and often scandalous, gave the schoolboy yet more useful information about the greatness of Rome.[3] Following Suetonius, Aurelius Victor continued the biographies of the Caesars. His rhetorical style, now considered 'tasteless and tedious'[4] was better received in the Renaissance, for judging by the many printed editions of his history, he was at least bought, if not always read.

Some of the Greek historians and biographers should be mentioned here, too, if only because they were commonly more familiar to most in Latin translation. Plutarch, of course, was always 'highly valued among the learned',[5] and Drummond had the Latin edition of his *Parallel lives* among his books. Diogenes Laertius, it has been claimed, had more influence on European education than his merit demanded[6]: his *Lives of the eminent philosophers* was available, the subject was popular, thus the work was much used — no 'University Scholar' according to Holdsworth, 'ought to be unacquainted with' it.[7] The history of Dio Cassius (a work written in the third century AD) was again valued for its subject: a general history of Rome, it was derived for the most part from Tacitus, Livy, Sallust and Caesar, and was particularly useful for the account of the decline of the republic, at a time nearer Dio's own age. Some parts of his history are missing, although some of the gaps are filled in an eleventh-century epitome made by Joannes Xiphilinus. Drummond, too, had Josephus' works which, although their information about Christian origins was sparing, nevertheless said something, and so were read.

Looking at Drummond's books of classical prose as a whole, we can be sure that they represent only a part of those he had read and knew. At least — to qualify this a little — Drummond's familiarity with classical culture was certainly not limited to the books in his library. Like any other man educated in the Renaissance, he would be referred to classical authority on occasion after occasion in every subject, not only in philosophy, law and literature, but in the practical subjects also. For agriculture he would be directed to Columella, for architecture, Vitruvius. A man too might pick up much classical learning without ever going to the source, for the anthology or compendium was always popular. Frequently these were collections done for the schoolroom, but even the schoolroom texts are not uncommon in the gentleman's library (there does not seem to have been much snobbery amongst book owners like Drummond). The pattern for many of the collections was, typically, a classical work: Aulus Gellius' *Attic nights*. This 'well-stuffed rag bag' was a choice plundering of other men's flowers, and Gellius had an eye for the best.[8] Although more interested in literature than anything else — he collected opinions on grammar, textual matters and literary criticism — he gathered much on law, history, biography and antiquities. His most faithful Renaissance imitator was Alexander ab Alexandro, whose *Geniales dies*, first printed in 1522, was a storehouse of miscellaneous learning on every subject of Roman antiquities and philology. Alexander was not popular with his contemporaries —

Erasmus said: 'He knows every one, no one knows who he is'[1] — but by Drummond's time he came to be much appreciated.

Erasmus himself was one of the first humanists to turn the classical collection to account, for he saw how useful it could be in the schoolroom. The compendium had flourished in the Middle Ages (one of these, the *Flores doctorum*, was evidently still in use in 1600). R.R. Bolgar has shown how Erasmus' educational works supplement each other, how they are designed to demonstrate in sequence the process of imitation of the best, that is, of the classics.[2] The *Copia*, first, provides the theory of classical imitation, for here Erasmus shows how the best words and phrases can be gathered and organized, and how they can be used to illustrate the best moral themes. The *Adages* are the illustration of the theory, 'popular sayings pithily and attractively put', rhetorical examples of the classical terms. The *Colloquies* and the *Praise of folly* show the theory in action: the classical techniques used with understanding and skill for a moral purpose that a Christian could applaud. Here was the first really successful attempt to join the imitation of the ancients with the imitation of Christ. Far from providing the humanist with an excuse for self-indulgence—as was fashionably claimed in fifteenth century Italy—the classics read properly could only strengthen a scholar's virtue. The *Adages* themselves were a survey of all that was best in the moral ideas of the ancients, and for Erasmus they seemed to teach an ethic 'as near as made no matter' to Christianity.

Erasmus' marriage of scholarship and morality appealed especially to the humanist teachers of the northern countries, and after the greater part of his works were condemned by the Index of 1559, his influence on Catholic countries was somewhat diminished. In the Protestant world he became regarded almost as an honorary reformer; his influence was profound and his books (as is clear from Drummond's collection) remained popular. His adages and apothegms were borrowed and put to use by generations of writers on morals, and indeed the usual pattern of the essay owed much to Erasmus' style. Francis Bacon, Robert Johnson or Owen Feltham (from among Drummond's English essayists) were all writing for an audience accustomed to Erasmus' treatment of the moral precept.

A man hardly needed to go to the classics—or to Erasmus—to pick up a smattering of learning, for there were many who compiled collections of apothegms, epithets, jokes, and moral saws from the works of the ancients. The most popular of these were despised by the academics: Roger Ascham singled out Ravisius Textor's *Epitheta* in the *Scholemaster* as especially likely to hurt the grammar schools, and said again in the *Toxophilus* that his *Officina* 'weueth vp many brokenended matters and settes out much rifraffe, pelfery, trumpery, baggage & beggarie ware clamparde vp of one that would seme to be fitter for a shop in dede than to write any boke'.[3] But the *Epitheta* and the *Officina* were certainly put to use, and critics like Francis Meres felt free to plunder not only classical lore, but even Textor's very system of comparisons, and to copy out his list of neo-Latin poets.[4]

1. Hallam, I, p. 451-2.

2. Bolgar *The classical heritage and its beneficiaries* (Cambridge 1954) p. 336 et seq. The following section is based on Bolgar.

3. Ascham, *English works* (Cambridge English Classics, 1904) p. 259, 50.

4. Meres' debt to Textor is examined in Don Cameron Allen's *Francis Meres' treatise 'Poetrie'*, University of Illinois Studies in Language and Literature (Urbana 1933) XVI, nos. 3-4. Allen's study shows the danger of taking Elizabethan learning at its face value—Meres was once considered an erudite and even important critic, but Allen shows that his learning was shamelessly poached.

Other compilations were modelled on the collections of Scriptural 'Common Places' (such as Melanchthon's *Loci communes*) or offered a medley of *sententiae* from ancient and modern, from pagan and Christian. Such a work was Joannes Heidfeldius' *Sphinx philosophica*, which strayed into the fields of philosophy and a rather uninspired Protestant theology. Here classics were again used to back up Christian dogma. 'Concerning God. What is the oldest thing of all? Thales of Miletus replies: God. And why so? Because he has always existed.'[1]

The history of the Ciceronian controversies in the Renaissance is in a large part the history of later humanism, for in these controversies we can see all the arguments, excesses and enthusiams produced by the supposed rebirth of the classical spirit. Petrarch is called the first humanist.[2] Petrarch earned this title by his enthusiasm for the spirit of the classics, and his main guide and inspiration was Cicero. Petrarch recommended the imitation of the classics, not by an exact reproduction of classical grammar and syntax, but by using a classical vocabulary and classical phrases, and by a concern with good style. Cicero himself was not passionate about 'correct' Latin, but rather with the effects of style, and the differences created on the audience by the two contrasting manners, the spare Attic and the florid Asiatic —his own style being a judicious compromise between the two. Coupled with his advocacy of good prose, Petrarch became an apologist for Cicero's ideas.

This, then, is what is meant when it is said that Petrarch 'besought his countrymen to close their Aristotle and open their Cicero'.[3] Cicero was far from unknown before Petrarch became his disciple: although treated primarily as a master of language, with his ideas subservient to his style, his works were read and admired in the Middle Ages. Scholasticism lived on, yet Petrarch's erection of Cicero into the epitome of all that was best in the ancient world, in morals as well as style, does mark the opening and set the tone for humanism in the Renaissance.[4]

In his *Letters* Petrarch's conception of Cicero is at its clearest. Boccaccio, sharing his ideals, did yet more to spread the classical gospel, and though his own Latin prose style was dry, and his mind rather pedantic, his classical compilations were especially popular throughout the Renaissance. His *Genealogies*—of the gods and demi-gods—were printed six times in the first century of printing, and his histories of famous women and famous men were also favourites. These works of Boccaccio were the illustration of Petrarch's thesis. In the High Renaissance in Italy there then developed that enthusiasm for the Ciceronian style whose excesses were to be attacked later by Erasmus and his successors; and though that enthusiasm was a direct and even a natural development of Petrarch's 'discovery' of Cicero, Petrarch can hardly be held responsible for the excesses. The imitation of Cicero's style was brought to a point of great perfection: Poggio, for instance, was famous among his contemporaries for his Latin, but yet more famous for his discoveries of lost classics.[5] Æneas Sylvius Piccolomini (Pius II) was another of the best Ciceronians, and his *Letters*, written on the pattern of Cicero's, are

1. *Sphinx philosophica*, p. 1.

2. The following on Petrarch is taken from Bolgar, p. 265 et seq. For more detailed information on Petrarch, particularly biographical, see Ernest H. Wilkins *Studies in the life and works of Petrarch* (Medieval Academy of America, No. 62, Cambridge, Mass. 1955), and the same author's *Petrarch's eight years in Milan* (no. 69) and *Petrarch's later years* (no. 70).

3. Bolgar, p. 255.

4. See Remigio Sabbadini *Storia de Ciceronianismo* (Turin 1885) pp. 5-11. I am indebted to Professor Denys Hay for directing me to this valuable work.

5. See Sandys, II, pp. 25-34 for a summary of these discoveries.

models of good style and familiar instruction. Like Cicero, Æneas Sylvius records the small and great events of his life, discusses his literary activities, chronicles his travels. It is a life of much interest, for he rose to be Pope, and his *Letters* reveal his growth of piety — a transformation reflected in the typically Renaissance change from his early scabrous *History of two lovers* to his last devout work inciting the pious to yet another crusade, a metamorphosis as complete as his change of name from the pagan Æneas to the Christian Pius.

Even in the fifteenth century, when much that was best in Ciceronianism, and indeed, humanism, was in its full vigour, there were some who refused to bow down before Ciceronian idols. Lorenzo Valla, having done pioneer scholarship on the texts of Virgil and Horace, decided to oppose the current uncritical worship of Cicero's style, and basing his criteria on correct usage, preferred the Latin of Quintilian.[1] Politian in the second half of the fifteenth century, was the most eminent of the Anti-Ciceronians; as a poet he was admired, as a scholar he was revered. He felt that the classics should be read for their beauty, not only their utility; they were good not only because they were old and full of wisdom but because they were works of art. Other writers reserved to themselves the right to choose all that was best from all the classics. Joannes Jovianus Pontanus, who spread his opinions from his academy in Naples, was never a strict Ciceronian, for he claimed the need to be eclectic in imitation. Beroaldus abandoned Cicero altogether, and chose instead to model his style on the prose of Apuleius — a style that has been called meretricious.[2]

By the beginning of the sixteenth century it was hardly possible to be neutral. Bembo became an 'exclusive Ciceronian',[3] and though his style reached a purity that was hardly to be challenged, his matter was too often trivial. Longolius — a Frenchman turned Italian — sought Bembo's advice on a pilgrimage to Rome in 1517, and afterwards applied himself to the exclusive study of Cicero, and did so with such zeal that he became for his own and later ages the model of all that was worst in Ciceronianism: Cicero's 'little crow'.[4] Like Longolius, Paulus Manutius was so much a Ciceronian that he refused to use even the words of Cicero's correspondents, unless he could find them in Cicero himself. Yet Paulus — the son of the famous Aldus — represents, too, the best in humanism, for he was an excellent scholar, and his commentaries and editions of Cicero were unsurpassed. Between the years 1540–6 he produced his complete edition of Cicero, and afterwards several separate works, usually with a commentary. His commentary on the *Ad Familiares* was only printed in 1592, eighteen years after his death: Ciceronian scholarship flourished through the whole course of the Renaissance.[5]

We can do no more than summarize a part of the attack on Ciceronianism. It lasted throughout the sixteenth century, and carried on well into the seventeenth; it was conducted on several levels, from the most scholarly to the lowest polemics. It became entangled with nationalism and religion: sometimes as the North against Italy, sometimes as Protestant against Catholic. Style was the

1. Sabbadini, pp. 25-32.

2. By R. Weiss, in *New Cambridge Modern History* (Cambridge 1957) I, p. 98.

3. Hallam's phrase, I, p. 447.

4. Harvey, p. 55.

5. See Wilson's notes, Harvey, p. 111.

main object of attack, but by no means the only one, for at times the arguments turned more on the paganism of the classics as opposed to the morality of the true Christian.

Erasmus is credited with striking the first blow, in his *Ciceronianus* (1528),[1] when he ridiculed 'the apes of Cicero', and after him a succession of writers joined the attack: Ramus, Sambucus, Sturm, Freigius, and Gabriel Harvey among the many. From the last (published in 1577) we can get an idea of the whole course of the controversy, for Harvey is cautious enough never to advance an opinion without giving it a respectable pedigree. He describes first his acceptance of the current worship of Cicero, then the gradual opening of his eyes to the sins of excess. The *Ciceronianus* of Joannes Sambucus sent him to the *Ciceronianus* of Ramus, and only a little later Sturmius directed him to the *Ciceronianus* of Erasmus. By the time Freigius' *Ciceronianus* was printed in 1575 Harvey was convinced, and he wrote his own *Ciceronianus* for delivery to his Cambridge students the following year. If Harvey's discourse shows the course of literary succession, it also shows quite clearly the nature of the attack on Ciceronianism. Ciceronianism itself was a worthy thing, but the true gospel had been distorted till it had become a heresy, and all the ideals that Cicero stood for cast aside for the mindless imitation of mere rhetorical tricks. As Ramus said:

> '. . . in imitating Cicero the imitator ought to study not only his Latinity but his resources of wisdom and factual knowledge, and most of all his virtues of conduct and character; nor should he heed only Cicero's letters, speeches, lectures, and treatises, but much rather the teachers, the course of studies, the labours of memory, and the vigils of thought by which so great an orator was made. Thus he ought to contemplate the genesis rather than the consummation of the Ciceronian eloquence.'[2]

Only the excesses of Ciceronianism were criticized by Harvey and his predecessors; the ideal was seen to be good: style itself should not be the sole concern of the writer; words should not be valued above content, nor language more than thought. Once, Harvey confessed: 'I preferred the mere style of Marcus Tully to all the postulates of the philosophers and mathematicians; I believed that the bone and sinew of imitation lay in my ability to choose as many brilliant and elegant words as possible, to reduce them into order, and to connect them together in a rhythmical period . . . that was what it meant to be Ciceronian.'[3] Now, with the help of the great masters Erasmus and Ramus and their followers, we come to see the truth. Imitation must be imitation of the spirit and thought of Cicero, not merely the words.

If I seem to have lingered on Harvey—and Drummond, after all, is not known to have owned the *Ciceronianus*—it is because Harvey provides a key to much of Renaissance Latin prose. The Ciceronian controversy is inescapable, and there were few if any prose writers who did not place themselves on one side or the other: Harvey shows us how the quarrel looked to an enlightened Elizabethan. Moreover, he shows us that this was a debate that still

1. See Sabbadini, p. 59 et seq., for Erasmus' attack on Longolius and the Ciceronians, and p. 62 for examples of the words and phrases (found or not found in Cicero's works) crucial to the controversy.

2. Harvey, trans. Wilson, p. 73.

3. Harvey, p. 69.

mattered in the last half of the sixteenth century, and that the words and opinions of men long dead were still valid and exciting. Gianfrancesco Pico della Mirandola's correspondence with Bembo on eclectic imitation (often printed under the title *De imitatione libellus*) remained fresh and new, and the words of Erasmus and Ramus were as up to date as the latest book from Freigius. Harvey's own contemporaries Muret, Turnèbe, and Lambin, all famous in their day as scholars, and Nizolius, author of the *Thesaurus Ciceronianus*, would be as familiar to Harvey's audience as they were to Harvey himself[1]: scholarly controversy was hardly bounded by national frontiers, for Latin was the known and common language. And if Harvey's discourse shows us a common Latin culture, it also shows us how that culture was divided: we need not the sweetmeats of the Italians, says Harvey, but the solid food of the Germans, French and British.[2]

We can do no more than briefly refer here to the larger questions of this division, to what has been termed the 'Counter Renaissance'.[3] This movement against the vanity of learning certainly accompanied the scholarly controversies conducted between the North and Italy, between the followers of Erasmus and the Italian humanists, but it remained distinctly separate. If Luther was content 'to bellow in bad Latin', his fellow German Melanchthon was not, and indeed was devoting nearly all his energies as a teacher to the study of Cicero.[4] As we saw from Harvey, the Ramists were defenders of a pure Latinity, and they were hardly anti-intellectuals. Besides, there is little evidence of the 'Counter Renaissance' among Drummond's Latin books; when anti-intellectualism was expressed, it was usually put in the vernacular.

The natural model for those who rebelled against Ciceronianism was Seneca; using him as an example they could feel justified in culturing a certain artificiality and decorativeness. The Senecan style sought to be neat, to avoid the obvious, to exercise the wit and appeal to the intellect. With it an audience was not likely to be swayed with rhetorical passion, but rather asked to admire the ingenuity of the rhetorical figures. If the dramatists went to Seneca for bombast, the prose writers went for rhetoric; they both found a measure of exaggeration: in the Senecan tradition we can put Bacon, and in English, writers such as Drummond himself.

The authors of Renaissance Latin prose were preoccupied with two subjects: style and classical antiquities. The former, as we saw, meant chiefly Ciceronianism, or for the academic, the mechanics of rhetoric in action. The formal oration was popular both in the university and in the private library, and Drummond owned many, from those of Ramus' scholarly opponents to the undistinguished and dull *Lucubrationes* of the Englishman Haddon.[5] In a handbook of model orations—Famianus Strada's *Prolusiones academicae*—we have an example of the kind of work that appealed greatly to Drummond and his contemporaries—and would be judged unreadable today. Drummond himself called it a 'pleasant and wise' book, and he wrote to one of his noble correspondents telling him that Strada would serve to 'recreate your L. in some solitarye dayes'.[6] Holds-

1. These and the names of other scholars are common to Harvey's discussion and Drummond's library. And Harvey could have mentioned other scholars like Maria Antonio Conti (Majoragius) who conducted several scholarly battles both for and against Cicero's works, e.g. his attack on the *Paradoxes* (1546), which brought him into conflict with Nizolius.

2. Harvey, p. 81.

3. See Hiram Haydn *The Counter-Renaissance* (New York 1950).

4. Melanchthon devoted nine-tenths of his Latin courses in the university to Cicero. Bolgar, p. 348.

5. See Wilson's introduction for a discussion of the lack of merit in Haddon's orations. Harvey, p. 31.

6. *Arch. Scot.*, IV, 95.

1. Fletcher, II, pp. 221-2.

2. Fletcher, II, p. 264 et seq. Strada was a Jesuit, but this seems to have had no effect on the popularity of his work in Protestant countries; it was, after all, 'non-controversial'. A common kind of model presented a delicately balanced ethical problem and offered opposing orations in solution. This was the method of Alexander van den Busche (or Silvayn) in his *The orator*, whose problems were taken both from Livy and his own invention, and included a *Declamation* 'Of a Chirurgion who murthered a man to see the mouing of a quicke heart'. The chirurgion defended himself on these grounds: 'I haue ben the death of one man to saue the liues of an infinit number of others, not onelie by the cures which I hope to performe during my life, but by that which I will leave behind mee in writing after my death. . . .' The answer was 'neuer can anie bad act, bee the beginning of anie good deed . . .'. Neither declamation was brief (pp. 326-32). Mason makes the point that Renaissance rhetoricians felt that oratory should have the same practical political effects that it had in Rome, and were frustrated when it failed. (Mason, op. cit., p. 66). Busche's practical claims for his *Rhetorical declamations* were that 'If thou studie law, they may helpe thy pleadings, or if diuinitie (the reformer of law) they may perfect they [*sic*] persuasions. In reasoning of priuate debates, here maiest though find apt metaphors, in incouraging thy souldiours fit motiues. Fathers here haue good arguments to moue affections in their children, and children vertuous reconcilements to satisfie their displeased fathers: briefly euery priuate man may in this be partaker of a generall profit, and the grossest vnderstanding find occasion of reformation.' From *To the reader*.

3. Tilley, pp. 273–6.

4. The best treatment of Budé's early works is still Louis Delaruelle's *Guillaume Budé, les origines, les idées maîtresses* (Paris 1907). Delaruelle makes a study of the digressions of *De asse*, particularly showing Budé's French nationalism, and his scholarly rivalry with the Italian humanists (Delaruelle, pp. 158-98 et passim). Works like Budé's no doubt encouraged the gentleman scholar to study and collect coins: numismatics was a common pursuit by Drummond's day—Simonds D'Ewes, for instance, was a keen collector, and owned some fifty books in the subject. See Andrew G. G. Watson *The library of Sir Simonds D'Ewes* (London 1966) pp. 13-15.

worth at Cambridge advised his students to read the same book on the grounds that it might bring them 'to some more rais'd and polish'd works'.[1] What were these 'Prolusiones?' According to Fletcher they were model arguments on oratory, history and poetry, in form taken from the usual textbook of the time (which was based in the first place on Rudolph Agricola's work). In effect, this meant that Cicero was the model, and the arguments after the fashion were designed not only to convince the opponent but to flatten him. Strada reasoned with 'a consummate viciousness that gave no quarter and expected none'.[2]

The second main subject of the Latin prose works—besides the dictionaries and grammars which were adjuncts to the good style—were the classical antiquities. The relics of Rome had been one of the early enthusiasms of the Italian humanists, and this enthusiasm was set alight by the discovery of pieces of Roman sculpture, by the excavation of Roman ruins, and perhaps most of all by the scholarly investigation of the everyday habits and products of classical life. The *Academia Romana* run by Pomponius Laetus was dedicated to archaeology, following the directions and inspiration supplied by Flavio Biondo in his *Roma instaurata*—the first precise attempt to make a topographical reconstruction of ancient Rome. During the first decades of the sixteenth century, the digging up of Roman relics became almost a frenzy, with princes, popes and bishops all competing for the sake of scholarship and their private collections. Such masterpieces as the Laocoön and the Apollo of Belvedere were their reward. This archaeology was of course recorded for posterity—and the existence of a work like Francesco Albertini's *Mirabilia Romae* a century later in Drummond's library is evidence of the continued interest in classical wonders throughout the Renaissance. In 1600 Philemon Holland still thought it worthwhile to translate Marlianus' *Topographie of Rome*.

The Renaissance interest in classical antiquities was by no means restricted to archaeology. The Italian humanists first began to explore Roman culture, but too often found themselves without the necessary philological knowledge. At the beginning of the sixteenth century Guillaume Budé, the great French scholar, set out to fill the gap. His *Annotationes* on the Pandects began the humanist revolution in law, but the learning that Budé displayed in this work rippled out over the whole field of humanistic studies; Budé in the generosity of his scholarship threw in quantities of facts on the Latin language and the classical antiquities. He devoted nineteen pages to the Roman and Greek public games, and some sixty to the Roman Senate. He displayed his knowledge of classical authors from Plautus to Boethius, and to encourage his less learned readers he translated the many Greek passages he quoted. His approach to the Pandects was that of the philologist.[3] In his *De asse* he gave his fellow humanists an accurate yardstick whereby they could compare the wealth and luxury of the ancients against that of modern times, but in doing so, he was hardly content to limit himself to the history and value of the ancient coinage, but enlarged his investigation till it covered the whole of classical culture.[4] Budé, unlike many of the Italian humanists—Pomponius Laetus, for instance, was all but pagan in his worship of all things classical—refused to forget his age or his religion, for he infused his classical scholarship with Christian and social comment. In his last and largest work, *De transitu Hellenismi ad Christianismum*, he described the philosophy of Greece as a preparation for Christianity, and he defended the study of Greek from those theologians who felt that any investigation touching Christian and Biblical origins was heresy.[1]

Drummond lacked the *De asse*, and also the *Commentarii linguae Graecae* (a compilation of Greek legal terms, a 'hotch-potch of notes interspersed with short essays'[2]), but he did have Budé's treatises on morality and education, and his short piece, *De philologia*. The latter, in the form of a dialogue between Budé and Francis I, is a defence of classical scholarship.[3] Budé, in the wide range of his interests, showed his contemporaries the way that Roman and Greek culture could be studied, besides providing them with tools for this study. Many subjects now came under review: Drummond had works on inscriptions in marble and monuments, and even the triclinium (the manner of dining among the ancient Romans) was worth a scholarly treatise.

Compared to the wealth of classical history, there seems little enough Renaissance history in Drummond's library. This is a fair indication of the amount written, for compared to poetry and rhetoric the histories in Latin were not abundant. Van Tieghem explains this by arguing that the Renaissance insistence on classical imitation somewhat cramped the historians' imagination: it was difficult to remain faithful to the language of Caesar, Livy or Sallust and still describe modern institutions without excessive circumlocution.[4] Yet the classical models were invaluable, for the Italian humanists had the difficult task of breaking clear from the old kind of historiography, which in its traditional preoccupations was quite apparently less 'scientific' than the methods of the ancients. Up to and even past Drummond's time the chronicles stayed popular: every nation proudly claimed its foundation from the fall of Troy, and traced its nobility back to classical or biblical heroes. The matter of France was the history of France; King Arthur and his knights were accepted as factual. Wars, battles, famines, were sent by God as signs of His displeasure to correct His children, kings were divinely punished and their inheritance dispersed at the express command of heaven. The writers of these histories were preoccupied by a search for God's order, and they continually strove to present their matters so that they could show history's unbroken course from Adam to the present. Besides this kind of genealogical organization, they still used the medieval convention of the four monarchies, which treated universal history as the narrative of the empires of Assyria, Persia, Greece and Rome:

> First in the orient raign'd th' assyrian kings,
> To those the sacred persian prince succeeds,
> Then he by whom the world sore-wounded bleeds,
> Earths crowne to Greece with bloodie blade he brings;
> Then Grece to Rome the Raines of state resignes. . . .[5]

1. Sandys, II, p. 171.

2. Bolgar, p. 377.

3. Sandys, II, p. 171.

4. Van Tieghem, p. 224 et seq. In the following section I have generally followed E. Fueter *Geschichte der neueren Historiographie* (Munich 1936).

5. Kastner, II, p. 229.

127

Thus Drummond praises his friend Sir William Alexander's *Monarchicke tragedies*—*Darius*, *Croesus*, the *Alexandrean tragedy* and *Julius Caesar*. The convention was a popular commonplace, and it received new life when early in the sixteenth century it was linked to Protestant propaganda and used to forecast the early dissolution of the papacy. Philip Melanchthon seems to have been responsible for starting this, when he inserted into Joannes Carion's *Chronica* an interpretation of the prophetical verses in the seventh chapter of the Book of Daniel, and identified the fifth monarchy—which would end with the establishment of God's kingdom on earth—as the heir to Rome. In the later Protestant editions of Carion's work the message was made explicit: the Church of Rome was ripe for destruction[1]; in Catholic translations such as the Spanish the prophesy was of course ignored, and the fifth monarchy named only as that of 'los Cesares y Emperadores Alemanes'.

Working against this tradition, the Italian humanists prepared the way for a new historiography, subjective, analytical and comparative, which later came into full flower with the vernacular histories of Machiavelli and Guicciardini. In the fifteenth century Leonardo Bruni and Flavio Biondo were the pioneers—Bruni in modelling his work on the Romans, making great use of the rhetoric and the Livian oration, Biondo in showing how documents and records should be treated with scholarly care. Coupled with this interest in style and appreciation of the value of source material, the humanists employed a cultured scepticism towards myth and legend. Italians made this approach to history almost exclusively their own. At home Merula wrote his history of the Duke of Milan, Rucellai told the story of the invasion of Italy after the plan of Sallust, and Paolo Giovio practised the art of biography and discussed such pressing topics as the success of the Turks in war; abroad Paolo Emilio became the royal historiographer of France, Marino Siculo and Peter Martyr studied and wrote in Spain, and Polydore Vergil in England. Amongst the theoreticians there was now general agreement that history was a literary art in which rhetoric could be exploited to emphasize the moral lessons which history naturally taught.[2]

Objectivity, however, was hardly a virtue of later histories, and the humanist method was often corrupted with chauvinist bias. With the exploration and conquest of the New World and the growth of mercantile nationalist philosophies, and no less with the increasing religious antagonism of the later sixteenth century, histories frequently became the justification of a nation's right to power and glory. Cortes told of his deeds in Mexico with a soldier's simplicity; Acosta later defended the conquest with elaborate sophistry. Protestants felt obliged to rewrite their nation's history, to justify their succession and to castigate their Catholic predecessors. On the lowest level polemicists such as John Bale turned out propaganda; Polydore Vergil's *Historia Anglia* was rejected in favour of accounts more flattering to Elizabethan taste. (By Drummond's time Vergil had the reputation of that man 'who did our Nation that deplorable injury' by burning all the records he could find so that his own history, as Peacham supposed, 'might passe for currant'.)[3]

1. See Karl Hartfelder *Philipp Melanchthon als praeceptor Germaniae* (Nieuwkoop 1964) pp. 300-2. For an example of Protestant propaganda see Nossenio's *Annali* (cat. 1250). According to Pierre Bayle the French sceptic, Carion's history was for generations of Protestants 'extolled at a high rate'. See *A general dictionary, historical and critical,* trans. from the French (London 1734-41) II, p. 322 et seq. Sir David Lindsay, for example, made use of Carion in completing *The monarche*.

2. See Beatrice Reynolds 'Shifting currents in historical criticism' *JHI*, XIV (1953) 471-92, for a discussion of sixteenth-century historical theory.

3. Peacham, p. 51.

128

33. Architectural shapes. Hygenus Gromaticus, *De limitibus constituendis* (Cat. 498).

DE LIMITIB. CONSTIT.

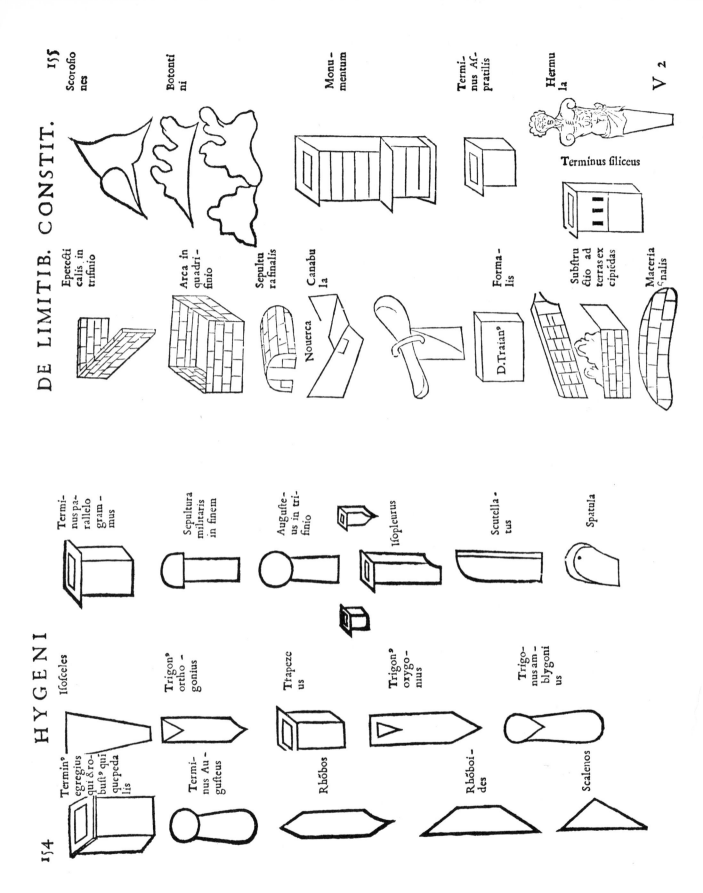

Scorofio nes

Botonti ni

Monu- mentum

Termi- nus Af- pratilis

Hermu la

V 2

Terminus filiceus

Epetecti calis in trifinio

Arca in quadri- finio

Sepultu rafinalis

Canabu la

Nouerca

Forma- lis

D.Traian⁹

Subftru ctio ad terras ex cipiedas

Maceria finalis

HYGENI

Termin⁹ egregius qui & ro- buft⁹ qui quepeda lis

Terminus pa- rallelo- gram- mus

Sepultura militaris in finem

Augufte- us in tri- finio

Ifopleurus

Scutella- tus

Spatula

Ifofceles

Terminus Au- gufteus

Trigon⁹ ortho- gonius

Rhôbos

Trapeze us

Trigon⁹ oxygo- nus

Rhôboi- des

Trigo- nus am- blygoni us

Scalenos

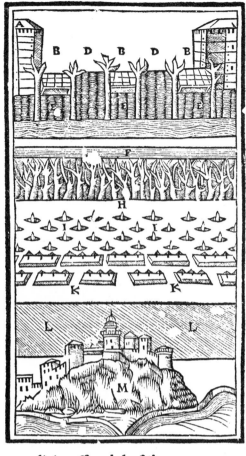

Alexia oppidum Mandubiorũ in summo colle positũ edito loco, quod nisi obsidione expugnari nõ posse uidebatur. Huius collis radices subluebantur duobus fluminibus duabus ex partibus. Cætera ex descriptione Cæsaris & ex hac figura patent.

a Turres coniunctæ aggeri & uallo, quæ inter se distabant pedes LXXX.

b Plutei qui tegebant interuallũ quod erat inter pinnas.

c Pinnæ quæ interstuctæ erant inter pluteos.

d Cerui grandes positi inter pinnas aggeris ad commissuras pluteorum & aggeris ipsius, in quibus erant suspensi plutei, sub quibus tecti milites ascensum hostium & conatum omnẽ repellebant.

e Vallum cum lorica. Lorica enim ex cratibus uel storijs apponebatur uallo & aggeri, ne facilè harpagonibus uel alijs instrumẽtis demoliri posset ab hostibus.

f Fossa pedum quindecim lata & profunda, in qua per campestria loca & demissa, aqua ex flumine deriuabatur.

g Fossa alia item pedum quindecim lata, & profunda, sicca & sine aquis.

h Stipites ex truncis arborũ, aut admodũ firmis ramis abscissis, præacutis cacuminibus, in perpetuam fossam demissi, & ab infimo reuincti, ne reuelli possent, ab ramis eminebant, quò qui intrauerant, se ipsi acutissimis uallis induebant. hos cippos appellabant.

i Stipites teretes fœminis crassitudine, ab summo præacuti & præusti, demissiǿ; in scrobibus obliquè in quincuncem dispositis. hos ex similitudine floris lilium appellabant.

k Taleæ pedem longæ, ferreis hamis infixæ, in terram infossæ mediocribus spatijs intermissis, omnibus locis differebantur. hos hamos stimulos appellabant.

l Fossa pedum XX. lata & profunda directis ad perpendiculum lateribus, à qua reliquæ munitiones distabant pedes quadringentos.

m Alexia oppidum superius descriptum.

Nationalism, however, did stimulate interest in a country's past, and by the end of the sixteenth century there was an increase in antiquarian scholarship. In France De Thou, in England William Camden and John Selden, are eminent examples of this. Their researches were helped by the collections both they and their friends amassed: men like Cotton, Ussher and D'Ewes were greedy and ambitious collectors — D'Ewes, for instance, gathered over 10,000 charters and 1,000 rolls.[1] Peacham counselled his English gentleman: 'bee not a stranger in the History of your owne Country . . . [which is] no whit inferior to any other in the world, for matter of Antiquity, and rarities of every kind worthy remarke and admiration.'[2]

Drummond, being interested in the subject as an historian in his own right, had a considerable collection of histories, not all of which have survived. From the evidence of his *Five James* his inclinations were towards the humanist school; that is, he favoured a polished style and a history which was morally instructive. His work is old-fashioned in conception, and as far as history goes, offers very little advance on Hector Boece and George Buchanan,[3] but accurate reporting was not Drummond's main concern. The *Five James* is propaganda for responsible monarchism, an impassioned warning to his rebellious fellow-countrymen.

The grammars and dictionaries form the last sizeable group among the Latin prose works. These range from the school grammars such as James Carmichael's to the scholarly works of Aldus and the Estiennes. For the sixteenth century the grammars first of Sulpicius and then of Despauterius replaced the Medieval stand-bys like the *Doctrinale* of Alexander of Villedieu (which relied on mnemonic techniques and doggerel verse to make its points). Despauterius' work had the widest acceptance in the schools, perhaps since it was not radically different to the *Doctrinale*, although it did incorporate many of the humanist simplifications, and it did replace a strict concern with the logic of grammar with attention to usage. The most famous Renaissance work on the Latin language, Valla's *Elegantia linguæ Latinæ*, was not in Drummond's collection. Valla's book was an acknowledged masterpiece of scholarship, for it set standards of linguistic accuracy that might be improved in detail but hardly in principle. Thomas Linacre's *De emendata structura Latini sermonis* is an example of the humanist Latin grammar especially written for the schools (it was commissioned by Colet for St Paul's); it was printed with a foreword by Melanchthon recommending its use in the schools of Germany, and judging by its appearance in Drummond's library it was still read a century later. The scholar and the literary gentleman had a wide choice of grammars and dictionaries by the end of the sixteenth century, and there is a good selection of both in Drummond's collection. Robert Estienne's French grammar and his French dictionary were scholarly productions, certainly more learned than the general dictionary of Calepinus, which, however, was common and popular.[4] Drummond also had Greek and Hebrew grammars.

The remaining books in this prose section are somewhat miscellaneous. There are a few works of fiction, and a few works on

1. Watson *The library of Sir Simonds D'Ewes* (London 1966).

2. Peacham, p. 51. For a discussion of the accepted Elizabethan and Jacobean reasons for studying history see F. Smith Fussner *The historical revolution* (London 1962) pp. 26-59, and the same work, pp. 96-116, for a description of antiquarian scholarship and collecting.

3. See David Masson *Drummond of Hawthornden* pp. 648-71 for a disheartened account and criticism of the *Five James*. In Edward Hall's Preface to the Reader we are told that Drummond 'hath sufficiently made it appear, how conversant he was with the Writings of Venerable Antiquity, and how generously he hath emulated them by a happy imitation; for the purity of his Language is much above that Dialect he writ in; his Descriptions lively and full, his Narrations clear and pertinent, his Orations Eloquent, and fit for the persons that speak (for that since Livys time was never accounted Crime in an Historian) and his Reflections solid and mature. . .'.

4. Denys Hay, in *New Cambridge Modern History*, II, p. 373.

34. The defences of Alexia. Caesar, *Commentarii* (Cat.436).

1. As the title of the English translation has it.

politics. Thomas More's *Utopia* is the chief of these. Drummond had Adam Blackwood's attack on George Buchanan's *De jure regni* (which was written to justify the deposition of Mary Queen of Scots). He had also Furio Ceriol's 'treatise declaring howe many counsells and what maner of counselers a prince ought to have[1];' but few other works on political theory in Latin, apart from an edition of Aristotle's *Politica*. Perhaps again this is a part of his library that is now lost, for being particularly preoccupied with political theory during the last years of his life, when he busied himself with writing a series of tracts and pamphlets designed to avert the disasters threatening his king and country, he may well have surrounded himself with a library of political works. Of fiction there is little, nor was much Latin fiction written. He had John Barclay's *Argenis* in English translation: it told of heroic adventures of war and love, and satirized the strife between the opposing nations of England and France. Achilles Tatius' ironic, racy and frequently broad romance, *Leucippe and Clitophon*, was there in a Latin translation; it was twice translated and printed in English in Drummond's day. Even more popular was Apuleius' *Golden ass*, for that went through five English editions (in Adlington's translation) in seventy years.[2]

2. See the *STC*.

Finally, what conclusions can we draw from Drummond's selection of prose works? If we say that style was a prime concern of the Renaissance, we will be right, but if we then say that a man like Drummond would choose his books for the sake of style we may be wrong. The classics were commended to him wholesale, and they were available in both expensive and cheap editions. A buyer of books could hardly swim against the tide, for apart from a few old favourites like *Reynard the fox* there was very little prose printed that was not written by humanists (outside the specialist subjects like law, theology and philosophy). Drummond's prose section is a very fair sample of humanist interests: Cicero, the classical historians, the Italian letter writers, Erasmus and his followers.

The classics are here supreme, and imitation of the classical form and spirit an accepted and cherished convention; for style, as Peacham took pains to show, was a reflection of a man's character, and style could only be learned from the greatest of the ancients.

Literature in the Vernaculars

Unlike many collectors, Drummond read his books. He copied out passages from some in his manuscripts, and on others he scribbled marginalia; in his Latin and Greek works this is the evidence we have that he did not buy for show. For his Italian, French, Spanish and English books we are luckier, for here we can trace the development of his taste quite closely. He left reading lists for the years he was buying most of these books, and these are most informative: we can see exactly when he took an interest in poetry, what books he first read in French, and just when he began to learn Italian. If we then look at his own poetry, we can see what use he made of his reading. Few literary men of his time have left behind more detailed evidence of their intellectual development, and few literary men can have had such a thorough European education.

If Drummond had one favourite among his books it was Sidney's *Arcadia*. He read it in 1606, the year after he graduated, and again in 1609. He put it first on his list of English books in 1611, and he copied out long extracts from it in his manuscripts. He knew it thoroughly, and it led him on to read Sidney's sources and imitators: by the time he abandoned literature there can have been few pastoral romances then in print he had not bought. His library was full of Arcadias, shepherds, and courtly lovers.

He seems to have travelled over the same course as Sidney himself. Sidney drew from Virgil's *Eclogues*, from Heliodorus, from *Amadis de Gaule*, from Malory, from Montemayor's *Diana* and Gil Polo's continuation of it, the *Diana enamorado*. With the exception of Malory, all these are in Drummond's library, or among the books he read. At the age of seventeen he nearly damaged his eyesight reading the Greek romance of Heliodorus. By twenty-one he had started upon the knightly romances in English translation: the *Mirror of knighthood* and the *Amadis de Gaule*. Virgil's *Eclogues* he might have had at the university; certainly he bought the complete Virgil in Paris in 1607. Montemayor and Gil Polo he read in English and again in French, and the Spanish original was also in his library.

The knightly romances are so unfamiliar to us now they may need some introduction — if we know them at all it may only be as the books that infatuated Don Quixote. The *Amadis* was the first and the greatest of the books of chivalry printed in Spain, an idealistic

35. Esplandian asleep aboard 'la grand' Serpente.' *Amadis de Gaule,* the fifth book (Cat. 961).

development of the medieval romance. It was, in a way, a purification of Arthurian and French cycles, and its hero, Amadis, a blend of Launcelot and Tristan. The *Amadis* was more fantastic, more sophisticated and more exotic than its sources, and it developed the conventions of the medieval romance to a high degree. There are false knights and fickle knights, secret births, blue blood recognized and kingdoms reclaimed, giants, monsters, wizards all to be overcome, fair maidens to be rescued, single combats in which the true knight always wins, and the action in a dizzy way covers the lands near and far from Scotland to Greece and the wilds of Turkey (Gaule is Wales). The *Amadis* was immensely popular, and it grew to satisfy demand. The original four books became in Spanish twelve, in French fourteen, and in Italian eighteen. The French translators added their own parts, and so did the Italians, and the French even borrowed back from the Italian translations.[1] The *Amadis* was not so popular in England: only the first four books were translated, and these by hacks, nor were they reprinted at the time.

Although the *Amadis* had not the vogue in England it had in France and Italy, there were other romances to take its place. Of these the *Mirror of knighthood* in a multiplicity of parts, books and continuations, was the most popular (the *Palmerin of England* was only printed once — Munday's bad translation cannot have helped it). *The Mirror of knighthood* was a faithful imitation of the *Amadis*, with the same extraordinary adventures, the same succession of combats, the same lucky coincidences. It has the same true and false knights — Rosicler and the Knight of the Sun — whose high birth would, at the right time, be revealed by the lucky discovery of appropriate birthmarks (a rose and a sun).

Enough of the Spanish romances; it is not for us to question their fame, but merely to record it. For Sidney and most literary men of the time the *Amadis* and its like were common light reading. At times editors and translators professed to see merit and profit in the romances, but as Margaret Tyler admitted (in her preface to the first English translation) they 'have bene rather devised to beguile time, then to breede matter of sad learning'.[2]

The Elizabethans did, however, prefer their reading to be ethical, and were not above grafting a didactic moral on to works of antiquity. Some of this was window dressing aimed to help the books sell to the middle-class and Puritan market,[3] and it is possible that few of the claims of the printers were swallowed whole by the more sophisticated readers, especially ones who like Drummond had the ability to read the work in its original language. The translator of *The Aethiopian History* of Heliodorus claimed it was a corrective to the 'wanton allurements to leudnesse' that were so often sold by the printers (and among these he included the *Amadis*). *The Aethiopian history* 'punisheth the faultes of evill doers, and rewardeth the well livers. What a king is Hidaspes! What a pattern of a good prince! What a happy success had he! Contrariewise, what a leaude woman was Arsace! What a paterne of evil behaviour! What an evil end had shee. . . .'[4]

One can see the appeal the Greek romances must have had to their

1. The history of the continuations and translation of the *Amadis* is most complicated. Besides adding six parts to a new Book 13 (or Books 13-18, as they were often called) the Italians wrote supplements that were inserted between the original Spanish books. See Henry Thomas *Spanish and Portuguese romances of chivalry* (Cambridge 1920) pp. 189 and 199-203.

2. Quoted by H.S. Bennett *English books and readers, 1558-1603* (Cambridge 1965) p. 253.

3. See Louis B. Wright *Middle class culture in Elizabethan England* (Chapel Hill 1935) for a discussion of middle-class tastes. Wright gives detailed information on popular and ephemeral literature (not covered here but certainly in evidence in Drummond's Library).

4. Quoted by Bennett, p. 218. Bennett wrongly implies that *The Aethiopian history* is actually a history; it is a romance.

Elizabethan and Jacobean readers. Certainly, virtue was always rewarded and vice always punished (a convention that could at least be represented in Christian moral terms); more important, the qualities of melodrama and rhetoric were highly attractive to an age loving both. Heliodorus pushes us *in medias res* with a startling scene: a band of robbers approaching the seashore from the mountains discover a ship full of treasure, and beside it on the beach, among the wreck of a banquet, the mutilated bodies of dead and dying men. On a nearby rock, like a vision of a goddess, is the heroine; at her feet, 'a young man disfigured by wounds', apparently dying, the hero.[1] The two, having preserved their lives, their love and their chastity throughout a series of complicated misfortunes, are not united until the last page of the book. Melodrama breeds rhetoric. Each time hero or heroine is a victim of fate, each time they are separated from each other, their happy union again frustrated, they can only cry, promise and bemoan. They are victims; they can be valiant, pure and beautiful, they can fight well enough when they have to, but they are always at the mercy of circumstance. In Achilles Tatius' *Leucippe and Clitophon*, Leucippe the heroine against all belief survives her tribulations as fresh and pure as the day she set out: her lover sees her disembowelled (and then marvellously restored), beheaded (but only apparently); her head is shaved, she is beaten, made a slave, forced to hoe the fields, but finally, triumphantly, she is able to go in to the cave of Pan and emerge—the true and heavenly test of a virgin. Virtue is long-suffering.

Reading Sidney's *Arcadia* one can see what Sidney took from these sources—the knightly stories like *Amadis* and the Greek romances—and how much he added to them. But Sidney himself did not invent pastoral romance; his was one of the greatest, but it was not the first: Jacopo Sannazzaro is given the credit for that. Sannazzaro's *Arcadia* was blended from the classical pastoral and the medieval romance: to Virgil's shepherd's songs he added action. He set out to write the classical eclogue in the vulgar tongue, but his plot was not at all classical. Half in verse and half in prose, he told of unhappy love, of exile, of the hero's wandering in search of his lover, of the heroine's death and transfiguration, and of the hero's quiet and philosophical acceptance of her fate and his own sad lot. This owed much to Tristan or Launcelot or to Petrarch's own history of love. The setting was exotic (and like the knightly romances, anything could happen); in Arcadia, where man was at peace with nature, shepherds and nymphs taught the lessons of love. Montemayor, in *Los siete libros de la Diana*, changed the form of the pastoral romance. He wrote it in prose, with occasional songs now properly integrated into the story and sung or recited by the characters themselves. He took Sannazzaro's plot of the separate lovers (although it is his heroine, Felismena, who is wandering and searching, not the hero) and added complications in the form of sub-plots. Wherever she goes, Felismena sees variations of her own situation, and the shepherds she meets teach her each side of love as they recite their own histories.

In 1606, the year in which he first read Sidney's *Arcadia*,

1. The phrase is quoted from Moses Hadas' translation.

36. Drummond's marginalia on a French/Latin dictionary written for the use of children. Judging by the hand, Drummond bought and used this book about the year 1607, when he was first in France. Robert Estienne, *Les mots francois* (Cat. 1037).

133

1. From the titles they sound like romances, though I have not been able to trace or read them.

2. I follow here John Buxton's chapter on the *Arcadia* in *Elizabethan taste* (London 1963) pp. 246-68.

3. In Drummond's *Works* (1711) pp. 159-62.

4. Ibid.

5. See Buxton, p. 261, who quotes the Elizabethan lawyer John Hoskyns.

Drummond also read Achilles Tatius in Latin, Aeneas Silvius' history of two lovers *Eurialus and Lucretia* (itself an imitation of the classical romance) in English translation, and two other romances in English, *Constant Calipolis* and *Paurino and Lusina*.[1] He came to the *Arcadia* with his head full of the stuff of romances, classical, pastoral, Italian, Spanish. What an advantage he had over us today! We read the *Arcadia* knowing little or nothing of its sources; we are unused to its rhetoric, and ignorant of its decorum. Instead of praising artificiality, we deplore it, and look for naturalness.[2]

To the Elizabethans and the Jacobeans the *Arcadia* stood apart. It was a noble work, written in noble language, the first proof that English was a tongue to compare with other civilized tongues. Sir William Alexander, in his *Anacrisis, or a censure of some poets ancient and modern* (which he sent to Drummond), considered it

'the most excellent Work that, in my Judgement, hath been written in any Language that I understand, affording many exquisite Types of Perfection for both the Sexes; leaving the Gifts of Nature, whose Value doth depend upon the Beholders, wanting no Virtue whereof a Humane Mind could be capable. As for Men, Magnanimity, Carriage, Courtesy, Valour, Judgement, Discretion; and in Women, Modesty, Shamefastness, Constancy, Continency, still accompanied with a tender Sense of Honour. And his chief Persons being Eminent for some singular Virtue, and yet all Virtues being united in every one of them, Men equally excelling both for Martial Exercise and for Cou[r]tly Recreations, showing the Author (as he was indeed) alike well versed both in Learning and Arms: It was a great loss to Posterity, that his untimely Death did prevent the Accomplishing of that excellent Work'.[3]

In the same passage Alexander goes on to mention that he himself was inspired to add to the *Arcadia* (and to fill the gap in Book Three where the 'new' *Arcadia* breaks off, before the story is patched with the old *Arcadia*) out of his love to the author's memory, although he had no hope of reaching Sidney's standard: 'it were enough to be excellent by being Second to Sidney, since who ever could be that, behoved to be before others.'[4]

The *Arcadia* deserved such praise not only for its perfections, but because it was more ambitious. We may notice, as the Elizabethans themselves noticed, that Sidney had gone to Heliodorus, Sannazzaro and Montemayor,[5] but while we will only find that he had married the romance to the pastoral, his contemporaries would have stated it in much grander terms. For Sidney *The Aethiopian history* was an heroical poem; for his contemporaries the *Arcadia* was an heroical poem. Sannazzaro in his *Arcadia*, Montemayor in his *Diana*, and Urfé in his *Astrée* could not, according to Alexander, rise to the level set by Sidney, who 'as in an Epick Poem did express such things, as both in War and in Peace were fit to be practised by Princes'. The other authors might have been capable of reaching the same heights, but they had chosen lower ground; they had clung too fondly to the pastoral and so they were 'bound by the Decorum of that which they profess'd, to keep so low a Course. . . .'[1]

In the first version of the *Arcadia* (the unpublished manuscript) Sidney divided his pastoral into five acts, each followed by eclogues, but in the 'new' *Arcadia* the addition of numerous episodes and complications destroyed this formal structure. His blend of different sources is far from haphazard, and adds great complexity to the traditional simplicity of the form. He has two heroes (like the *Amadis*) in love with two heroines, who are kept guarded in the deserts of *Arcadia*, for their father the Duke Basilio lives in fear of their marriage. Basilio had visited the Delphic oracle, and seeks to avoid the fulfilment of its cryptic prophecy. The heroes fall in love with the young princesses, but to win them they are forced to disguise themselves: Pyrocles as a young (and beautiful) Amazon, Musidorus as a shepherd. This disguise adds more complications, for the Duke begins to lust for Pyrocles (as a woman), and his wife, seeing through the disguise, lusts for him as a man. All the characters compromise themselves and their virtue through the false use of passion; all are brought to reason at the end. The shepherds provide a comic sub-plot, the entertainment of the eclogues, and the steadying example of true and proper love.

This is the *Arcadia* in the briefest summary, yet this hardly begins to describe it. Indeed, critics are still arguing as to what the *Arcadia* is really about. For many readers it has always been just a pleasant tale pleasantly told and certainly Sidney's confidential manner, his wit and good humour are the best kind of evidence for this argument. At the same time it must be, as Fulke Greville said, a political parable. The Duke Basilio is wrong to retreat from his court to the desert, and the riots and revolt which follow are the natural result. Again, with Greville, it has to be read as a lesson in ethics, a tale which shows the disasters which come when passions are put before reason. It was foolish of Basilio to want to know the future (that always tempts fate), and knowing it, it was more foolish of him to try to avoid it. His passion for the youth Pyrocles was unnatural in nature and adulterous in fact; that of his wife equal in blame. The two heroes shed reason with their clothes; one abducts and tries to rape his princess, the other seduces his with her own consent. All stand in need of correction.[2]

What lies between us and the *Arcadia* now is the style (that is, as well as our ignorance of the genre). The speeches are long-winded, the rhetoric inflated, and the eclogues dull. We notice some of the verbal tricks, but they seem ingenious rather than admirable. To an Elizabethan it was these qualities that were much appreciated. For generations trained in rhetoric Sidney put the English language through textbook Latin hoops, and his audience applauded, not deplored. Much of it was, of course, superficial; but the point is that it was not a barrier to the Elizabethan reader, but an entertainment.[3]

What the *Arcadia* was to English prose, *The faerie queene* was to English poetry. With *The Shepheardes calendar* Spenser staked his claim to be the new poet who would raise English to Italian and French heights; his pastoral would now be followed by epic, for like Virgil he intended to give his nation the supreme gift. *The faerie*

1. *Works* (1711) p. 161.

2. Summaries and discussion of modern critical opinions can be found in Walter R. Davis and Richard A. Lanham *Sidney's Arcadia* (New Haven 1965).

3. Drummond (a man who was attracted to the superficialities of prose and poetry) was quite typically enchanted by the rhetorical and poetical tricks and copied numbers of them out in his note-books. A device such as *vers rapportés* he thought quite worth imitating: Sidney's 'Vertue Bewty and Speeche, did stryke, wounde, Charme, / My Hart, Eyes, Eares with wonder, Love, Delight . . .' is written down in the Hawthornden manuscripts, and Drummond's (poor) attempt at the same form comes in Sonnet iv of his *Urania*. In an age unsympathetic to such artifice it is easy to condemn the ornaments and rhetoric of the *Arcadia* as blemishes, without understanding that they were jewels in the eyes of Sidney's contemporaries. Besides, it is worth remembering that courtly and even everyday speech then was much more formal than anything we are used to. See Davis and Lanham, p. 237.

queene was to be an English *Aeneid*, with, as its immediate contemporary model, the *Orlando furioso* of Ariosto. And with national pride Spenser claimed an English model; Chaucer (although he gave him little more than lip-service).

Spenser's pretensions were accepted to the full by his contemporaries, although they regretted he did not live to fulfil his ambitions, and that he completed only a half of his plan. Drummond read *The faerie queene* in 1610, and, since by that year he had already read many of Spenser's rivals, he was well qualified to set Spenser into a European framework. He had been through the *Orlando furioso* in both English and French the previous year, as well as Tasso's *Gerusalemme liberata* in English, and Ronsard's *Franciade* in French. He had read Du Bartas, too, and so he was well primed in the epic. The only major omission from among Spenser's direct sources is Trissino: Drummond does not seem ever to have read or owned *L'Italia liberata dai Goti.*[1]

We have already noticed that Sidney's *Arcadia* was considered to be an epic, even an heroical *poem*, so it hardly needs saying that the conception of the epic was then very different from our modern ideas. The Italian poets like Boiardo, Ariosto, Trissino and Tasso had blended fantasy, romance, chivalry, allegory and history into their poems — a mixture that is familiar enough to us from *The faerie queene* — and these for their age were epics. Boiardo in his *Orlando innamorato* went to the matter of France — Charlemagne, his knights (notably Roland) and the struggle between Christian and infidel, but to please his audience of courtiers his emphasis was on love: the love of Roland for Angelica, daughter of the king of Cathay. He included anything that would amuse and delight: giants, dragons, marvellous gardens, flights through the forest, fairies, magicians — all the props of the romance. Boiardo celebrated chivalry, but with magic he was only half serious; he treated his enchantresses and their spells with a quiet humour.

Ariosto took over the matter of Orlando where Bioardo stopped off, but in his *Orlando furioso* chivalry is sacred no more. We see the same collection of characters from the romances as ever before — giants, dwarfs and hermits, magicians and monsters — and added to them creatures from myth and legend like the Hippogriff, allegorical figures such as Discord and Jealousy, Old Testament prophets like Enoch and Elijah. Ariosto is full of fantasy, and as full of wit, an artist after the Renaissance taste, smooth, fluent and varied, one who could handle with ease six interwoven plots at once, and change his verse to suit the mood of each. He was equally accomplished at describing the combat of knights or the wooing of maidens, or entertaining with some such fantasy as Astolfo's mission to the moon in search of Roland's wits. The *Orlando furioso* was immensely popular; it went through over two hundred editions in Italy before 1600, it was translated into French by Gabriel Chappuis, and into English by Sir John Harington.

With Torquato Tasso's *Jerusalem delivered* the long narrative poem takes yet another turn: it becomes historical and self-consciously moral. Tasso was very much aware of late-Renaissance

1. But then Trissino was not popular, especially outside Italy. See Jefferson B. Fletcher *Literature of the Italian Renaissance* (New York 1934), p. 245.

literary theory, and he wrote his epic with, as it were, the classics at his elbow. His theme is the liberation of Jerusalem in the first crusade, but his historical figures like Godfrey of Bouillon are hardly as important as his fictional ones. His chief hero is still Rinaldo, who is prevented from performing as a true knight by the magic skills of the enchantress Armida. *Jerusalem delivered* was conceived as a Christian epic: Christians triumph over infidels, Armida is converted to the true religion and gives herself in Christian marriage, and the reader is forced as Tasso intended to admire the miracles brought about by a Christian God. At the same time the classical proprieties are observed, and even details of the classical epics are faithfully imitated (thus, the king of Jerusalem, like Homer's Priam, is given fifty sons.)

There is no difficulty in seeing why Ariosto and Tasso were popular in their day, and modern critics are almost as ready to praise the beauties of their verse as were their contemporaries. But some poets whose reputations were once high are now quite disregarded, and indeed the problem is often to explain how they could ever have been read at all. Such a poet was Du Bartas. Drummond's copy of the *Semaines* in the original French has gone astray (and he must have owned one), but his Latin and Italian editions are in the catalogue. We know, too, that he read and liked Sylvester's English translation of *Judith*,[1] and it is probable that he had Sylvester's complete *Divine weekes*. The number of English translations and editions of Du Bartas is proof enough of his English popularity; Alexander found him full of perfections,[2] and Drummond himself placed him in the company of those poets that had captured the essence of poetry, the true immortals—Homer, Virgil, Ovid, Petrarch, Ronsard, Boscan and Garcilaso.[3]

Du Bartas was a Protestant poet, and his reputation was at its height in the Protestant countries. His chief work — the *Semaines* — is a Biblical epic laced with lore and commentary, didactic and frequently familiar. Added to the history of the creation is a discussion of the destiny of man, and a great deal of fabulous, scientific and even commercial information. Catholic readers were undoubtedly put off by Du Bartas' Protestant bias, but it suited most English readers very well. Sylvester in his translations made Du Bartas homely, familiar and racy, and did not hesitate to add local details when it took his fancy. Du Bartas' long poem *Judith* was also translated by Sylvester, and Drummond admired the translation. 'His Pains are much to be praised', he said, 'and happy Translations, in sundry parts equalling the Original'. Whereas he found Sylvester's version of *Judith* 'excellent', he thought Hudson's poor.[4]

Du Bartas was admired because his verse was elevated and improving, discursive and didactic — qualities all approved of by the taste of the time. The Elizabethans liked their poets to instruct as well as delight them, and were quite ready to give the rank of epic to works that were heroic in tone though not in plot. Theology, history and even geography were all suitable subjects for the ambitious poet. The models were as usual classical: Lucretius had written his philosophy in verse, Lucan his *Civil wars*, and Homer, too, was ranked

1. 'Character of several authors', in *Works* (1711) p. 227.

2. *Works* (1711) p. 160.

3. Letter to Arthur Johnston *Works* (1711) p. 143.

4. *Works* (1711) p. 227.

an historian. Contemporary Latinists followed on: Danaeus, and Honterus, for instance, had both written long expository poetical geographies.

Drummond had a number of these 'epics' in his library. They were popular in their day; now they are forgotten. Francis Meres' opinion of William Warner is well known but still worth quoting, if only to show how tastes have changed:

> '*Warner* in his absolute *Albion's Englande*, hath most admirably penned the historie of his own country from *Noah* to his time, that is, to the raigne of *Queene Elizabeth*: I have heard him termd of the best wits of both our Vniuersities, our English *Homer*. . . .'[1]

Meres has been shown to be a gossip and a somewhat derivative critic, but even if we take his judgement with reservations we must accept that Warner was admired and read.[2] Certainly his *Albion's England* sold well, and he thought it necessary to add to it and carry it up to date. It is a celebration in fourteener verse of the history of England from Biblical times that goes on and on and on. To modern taste it is almost completely unacceptable.

Daniel in his *Civil wars* (following Homer and Lucan, as he himself claimed)[3] and Drayton in his *Barons' wars* both conceived their poems as major works to celebrate in the accepted grand manner the glories of their country's history and its now assured peace. As Jonson told Drummond, 'Daniel wrott ciuill warres and yett hath not a batle in all his Book'—a half-truth unfortunately typical, motivated by spleen and anyway irrelevant, for Daniel's real purpose was to hymn the Elizabethan peace and to contrast it with the confusion of the Yorkist-Lancastrian struggle. It has been shown that Daniel was 'a sincere classiciser', and that had he completed his *Civil wars* they might well have fulfilled his highest hopes. He was better suited for the task than Drayton, who was much more at home with the descriptive lyric, and who in the *Barons' wars* had trouble rising to heroic heights.

Yet Drayton felt he had to write epic, and after the *Barons' wars* he turned to a still more ambitious undertaking, his *Poly-Olbion*. This is part history, part geography, a generous relation of the story of England, done county by county, through its heroes, myths, towns and woods. It came out described as a 'chorographicall description of Great Britain', printed in a handsome folio, dedicated to the Prince of Wales (the first part was printed in 1612 just before his death), with elaborate and ornate maps of the regions described. Drummond wrote that he liked the *Poly-Olbion*, and he tried to arrange for the publication of the second part by Andrew Hart the Edinburgh printer, but though he did not say so in so many words, it is clear he thought it a failure as an epic. He praised the songs, but seems to have found the history tedious. And here, we might add, his opinions agree with modern critics.

Looking again at Drummond's reading lists, one cannot but notice the translations. The abundance of translations in the late sixteenth and early seventeenth centuries meant that literature passed down the line with ease, and nations such as the English could share

1. Francis Meres *Poetrie*, edited by Don Cameron Allen, University of Illinois Studies in Language and Literature (Urbana 1933) pp. 75-6. Allen's introduction shows the extent of Meres' debt to other critics, from Textor to Sidney.

2. Jonson's remark that Warner 'since the Kings comming to England [had] marrd all his Albions England' refers to Warner's continuation of the poem, bringing it up to date. Jonson tacitly approves of *Albion's England* in its original state. See Herford and Simpson, I, p. 154.

3. See E.M.W. Tillyard, *The English epic and its background* (London 1954) p. 323.

in the glories of Italy. Some authors, such as Machiavelli, were for religious or political reasons not translated immediately, if at all, although, as with Machiavelli, their reputation filtered into the country, perhaps in a distorted form. Others, such as Castiglione, were translated and reprinted again and again. For a gentleman who read French the choice was of course much wider. Before Drummond ever began to learn Italian he had read *The courtier* in English, as well as Guazzo's *Civil conversation*, Ariosto's *Orlando furioso* and Tasso's *Gerusalemme liberata*. When he started to learn French in 1607 while he was at Paris and Bourges there were at once French translations in his reading list: Montemayor's *Diana* (from the Spanish), Tasso's *Aminta*, Sannazzaro's *Arcadia* and the *Circe* of Gelli. Although there are one or two works on grammar and several dictionaries in Drummond's catalogue (he had, for instance, Florio's *Worlde of words*), the number of books in more than one language is evidence of his method of learning a foreign tongue: he must have taught himself by comparing the Italian original with its English or French translation. Thus in 1610 — the year in which he seems to have begun his Italian studies seriously — he read Sannazzaro in both Italian and French, and did the same with the first part of Petrarch's *Rime*, Guarini's *Pastor Fido*, Tasso's *Aminta*, and Bembo's *Gli Asolani*. The *Gerusalemme liberata* he read in Italian and English.

The reading lists for the last four years (1611–14) show Drummond's taste at its most catholic: he exploited his facility with languages, jumping from theology to amorous verse, from history to pastoral, from classical Latin to English controversy. He worked his way in Italian through most of Tasso, Bembo and Luigi Groto, went back to Dante and Boccaccio,[1] read some literary criticism (De Nores) and some theology. In French he tackled everything from satire (*Pater Noster des Jesuites*) to De Mornay on the Christian religion,[2] with amorous verse for leavening. In English he read all of Alexander, most of Drayton, some of Donne, Daniel, Jonson, Sir John Davies, Bacon's *Essays*, Lodge's *Phillis* and the *Zepheria*. His inclination here was clearly to poetry, particularly the amorous lyric, yet in 1611 he set himself to read the prophetical books of the Old Testament. By 1614 he had added Spanish to his languages, and in this list Boscan, Garcilaso and Granada all appear. Finally, it is interesting to notice that Drummond never stopped reading Latin: in 1613, for instance, he read Petrarch's *De contemptu mundi* and in 1614 Cicero's *Tusculan disputations*.

Drummond's literary appetite listed in this way seems formidable, but I feel certain he read for his own enjoyment. ('For fun' would have been to him a trivial and meaningless phrase; one has to credit him with looking for instruction in all he read, although that by no means precludes enjoyment.) It we are to look for his lightest reading it must be in drama.

Here it may be worth repeating a few critical commonplaces. The Elizabethans held the stage in low repute, and regarded most of its writers as hacks. They admired of course classical drama: Drummond owned Aristophanes, Seneca, Plautus and Terence (and in 1607 noted reading a French translation of Seneca). Only a few gentlefolk

1. Dante was not much more than a name to most English and Scots.

2. Sidney began a translation of this work. De Mornay's religious works were popular in the Protestant countries.

1. So, too, Marlow's reputation was based on *Hero and Leander*, rather than his plays. *Hero and Leander* went through ten editions before 1640. See *STC*.

wrote plays, and when they did they went to the best model, Seneca: Greville with *Mustapha*, Alexander with his *Monarchicke tragedies*, or the Countess of Pembroke in her translations of Garnier. Our present preoccupation with English drama the Elizabethans would have thought unnatural: for us, Shakespeare lives as a playwright, for his contemporaries, he was the sweet-tongued poet, the author of *The rape of Lucrece* and *Venus and Adonis*.[1]

This is not to say that the plays were never read. They were printed, and they seem to have sold well, and if a man like Drummond is in any way an example of the common reader, they were enjoyed. He read *Romeo and Juliet*, *Love's labour's lost*, and *A midsummer night's dream* as early as 1606 (as well as three other comedies and a tragedy), which is proof enough of Shakespeare's popularity, and his copies of the first two plays, with his overlining still visible, show he was interested in the language and the wit. *Hamlet*, it is known, was much admired in Shakespeare's own lifetime: Drummond's copy is lost, although we know he read the play (he borrowed from it for his *A midnight's trance*). Drummond had a normal attitude to plays: like his contemporaries he regarded them as not quite respectable, but he read them in quantity. He preferred comedies, and he seems to have gone through his favourites culling witticisms and purple passages.

Looking back over Drummond's whole collection of vernacular literature, one can see few major omissions. In addition to the works mentioned above, he had the Italian courtesy books — Castiglione's *Courtier*, Della Casa's *Galateo* and Guazzo's *Civil conversation* — and on these he must have relied for his knowledge of manners and correct behaviour. He had some plays of Aretino, Ariosto and Luigi Groto, and even the dialogues of the wandering players. He had the famous *Celestina* in Spanish and several editions of Huarte's educational and psychological discussion on 'men's wits'. He had Machiavelli and Machiavelli's controversialist, Gentillet. He read, and owned (and imitated) nearly all the members of the Pléiade, and possessed important French histories and chronicles, notably Pasquier and De Serres, and best sellers like Blaise de Montluc's *Commentaires* ('the soldier's Bible') or François de la Noue's *Discours*. In English he could add to his collection of first rank poets numerous lesser figures: Churchyard, Derrick, Breton, Fraunce, Quarles — the list is a long one. There are idiosyncrasies in Drummond's choice — the love lyric is especially favoured, for example — but on the whole the collection is as remarkable for its balance as for its size.

PART III
Catalogue of the Library

The Arrangement of the Catalogue

The catalogue is an attempt to reconstruct Drummond's library as it was before he donated a large part of it to Edinburgh University in 1626. He bought very few books after this date; his library, therefore, was at its best in the early 1620s.

The catalogue is made up from two sources: books that still exist and books that have now disappeared. Most of the books that have survived are in Edinburgh University Library (and the majority of these have remained there since the donation of 1626), but a considerable number have found their way into other libraries, both in Britain and in the United States. The books that are lost are known about from a variety of sources, the largest and most important being a catalogue of his library made by Drummond in 1611. This is preserved among the Hawthornden MSS, and includes 546 books, of which about a third has survived. A second source is the catalogue of this first donation, the *Auctarium bibliothecae Edinburgenae . . .*, printed in 1627. Since that year over eighty of Drummond's books from this donation of 1626 have been lost or stolen from Edinburgh University Library; the *Auctarium* is a reliable enough proof of the one-time existence of this group. Some of the books that Drummond gave in later years have also been lost, and a few of these have been identified from the Library's catalogues. The fourth source is a number of small lists in Drummond's hand, preserved in the Hawthornden MSS, some of which I first suspected might have been lists of books he once wanted to buy; but so many of the titles have turned up in the flesh, so to speak, that I am quite confident that the books were in his library. None of these lists would appear to be any later than 1626.

In his catalogue of 1611 Drummond arranged his books by language and subject. I have followed his system as closely as possible, but for the sake of easy reference I have put authors in alphabetical order. With books that exist I have used the normal cataloguing practices, with these modifications. I have taken authors' names from the British Museum short-title catalogues, but where seventeenth-century (and modern) common usage demands, I have kept that usage. It seemed sensible to call Ramus 'Ramus', rather than conceal him under the name of 'La Ramée'. I have quoted titles at some length, because this is one way of keeping the 'flavour' of the books — besides, much useful information is given in these long-winded titles; the bias or religion of the author, the name of the pamphlet he is replying to, the audience he is hoping to reach. Even the purely honorific salutations tell us something about the age.

Whenever I had access to the book itself, I have taken my title from it directly, and not used a printed catalogue. I have not meddled with spelling or punctuation, but reproduced titles with as little modification as possible, short of breaking into bibliographer's quasi-facsimile. It is impossible to be consistent about capitalization (short of quasi-facsimile), for printers — especially English printers — can vary their practice from page to page. I have therefore followed the usage adopted by the editors of the *Short-title catalogue*, where all save proper names and places are reduced to lower-case. Similarly with *I* and *J* and *V* and *U* I have followed STC practice: medial *V* (appearing in capitals on a title-page) is of course rendered lower-case *u*, *v* being reserved for the initial position. Printer's errors are neither corrected nor indicated; printer's abbreviations are reproduced as they appear on the title-page (there are few that are not self-explanatory in context). Titles that are quoted from such sources as the British Museum catalogues are not altered; this accounts for an unfortunate, but unavoidable, discrepancy between the titles of the books that exist and the books that are lost. With imprints I have taken some bibliographical liberties. I have translated printers' names as much as possible into the vernacular, and I have done the same with place names. Only bibliographers will know that Rothomagnum is Rouen. (Printers' names are taken from McKerrow or Renouard; place names from the British Museum general catalogue.)

With books now lost the procedure necessarily had to be different. The chief problem was identifying the books correctly. Drummond was making his catalogue for his private use (not for the convenience of a twentieth-century cataloguer) and so his titles are sometimes brief and cryptic. His handwriting is not always easy to read, and the title he gave to a book is not always what it is now in a modern catalogue. I have been greatly assisted in deciphering Drummond's titles by a number of scholars; other titles I have stumbled upon by luck, and perseverance has brought its rewards. A few titles I cannot identify, and several are doubtful (these I indicate with a query in the catalogue). I am fairly confident about the others, for one of the satisfying parts of this work has been to have guesses proved right, and the book appear on the shelves of a library. In quoting un-identified titles I keep Drummond's spelling. An asterisk after a catalogue number means that Drummond's copy is thought not to exist.

The entries for the lost books are taken from the printed catalogues of the British Museum, the Bibliothèque Nationale, Edinburgh University Library, and in the case of English and Scottish books, Pollard and Redgrave's *Short-title catalogue*. This variety of sources accounts for the slight variations in the treatment of these entries. It was impossible to guess the edition that Drummond owned and, as there was little point in quoting the earliest edition, I instead took my entry from the one printed nearest to the date he might have

37. Catalogus librorum. The first page of a rough list
Drummond made of his books, before 1611.

10 ℔ Dictionarium Calepini septem linguarum.

☉ 6 Dictionarium græcum Scapulæ e Henrici Steph...

Dictionarium Hebræum.

6 ℔ Biblia latina.

Biblia Hebræa

Commentarium Julij Pacij cum lo: græco in organon Ar...

Commentarium Francisci Piccolomini in libros Ar. de c...

de ortu et interitu & latino.

Commentarium Jacobi Zab... in libros acromaticos, de...

et interitu, et 4 meteorologicos Ar.

3 ß Commentarium Ja. Zab. in logicam Ar.

50 ß commentarius academiæ Conimbricensis in p... Ar.

Petri Rami Scholia in omnes libros artes li...

mathemata.

7 ℔ 6 10 ß Hieronymi Zanchij opera de operib... d...

Alexandri Piccolominei opera

30 ß Guilielmi Budæi Pandectæ utriusq...

Naxxogonia Jacobi Zabarellæ

Toleti commentaria in logicam Ar.G. 1. 2 libros acrox...

et de generat. et corrup. 3 in libros de anima...

Francisci Piccolominei commentaria e græco

48 ß Fran... Piccolominei commentarius.

30 ß In Funiualem commentarius.

In epistolas Ovidij commentarius.

50 ß Suetonius Tranquillus

50 ß Compendium theologicum

40 ß Herbarium antiquum

5 ß L. Flori opera Romanorum

5 ß Meteora Pontani

6 ß commentarius in Porphirionis præf...   oxoxond.

-12ß 8ß 6 ß Salustius, Sp... onica Caruionis Encomium moriæ

6 ß commentarius Pacij in 8 ß ß. ar.

30 ß commentarius de cælo motus. de s... et p...

28 ℔ A.G. libri de cælo motus. de ... floridotoxum

15 ß 14 ℔ Plutarchi apophthegmata & epistolæ amatoriæ gallicæ.

6 ß 6 ℔ Calvini institutiones Gallicæ, & epistolæ

30 ß 14 ß Petri Rami opera & declamationes

20 ß 14 ß 16 ß Herodiani Hystoria Theodori ...

20 ß Homeri Iliados & Odysseæ ... omnes ...

24 ß 8 ß Philo de anima libri & ... grammatica ...

5 ß 8 ß Psalmi Hebraici & ... grammatica

5 ß Catalogus Lutheri Hebraici arte latina ...

5ß 8ß 14 ß 20 ß ...andij opera Horatij & Lucretij 4 Boethij de c...

10 ß 20 ß ... Papinij opera & Silij Italici poema

11 ß 9 ß Marullus cum p... & Daniels Heysij poemata

atq... illæ Statius & lib amorum

8 ß 24 ß 4 ... nov... Eutropia & Glareani ...

4 ß 8 ß ... noti Eutropia & ...

20 ß Ciceronis epistolæ ad Atticum

10 ß Paraphrasis Erasmi in epistolas Pauli

20ß 14 ß Augustinus, Biblia ... Hieronymi   fi.

5 ß 7 ß institutiones Pacij in dialecticen logica piccolomini

8 ß 19 ß ... dialectica. Hunnij dialectica

8 ß Alberti magni Secreta & Michaelis Scoti ...

Table of my Italen bookes
anno 1611.

Gierusalem conquistata
del sigr. T. Tasso, of the edition
of Paris ——————————— 2 ß Ingſ.

Gierusalem as printed at
vith ——————— 18 d. Ingſ.

Le sette giornate del S. T. Tasso — 20 d. Ingſ.

Rime et prose del sigr. T. Tasso
foure Tomes ——————— 4 ß Ingſ.

Lettere familiar del S. T. Tasso —— 10 ß fra.

Orlando furioso di M. Lodovico
Ariosto ——————————— 2 ß Ingſ.

Rime Di. M. L. Ariosto — 18 d. Ingſ.

Gli asolani di M. pietro Bombo — 1 ß Ingſ.

Rime di M pietro Bombo ——— 8 ß Fra.

Il Petrartha ———————— 1 ß Ingſ.

Creatione del mondo del S. Gaspato
Murtola ——————————— 2 ß Ingſ.

Rime di Iacomo Castellano — 18 d. Ingſ.

La comedia di Dante ———— 1 ß Ingſ.

Leone Hibro ——————— 1 ß Ingſ.

Il pastor fido Madrigali di Baptista
Guarini ——————— 1 ß Ingſ.

bought it: since he bought so many of his books second-hand this was only for the sake of consistency.

Principal Bibliographical References

A wide variety of bibliographical references were used to identify titles. Some of these are bibliographies of the sixteenth and seventeenth centuries, which because of their arrangement and inclusiveness were especially helpful, although they are not often accessible to bibliographers today. (Draud, for instance, is an essential tool for anyone trying to track down books of the early seventeenth century, for his index and subject headings are exhaustive and surprisingly accurate.) STC numbers with decimal points or addition signs that are not found in the 1926 edition refer to the revised (unpublished) edition; they are as yet tentative. 'Not identified' under an entry in the catalogue means that the work could not be found in a printed catalogue or bibliography.

A. & R.   Antony Francis Allison and David Morrison Rogers *A catalogue of Catholic books in English printed abroad or secretly in England, 1558–1640* (Bognor Regis 1956)

AUCT   *Auctarium bibliothecae Edinburgenae sive catalogus librorum quos Guilielmus Drummondus ab Hawthornden bibliothecae D.D.Q. anno 1627.* (Heirs of Andrew Hart, Edinburgh 1627)

BARBIER   Ant.-Alex. Barbier *Dictionnaire des ouvrages anonymes* (Paris 1872)

BAUDRIER   Le President Baudrier *Bibliographie Lyonnaise,* published and continued by J. Baudrier (Paris 1964)

BEALE   Joseph Henry Beale *A bibliography of early English law books* (Cambridge, Mass. 1926)

BM   British Museum (Catalogue of Printed Books or STCs)

BN   Bibliothèque Nationale (Catalogue of Printed Books)

BRUNET   Jacques C. Brunet *Manuel du libraire* (Paris 1860–5)

COPINGER   Supplement to Hain *Repertorium* (London 1895–1902)

COTTON   Henry Cotton *A typographical gazetteer* (Oxford 1831)

DRAUD   Georgius Draudius *Bibliotheca classica* (Frankfurt 1625)

DRAUD, *Exotica*   Georgius Draudius *Bibliotheca exotica* (Frankfurt 1625)

EULC   Edinburgh University Library (Catalogue of Printed Books)

GESNER   Conrad Gesner *Bibliotheca universalis* (Zurich 1545)

GREG   W.W. Greg *A bibliography of the English printed drama to the restoration* (London 1939)

HAIN   Ludwig Hain *Repertorium bibliographicum* (Paris 1826)

JÖCHER   Christian Gottlieb Jöcher *Gelehrten-Lexicon* (Leipzig 1750–1)

KASTNER   L.E. Kastner *The poetical works of William Drummond,* Scottish Text Society (Edinburgh 1913)

MCKERROW   Ronald B. McKerrow *Printers' and publishers' devices* (London 1949)

MELZI   Gaetano Melzi *Dizionario di opere anonime e pseudonime di scrittori italiani* (Milan 1848–59)

ONG   Walter J. Ong, S.J. *Ramus and Talon inventory* (Cambridge, Mass. 1958)

PALAU   Antonio Palau y Dulcet, *Manual del librero Hispano-Americano* (Barcelona 1945–65)

PANZER   Georg Wolfgang Panzer *Annales typographici* (Nuremberg 1793)

PELLECHET   Marie Pellechet *Catalogue géneral des incunables des bibliothèques publiques de France* (Paris 1897–1909)

PROCTOR   Robert Proctor *An index to the early printed books in the British Museum* (London 1960)

RENOUARD   Philippe Renouard *Les marques typographiques Parisiennes* (Paris 1928)

RENOUARD, *Estienne*   Antoine Augustin Renouard *Annales de l'imprimerie des Estienne* (repr. New York 1959?)

SCOTT   John Scott *A bibliography of works relating to Mary Queen of Scots, 1544–1700* (London 1896)

SILVESTRE   M. L.-C. Silvestre *Marques typographiques* (Paris 1867)

SOUTHERN   Alfred Collingwood Southern *Elizabethan recusant prose* (London 1950)

STC   A. W. Pollard and G. R. Redgrave *Short-title catalogue of books printed in England, Scotland, and Ireland, 1475–1640* (London 1946) STC² refers to the forthcoming revised edition

WATT   Robert Watt, M. D. *Bibliotheca Britannica* (Edinburgh 1824).

Provenance and Locations

All books in Edinburgh University Library and in other libraries listed below as Drummond's are signed by Drummond, or carry his recognizable annotations. Some other books are known to be his by association; that is, by being bound with signed books in bindings that date from his ownership. These facts are not usually noticed in this catalogue, but cases of doubtful Drummond ownership of the *actual* copy described are indicated by the word 'Unsigned'. No such entries are included unless there is evidence that Drummond owned a copy of the book. (Such evidence comes from his manuscript catalogues and lists.) Sometimes there is a copy of a missing book in Edinburgh University Library that probably was Drummond's actual copy, although it bears no signature or annotations: this is noticed by 'Copy in EUL.' The signatures of previous owners are not usually recorded, unless they are of interest. The following abbreviations are used in the catalogue to indicate provenance and locations.

AUCT   *Auctarium bibliothecae Edinburgenae . . .* (see under Bibliographical References). Books recorded in this catalogue and now lost.

AUL   Aberdeen University Library

BODL   Bodleian Library

BUL   Brown University Library

CHCH   Christ Church College Library, Oxford

DUL   Dundee University Library

EUL   Edinburgh University Library

FOLG   Folger Library

GUL   Glasgow University Library

HEND List made by Robert Henderson, Librarian, Edinburgh University, in 1701, of later donations made to EUL by Drummond (that is, after 1626). Only books which have since disappeared are entered under this heading

HUL Harvard University Library

JR John Rylands Library

LC Library of Congress

MORG Pierpont Morgan Library

MUL Manchester University Library

NLM National Library of Medicine, Bethesda, Md

NLS National Library of Scotland

PR Private owner (see Register of Private Owners)

PRESS 'Press' catalogue, 1636, EUL. A manuscript catalogue which includes (but does not distinguish) Drummond's donation. Only books listed in the *Auctarium* are quoted from this catalogue, and only when the books are now lost, and when the description given is in more detail than in the *Auctarium*

SALE Sale catalogues or booksellers' lists (see Register)

SAUL St Andrews University Library

TC Trinity College, Cambridge

UTL University of Texas Library

WELL Wellcome Historical Medical Library

WINC Fellows' Library, Winchester College

WORC Worcester College, Oxford

The following abbreviations refer to Drummond's 1611 MS catalogue which appears in the Hawthornden MSS in the National Library of Scotland (MS 2059 (vol. VIII) ff. 370r–397r).

It. (followed by number) Italian books

Fr. French books

Sp. Spanish books

Eng. English books

Gr. Greek books

Heb. Hebrew books

Theo. Theology books (in Latin)

Phil. Philosophy books (in Latin)

Jur. Law books (in Latin)

Poe. Poetry books (in Latin)

Pro. Prose books (in Latin)

List A. (B., *etc.*) Supplementary lists of books bought by Drummond, preserved in the Hawthornden MSS (see Register, below)

Bought in Paris, 1607 Date and place of purchase, as recorded by Drummond on the book itself.

Note on Drummond's Arrangement

Drummond listed his books in the 1611 MS catalogue quite carefully, and on close examination many of his apparent errors turn out to be quite logical. Thus, he does put some poets amongst his prose works, but they are poets with commentary, and the prose commentary evidently decides the case. There was some freedom in his day in deciding whether a work was theological, philosophical or geographical: Draud, for instance, occasionally puts a book in two categories just to be safe, and classifies a work like Hopkinson's description of Paradise under geography. Orations, particularly, are tricky titles to catalogue; Drummond sometimes places them under philosophy — going by their subject — and sometimes under prose, that is, as coming under rhetoric. Many of my choices are no more than guess; Drummond might well have ordered them differently.

Register of Private Owners
Lord Ancaster, Drummond Castle Library: 169, 479, 578, 653, 1143.
Hubert Dingwall, Esq.: 1227.
Sir Alec Douglas-Home, The Hirsel Library: 931.
Sir Geoffrey Keynes: 407 (*Bibliotheca Bibliographici* No. 107).
Adrian McLaughlin, Esq.: 1263, 1264, 1266.
Roger Lamson, Esq.: 1212.
The Late Sir James Williams-Drummond, Hawthornden Castle: 454. 5? 831. 5? 922?
Reverend Hugh Purves: 1405.

Register of Sale Catalogues and Booksellers' Lists
William Brown (Edinburgh), catalogue, 1913: 131, 172.
McLeish & Son (booksellers) catalogue, 1948: 360.
Bernard Quaritch *General Catalogue* (London, 1887): 1173, 1308.
Thorpe (booksellers) catalogue, 1834: 426.
Sotheby sale catalogue (David Constable sale), 1827: 1204, 1236, 1249, 1270, 1274, 1239.
Sotheby sale catalogue, 1857: 1397.
Sotheby sale catalogue (Gibson Craig sale), 1887: 1300.
Sotheby sale catalogue, 1917: 1284.
Barnard Library sale catalogue, 1920: 639.
Culter Maynes library sale catalogue, 1869: 147.
Sotheby sale catalogue, 1968: 1193–5.

Register of Supplementary Lists, with Location in Hawthornden MSS, National Library of Scotland
A   Five books.   MS 2062 (vol. X) f. 145.
B   Twenty-two English books.   MS 2062 (vol. X) f. 69.
C   Seven books.   MS 2061 (vol. IX) f. 62.
D   One book.   MS 2060 (vol. VIII) f. 103.
E   Nine books.   MS 2060 (vol. VIII) f. 195.
F   Twenty-four books, inherited from Sir John Drummond and others.   MS 2059 (vol. VII) f. 10.
G   List of books lent and received.   MS 2059 (vol. VII) f. 10.
H   Catalogue of Comedies. (see appendix II)   MS 2060 (vol. VIII) ff. 122–3.
I   Order to a bookseller. (see above, p. 41)   MS 2060 (vol. VIII) f. 152.
J   One book.   MS 2060 (vol. VIII) f. 286.
K   *Catalogus librorum* (a rough catalogue of the library, incomplete, made about 1611. It is duplicated by the main 1611 catalogue, but it does give a few books not in the main catalogue, and others are sometimes given in more detail.)   MS 2059 (vol. VII) f. 3.

LATIN BOOKS

THEOLOGY

1 ABRAHAM, Aben Hassan, *the Levite*. Hæc sunt verba Dei, &c. Praecepta in Monte Sinai data Iudæis sunt 613. quorum 365 negatiua, & 248 affirmatiua, collecta per pharisæum magistrum Abrahamum filium Kattani, & impressa in bibliis Bombergiensibus, anno à mundo creato 5288 Venetiis, ab authore vox Dei appellata: translata in linguam latinam per Philippum Ferdinandum Polonum . . .
4° Cambridge, J. Legat, 1597.   EUL
STC 80

2 AEVOLUS, Caesar. Caesaris Euoli Neapolitani, de diuinis attributis, quae Sephirot ab Hebræis nuncupata.
4° Venice, F. Ziletti, 1573.   EUL

compendium theologicum [Theo. 14]
3 ALBERTUS, *Magnus, St.* Compendium theologice veritatis.
2° Strasburg, [J. Prüss,] 1489.   EUL
Hain *442. Proctor 544.

4 AUGSBURG: *Interim.* Interim, hoc est, constitutio præscribens, qua ratione sacrosancti imp. Ro. status in negocio religionis, vsq; ad decisionem concilij Tridentini, sese mutuò gerere, ac excipere debeant . . .
16° Lyons, T. Payen, 1548.   EUL

5 AUGUSTINE, *St.* D. aurelii Augustini Hipponensis episcopi de gratia & libero arbitrio, ad Valentinum & cum illo monachis liber vnus. Eiusdem de correptione & gratia ad eundem & cum illo monachis, liber vnus. Quibus præmittūtur epistolæ duę Diui Augustini ad Valētinū, cōtra eos qui negant liberum arbitrium.
8° Paris, J. Bonhomme, 1542.   EUL

6 AUGUSTINE, *St.* Diui Aurelii Augustini Hipponensis episcopi de spiritu & litera, liber vnus.
8° Paris, J. Fouchet, 2451 [1542].   EUL

7 [BARNAUD, Nicholas.] Dialogi ab Eusebio Philadelpho cosmopolita in Gallorum et cæterarum nationum gratiam compositi, quorum primus ab ipso auctore recognitus & auctus: alter verò in lucem nunc primum editus fuit. [In 2 parts.]
8° Edinburgh [Geneva?], J. Jamæus, 1574.   EUL
STC 1463

8 BARTHIUS, Casparus. Casp. Barthi de fide saluifica libri duo. De constantia libri duo.
8° Frankfort, house of Wechel for D. and D. Aubry and C. Scheichius, 1623.   EUL

Biblia [Theo. 12]
9* BIBLE. Biblia sacra.
Probably a Protestant version of which the most likely would be that done by Emanuel Tremellius and Franciscus Junius.

biblia Hieronimi [Theo. 15]
10* BIBLE. Biblia Sacrosancta . . . iuxta Diui Hieronymi vulgatam æditionem . . .

Bibliotheca expositionum Geneseos [Theo. 3]
11* BIBLE. Genesis. Genesis cum catholica expositione ecclesiastica . . . sive bibliotheca expositionum Geneseως . . .
Editions were printed at Morges in 1584 and 1585 under Calvinist auspices.

12 BIBLE. Psalms. Psalterium vniuersum elegiaco carmine explicatum. Autore Ioanne Spangenbergo, Herdesiano.
8° Frankfort, heirs of C. Egenolff, 1561.   EUL
Title wanting. Title taken from head-title.

13 BIBLE. Jeremiah. Complanationis Ieremiae prophetae, foetura prima, cum apologia quur quidque sic uersum sit, per Huldrychum Zuinglium.
2° Zurich, C. Frosshauer, 1531.   EUL
With *Annotationes et satisfactiones complanationis Huld. Zuing. in Ieremiam prophetam* . . .

Theodoreti commentaria in ezechielem [Theo. 2]
14* BIBLE. Ezekiel. Beati Theodoreti Episcopi Cyrensis, in Ezechielem Prophetam commentarius, Ioanne Baptista Gabio Veronensi interprete . . .
Probably with the text.

Testamentum nouum T. Bezæ [Theo. 18]
15* BIBLE. New Testament. Iesu Christi, Domini Nostri Nouum Testamentum . . . T. Beza interprete . . . Cui additur ex aduerso eiusdem Noui Testamenti ex vetustissima Syriaca translatione, translatio Latina I. Tremellii . . .
Copy, possibly Drummond's, of the Geneva, 1588 edition in University Library, Dundee.

paraphrases Erasmi pauli epist. [Theo. 21]
16* BIBLE. Epistles. Paraphrases Erasmi Roterodami in aliquot Pauli apostoli epistolas.
Copy, possibly Drummond's, of the Basle, 1522
edition in University Library, Dundee.

17 BIBLE. Revelation. Primasii Vticensis in
Africa Iustinopoli ciuitate episcopi, commentariorum libri quinque in apocalypsim Ioannis
Euangelistæ, ante mille annos ab auctore con-
scripti, nuncque primum æditi. [With the text.]
8° Basle, R. Winter, 1544.   EUL

18* BIBLE. Liturgical Epistles and Gospels.
Homiliae in evangelia dominicalia juxta literam,
adjectis homiliis in evangelia trium feriarum
paschalium, et totidem pentecostalium per F.
Joannem Royardum . . . Pars hyemalis . . .
                              AUCT

proteuangelium Iacobi [Theo. 16]
19 BIBLE. New Testament. Apocryphal Books.
Proteuangelion siue de natalibus Iesu Christi, &
ipsius matris Virginis Mariæ, sermo historicus
diui Iacobi minoris, consobrini & fratris Domini
Iesu, apostoli primarij, & episcopi Christianorum
primi Hierosolymis. Euangelica historia, quam
scripsit beatus Marcus, Petri apostolorum principis
discipulus & filius, primus episcopus Alexandriæ.
Vita Ioannis Marci euangelistæ, collecta ex pro-
batioribus autoribus, per Theodorum Bibliandrum.
Indices rerum ac uerborum . . .
8° Basle, J. Oporinus, 1552.   EUL

20 BIBLIANDER, Theodorus. De mysterijs
salutifera passionis et mortis Iesu Messiæ:
expositionis historicæ libri tres . . . Quibus
adiuncta est epilogi uice, oratio D. Martini
Lutheri . . . de reformanda Ecclesia [in German] . . .
4° Basle, J. Oporinus, [1551].   EUL
Gathering 'a' (which includes the title) is wanting.

legenda maior beati francisci [Theo. 24]
21 BONAVENTURA, St. Legēda maior beatis-
simi patris francisci a sancto Bonauētura . . .
8° Paris, J. Barbier, [c. 1520].   EUL
Repeated (in error?) as *legenda maior de bona
Ventura*, Theo. 26.

Catecheses [List K]
22* CATECHISMUS.
Not identified.

clemens Alexandrinus [Theo. 19]
23* CLEMENT, *of Alexandria.* ? T. Flauii
Clementis Alexandrini . . . opera omnia ante
annos quadraginta è græco in latinum conuersa . . .
Or perhaps Clement's commentaries on the
Epistles of James or John. See Draud, 208, 225.

24 CLICHTOVEUS, Jodocus. De doctrina
moriendi opusculū, necessaria ad bene moriēdum

prēparamēta declarās, & quomodo in eius agone
varijs antiqui hostis insultibus sit resistendū,
edocens. Accessere orationes aliquot D. Dionysij,
homini iam iam morituro, sanè q̄ necessariæ.
16° Antwerp, J. Grapheus for J. Steels, 1535. EUL

25 COLERUS, Jacobus. De animarum immortalitate, et statu, postquam ex hoc ergastulo
corporis humani egressæ sunt, orthodoxa, pia
& vtilis doctrina . . .
8° Wittenberg, C. Schleich, 1587.   EUL

26* CRAMER, Daniel. Flores fragrantissimi
meditationum precumque sacrarum, ex hortulo
animae veteri . . . excerpti . . . Septem semitis
distincti.
16°.   AUCT

Scola prophetica Crameri [Theo. 25]
27* CRAMER, Daniel. Crameri scholæ prophe-
ticæ classis I. II. III. IV. V. & VI.
Draud has an edition printed at Hamburg. Draud,
p. 516.

Acta martirum crispini [Theo. 6]
28* CRESPIN, Jean. Acta martyrum, eorum
videlicet, qui hoc seculo in Gallia, Germania,
Anglia, Flandria, Italia, constans dederunt nomen
Euangelio, idque sanguine suo obsignarunt: ab
Wicleffo & Husso ad hunc vsque diem. [Tr.
Claude Baduel from the French.]

Dionisii Ariopagitæ opera [Theo. 1]
29 DIONYSIUS, St., *the Areopagite.* Dionysii
Areopagitae opera omnia quae extant. Eiusdem
vita. Scholia incerti auctoris in librum de ecclesiastica hierarchia. Quæ omnia à Ioachimo
Perionio Benedictino Cormœiaceno, Henrici
Gallorum regis interprete, conuersa sunt. Accesserunt huic editioni indices duo, capitum uidelicet
librorum omnium unus, & rerum insigniorum
alter: item scholia quædam ad marginem non
inutilia, & multorum locorum emendationes.
2° Paris, M. de Vascosan, 1566.   EUL

30* DUNS, Joannes, *Scotus.* Scriptum oxoniense
in quatuor libros Sententiarum.   AUCT
Auct. has 'Venice, 1522'. Edition not traced.

31 DURAND, Nicolas, *Chevalier de Villegagnon.*
Ad articulos Caluinianæ, de sacramento euchari-
stiæ, traditionis ab eius ministris in Francia
Antarctica euulgatæ responsiones . . .
4° Paris, A. Wechel, 1560.   EUL

32 EGLISHAM, George. Crisis Vorstiani re-
sponsi. Quâ D. Conradus Vorstius denuo atheismi,
schismatis, & ignorantiæ arguitur . . .
4° Delft, J. Andriesz, 1612.   EUL

33   ENGLAND. Public Documents. Declaratio serenissimi magnæ Britanniæ regis, qua quid cum generalibus fœderatarum Belgij prouinciarum ordinibus super re Vorstii actum tractatumue sit, singillatim explicatur.
4° London, J. Norton, 1612.   EUL
STC 9232

Erasmus de preparatione ad mortem [Theo. 22]
34* ERASMUS, Desiderius. D. Erasmi ... liber ... de præparatione ad mortem, nunc primum ... æditus.   AUCT
Auct. has 'Antwerp, 1534'. There were two editions printed at Antwerp in 1534: both octavos; one by M. Hillenius, a second by M. Caesar for G. Dumaeus.

Eusebii Emiseni Homiliæ [Theo. 30]
35* EUSEBIUS, *Bp. of Emesa.* Eusebii ... Homiliæ ... recens in lucem emissæ per J. Gaigneum ...

Fidelis mundi structuri [Theo. 5]
36* FIDELIS, Ludovicus. L. F. Nervii ... de mundi structura opusculum.

Fulcius de elimosina [Theo. 4]
37   FULCUS, Julius. Eorum qui vel eleemosynas erogauerunt admirabiles fructus, vel de eleemosyna scripserunt insignes sententiæ, numquam antea in vnum ita collectæ.
8° Paris, G. Gourbin, 1585.   EUL
Bought in Paris, 1607.

Furii Ceriolani bononia [Theo. 7]
38* FURIO CERIOL, Federico. ? F. Furii Caeriolani Bononia, sive de Libris Sacris in vernaculam linguam convertendis, libri duo.

apologia innocentii Gentiletii [Theo. 20]
39* GENTILLET, Innocent. Apologia pro Christianis Gallis religionis evangelicæ seu reformatæ ...

examen consilii Tridentini [Theo. 8]
40* GENTILLET, Innocent. Examen Concilii Tridentini: in quo demonstratur, in multis articulis hoc concilium antiquis conciliis & canonibus regiæq́ authoritati contrarium esse ...

41   GUIDO, *de Monte Rocherii.* Manipulus curatorum.
8° Rouen, M. Morin, 1496.   EUL
Panzer II, 560. 12.

42   GULIELMUS, *Arvernus, Bp.* Guillermus parisiensis de septem sacramentis.
8° [Paris,] D. Gerlier, [c. 1500].   EUL
Hain *8309

43   [GULIELMUS, *de Occam.*] Disputatio inter clericum et militem, super potestate prælatis ecclesię atq́ principibus terrarum commissa, sub forma dialogi.
8° London, T. Berthelet, [1531?]   EUL
STC 12510

44   IGNATIUS, *of Loyola, St.* Exercitia spiritualia ...
32° Douay, J. Bogard, 1586.   EUL

45   JAMES, Thomas. Concordantiæ sanctorum patrum hoc est vera et pia libri canticorum per patres vniuersos tam Græcos quam Latinos expositio.
4° Oxford, J. Barnes, 1607.   EUL
STC 14452

46* JESUS CHRIST. Opuscula diuersa insignium poetarum de Christi Iesu vita ac morte.
8° Antwerp, S. Cock, 1536.   AUCT

47   JOHN, *of Capistrano, St.* Tractatus de cupiditate ...
2° [Cologne, J. Koelhoff [the elder], before 1483].   EUL
Proctor 1054, Hain 4376.

48   JOHN, *of Damascus, St.* In hoc opere contenta. Theologia Damasceni, quatuor libris explicata: et adiecto ad litteram commentario elucidata. I De ineffabili diuinitate. II De creaturarū genesi, ordine Moseos. III De ijs quæ ab incarnatione vsq̃ ad resurrectionē Christi. IIII De ijs quæ post resurrectionem vsq̃ ad vniuersalē resurrectione.
2° Paris, H. Estienne [the first], 1519.   EUL
With an interpretation by Lefèvre d'Etaples and notes by Jodocus Clichtoveus.

prognosticon futuri seculi Nicolai Bugnei [Theo. 29]
49   JULIAN, *St., Abp. of Toledo.* Liber prognosticorum futuri seculi aeternæque vitæ fœliciter sperandæ ... Nunc autem opera atque diligentia religiosi patris, Fratris Nicolai Bugnee, compendiensis, doctoris theologi ordinis prædicatorum, in lucem proditus.
16° Paris, P. Le Preux, 1554.   EUL

Vitæ Hereticorum langii [Theo. 10]
50* LAING, James. De vita et moribus atque rebus gestis hæreticorum nostri temporis, &c. Traductis ex sermone Gallico in Latinum, quibus multa addita sunt quæ in priori editione ... omissa fuere.
8° Paris, M. de Roigny, 1581.   AUCT
Translated by Laing from the French of Noël Taillepied and J. H. Bolsec.

51   LA ROCHE DE CHANDIEU, Antoine, *called Sadeel.* Posnaniensium assertionum de Christi in terris ecclesia, quænam & penes quos

existat: propositarum in collegio Posnaniensi, à monachis nouæ societatis, quam illi societatem Iesu, non sine blasphemia nominant, nisi fortè vnius Iudæ Iscariotæ posteri, ac hæredes haberi velint, analysis & refutatio . . .
8° Morges, J. Le Preux, 1584.   EUL

Di carthusianus de contemplatione [Theo. 28]
52 * LEUWIS, Dionysius de, *de Rickel.* ? D. Dionysii Carthusiani opuscula aliquot, quae ad theoriam mysticam egregie instituunt: Contemplationum lib. III . . .

53 LITURGIES. Breviaries. Breuiarium ad vsum Cister. ordinis nouissime ad veram et debitam (superfluis resecatis diminutisque suppletis) formam vtiliter redactum . . .
8° Paris, Y. Bonhomme, 1542. EUL

54 * LITURGIES. Hours. Thesaurus spiritualis, cū psalterio Christi deuotum: &c ꝗ plurimis orationibus pristine impressioni superadditis: cum regula fratrum minorum: ac testamento Sancti Frācisci: nuper diligēti accuratione recognitus.
16° Lyons, 1536.   AUCT
Copy in EUL.

55 LITURGIES. Church of England. Book of Common Prayer. Ordinatio ecclesiae, seu ministerii ecclesiastici, in florentissimo regno Angliæ, conscripta sermone patrio, & in Latinam linguam bona fide conuersa . . . edita, ab Alexandro Alesio Scoto . . .
4° Leipzig, W. Guenther, 1551. EUL
Incomplete: all after R3 wanting.

56 LOHETUS, Daniel. Sorex primus oras chartarum primi libri de republica ecclesiastica illustrissimi & reuerendissimi D. Archiepiscopi Spalatensis corrodens Leonardus Marius theologaster Coloniensis a Danielo Loheto Burgundo Laudonensi, eiusdem D. Spalatensis amanuensi, in muscipula captus, & eiusdem scalpello confossus.
8° London, J. Bill, 1618.   EUL
STC 16695

57 LOSSIO, Lucas. Catechismus, hoc est, Christianæ doctrinæ methodus. Item, obiectiones in eundem, vna cum ueris & breuibus earum solutionibus, ordine certo & perspicuo insertæ . . .
8° Wittenberg, J. Krafft, 1554. EUL

58 MARTINI, Matthias. De Deo, summo illo bono & causa omnis boni, libelli duo; I. De essentiæ divinæ unitate & essentialib. proprietatibus, II. De trinitate personarum & personalibus proprietatibus; erotematicè, maximé ad popularem institutionem scripti; quibus adjecta est brevis institutio de duabus Jesu Christi nativitatibus &

unica filiatione . . . [In 2 parts.]
8° Bremen, J. Wessel, 1616. EUL

59 MELANCHTHON, Philip. Sententiae Phil. Melanthonis Martini Buceri, Casp. Hedionis & aliorum in Germania theologorum de pace ecclesiæ.
8° n.p., 1607.   EUL
Bought in Bourges, 1608.

60 * METHODUS. Methodus confessionis ubi peccata & eorum remedia plenissime continentur.
Edition not traced. Auct. has 'Paris, 1531'. AUCT

61 [PARSONS, Robert.] Elizabethae reginae Angliae edictum promulgatum Londini 29. Nouemb. anni M.D.XCI. Andreae Philopatri ad idem edictum responsio.
8° [Rome?] 1593.   EUL

62 PATRIARCHS, *the Twelve, Sons of Jacob.* Testamentum duodecim Patriarchum, filiorum Iacob, per Robertum Lincolinensem episcopum, è Græco in Latinum uersum. Floruit author anno M.CC.XLII. Iuliani Pomerii, Toletani episcopi, contra Iudæos libri tres. Hic author floruit anno Christi D.C. LXXXVI.
8° Hagenau, J. Setzer, 1532. EUL

63 PEPIN, Gulielmus. Expositio euāgeliorū quadragesimalium . . .
8° Paris, J. Petit, 1529.   EUL

64 PEPIN, Gulielmus. Sermones quadragesimales . . .
8° Paris, J. Petit, 1529.   EUL

problema Perkinsii [Theo. 17]
65 * PERKINS, William. G. Perkinsi Problema de Romanæ Fidei ementito Catholicismo. Estq: antidotum contra Thesaurum Catholicum J. Coccii . . . Editum . . . opera . . . S. Wardi.

66 POLAND. *Ministers.* [*Begin.*] Ministri et pastores ecclesiarum in Minori Polonia, pio lectori salute in Domino.
8° Pinczow, D. Lancicius, 1560. EUL

67 QUINT' ESSENTIA. Quint' essentia magistralis in quatuor secta partes succinctis solutionibus præcipua in theologorum scholis controuersa resoluens.
12° Saint-Mihiel, F. Dubois, 1614. EUL

P. Ramus de relligione [Theo. 11]
68 * RAMUS, Petrus. P. Rami commentariorum de religione Christiana libri quatuor. Ejusdem vita a T. Banosio descripta.

de cælibatu sacerdotum Smytheus [Theo. 23]
69* SMITH, Richard, *D.D., Dean of St. Peter's Church, Douay.* Celeberrimi . . . R. Smythei, de coelibatu sacerdotum liber unus. Ejusdem de votis monasticis liber alter.

Aquinas [List E]
70* THOMAS, *Aquinas, St.* Summa theologica. Drummond ordered the *Summa*, expecting it to cost 16s ster. (see List I). He actually paid 12 *lb* (12 livres, French?) thus his copy could have been one of the current four volume editions.

71* TORÚN. Acta et conclusiones synodi generalis Toruniensis . . . 1595.
8° Torún, A. Cotenius, 1596.   AUCT
See *Bibliographica Polonica*, II, 1816.

Decreta publicata in sessione vltima Tridentini [Theo. 9]
72* TRENT, Council of. Decreta publicata in sessione nona et vltima, Sacri Concilii Tridentini . . . Diebus. III. et IIII. Decemb. 1563.

73 TURRECREMATA, Joannes de, *Card.* Glosa psalterij . . .
2° Strasburg, [printer of the 1483 *Iordanus de Quedlinburg,*] 1487.   EUL
Proctor 614, Hain *15707.
With the motto, in Drummond's hand: 'Mas honra que vida.'

74 VORSTIUS, Conradus. Conradi Vorstij S. theol. doctoris parænesis ad Doct. Sibrandum Lubbertum. Quâ recentes aliquot hujus in illum injuriæ, apertæque calumniæ, commentarijs ejusdem nuper editis insertæ, ac summatim in epistola, & præfatione libri propositæ, breviter refutantur.
4° Gouda, C. Tournay for A. Burier, 1613.   EUL

75 VORSTIUS, Conradus. Oratio apologetica habita in pleno consessu illustrium ac præpotentium Hollandiæ & VVestfrisiæ ordinum.
4° Amsterdam, W. Janszoon, 1612.   EUL

Consiliatio patrum cum sacra scriptura [Theo. 27]
76* WESTHEMERUS, Bartholomaeus. Conciliatio patrum et conciliorum & decretorum cum sacra scriptura; collecta, aucta, & edita a B. Westhemero.

77 WITZEL, Georg. Ordinandorum examinatio. Quid ad interrogata censuræ Moguntinensis de re ecclesiastica, à candidatis sacri ordinis, quàm breuissimè responderi possit . . .
8° Mainz, F. Behem, 1544.   EUL

Zanchius de operibus dei [Theo. 13]
78 ZANCHIUS, Hieronymus. De operibus Dei intra spacium sex dierum creatis. Opus tres in partes distinctum . . .
4° Neustadt in the Palatinate, N. Schramm for the heirs of W. Harnisch, 1602.   DUL
Bought in 1606. With the motto, in what is probably Drummond's hand: 'Vanity, vanity, all is vanity' (in Hebrew).

79 ZEPPER, Wilhelm. Ars habendi et audiendi conciones sacras. Hoc est: quid ante, sub et post conciones sacras, tam concionatoribus, quam auditoribus facto opus sit . . .
8° Siegen, C. Corvinus, 1598.   EUL

PHILOSOPHY

80 ÆTHICUS. Aethici cosmographia: Antonii Augusti itinerarium prouinciarum: ex bibliotheca P. Pithœi, cum scholiis Iosiae Simleri.
16° Basle, [T. Guarin,] 1575.   EUL

81 AEVOLUS, Caesar. Caesaris Aeuoli Neapolitani, de causis antipathiæ, & sympathiæ rerum naturalium.
4° Venice, F. Ziletti, 1580.   EUL

82 AGRIPPA, Henricus Cornelius. In artem breuem [Raymundi] Lul [lii] Henrici Corn. Agrip. com [mentaria].
8° Cologne, J. Soter, 1533.   EUL
Imperfect. All before d1 and all after i8 wanting. Title taken from running-title.

Alberti secreta et Scoti [Phil. 14]
83* ALBERTUS, *Magnus, St.* [*Supposititious work.*] Alberti Magni de secretis mulierum libellus, scholiis auctus . . . Item de mirabilibus mundi . . . Michaelis Scotis . . . de secretis naturæ opusculum.
The two editions of Michael Scott's *Liber physionomiæ* described in EULC as *Drummond Collection* have no apparent Drummond provenance.

84 ALCHABITIUS ['Abd Al-'Aziz Ibn 'Uthmān, *al-Kabisī*]. Alcabitii ad magisterium iudiciorum astrorum isagoge: commentario Ioannis Saxonij declarata.
4° Paris, S. de Colines, 1521.   EUL

85 ALSTEDIUS, Joannes Henricus. Compendium logicæ harmonicæ, exhibens universum bene diserendi modum juxta principia Peripateticorum & Rameorum celebriorum; distincteq́; proponens præcepta selectiora, canones illustriores, et commentaria brevia.
12° Herborn, 1615.   EUL

86* ARCHANA. Archana medicine. Candidus De genitura hominis . . . Conseruatorium sanitatis per

Io. philippum de lignamine . . . editū . . . Petrus
de abano De singulis venenis et curis eorūdē . . .
Arnaldus de villa noua De Arte cognoscēdi
venena . . . et cura eorūdem . . . Tractatulus de
peste et epydimia . . . Valasti de tarēta . . . Alius
tractatulus de peste et epydimia Iohānis Itrensis
. . .
2° [Geneva, 1505.]   HEND
AUCT lists the tracts separately. BM notes that
the *Conseruatorium sanitatis* printed here is the
De conseruatione sanitatis of Benedictus de Nursia.

Argenterius de somno et vigilia [Phil. 40]
87 ARGENTERIUS, Joannes. De somno et
vigilia libri duo, in quibus continentur duæ
tractationes de calido natiuo, et de spiritibus . . .
4° Florence, L. Torrentino, 1556.   NLM

88 ARISTARCHUS, *Samius*. Aristarchi de
magnitudinibus, et distantiis solis, et lunae, liber
cum Pappi Alexandrini explicationibus quibusdam. A Federico Commandino Vrbinate in latinum conuersus, ac commentariis illustratus.
4° Pesaro, C. Franceschini, 1572.   EUL

Academia conimbricensis in phis. [Phil. 4]
89* ARISTOTLE. Commentariorum Collegii
Conimbricensis . . . in octo libros physicorum
Aristotelis . . . prima (–secunda) pars . . .
Probably with the text in Greek.

Hiperii compendium phisices [Phil. 27]
90* ARISTOTLE. Andreæ Hyperii [*i.e.* A.
Gerardus, Hyperius] compendium physices
Aristoteleæ . . .

91 ARISTOTLE. Aristotelis . . . parua quae
vocant naturalia: de sensu et sensili; de memoria
et reminiscentia; de somno et vigilia; de insomniis; de diuinatione per somnia; de animalium
motione; de animalium incessu; de extensione
et breuitate vitae; de iuuentute et senectute,
morte et vita; et de spiratione . . . conuersa . . .
a Nicolao Leonico Thomaeo . . . (N. Leonici
Thomæi opuscula.) [In 2 parts.]
2° Paris, L. Cyaneus for S. de Colines, 1530.   LC
Bought in Paris, 1607.

92 ARISTOTLE. Aristotelis liber, qui decimus
historiarum [animalium] inscribitur, nunc primum
Latinus factus à Iulio Cæsare Scaligero viro
clarissimo, & commentariis illustratus.
8° Lyons, A. de Harsy, 1584.   EUL

Aris. libri de celo meteor. de sensu et sensili &c
[List K]
93* ARISTOTLE. De caelo. Meteorologica. De
sensu et sensilibus.
Edition not traced.

Portii comment. in. lib. de coloribus [Phil. 41]
94* ARISTOTLE. [*Supposititious work.*] De
coloribus libellus, a Simone Portio . . . latinate
donatus, & commentarijs illustratus: vna cum
eiusdem præfatione . . .

95 ARISTOTLE. [*Supposititious work.*] Phisio-
gnomia Aristotelis ordine compositorio edita, ad
facilitatem doctrinæ. Commentarijs illustrata
breuissimis, & propter methodum præspicuam,
facillimis. In gratiam eorum præsertim qui mores
hominum præspicere student.
8° Paris, J. Paquet, 1611.   EUL
Attributed to Polemon.

96 ARISTOTLE. [*Supposititious work.*] In hoc
libro continentur probleumata Aristotelis varias
questiones cognosci admodum dignas & ad
naturalem philosophiam potissimum spectantes
discutientia.
8° [Paris,] J. Petit, [1539?]   EUL

97 AZOTH. Azoth, siue aureliæ occultæ philosophorum, materiam primam, et decantatum illum
lapidem philosophorum filiis Hermetis solide,
perspicue & dilucide explicantes, per ænigma
philosophicum, colloquium parabolicum, tabulam
smaragdinam Hermetis, symbola, parabolas &
figuras saturni, F. Basilii Vicentini. M. Georgio
Beato Fr. interprete.
4° Frankfort, J. Bringer, 1613.   EUL
Title-page mutilated, with Drummond's signature
over the repair. Attributed to 'Basilius Valentinus', the supposed author of a number of occult
works and the supposed discoverer of antimony.
This work is a translation from the German
*Occulta philosophia. Von den verborgenen philoso-
phischen Geheimnussen der heimlichen Goldblumen.*
(See BM)

98 BIESIUS, Nicolaus. De vniuersitate libri tres,
quibus vniuersa de natura philosophia continetur
. . .
4° Antwerp, M. Nuyts, 1556.   HUL

Tabularum Iohannis Blanchini canones
[Phil. 52]
99* BLANCHINUS, Johannes. Tabularum J. B.
canones.
A copy of the Venice edition of 1495 is in EUL,
and included in this edition is *Tabulae astrono-
micae et canones in eas.*

100 BRUNO, Giordano. Summa terminorum
metaphysicorum . . . Accessit eiusdem praxis
descensus, seu applicatio entis ex manuscripto,
per Raphaelem Eglinumiconium . . . Cum supplemento Rodolphi Goclenii senioris.
8° Marpurg, Hutvvelckerus, 1609.   EUL

101   CAPELLA, Martianus Mineus Felix. M. Capella. Martiani Minei Capellæ Carthaginensis de nuptijs philologiæ, & septem artibus liberalibus libri nouem optime castigati.
8° Lyons, heirs of S. Vincent, 1539.   EUL

Cardanus de insomniis [Phil. 48]
102 * CARDANO, Girolamo. De insomniis commentaria.

Cardianus de varietate [List G]
103 * CARDANO, Girolamo. De rerum varietate libri XVII.

casei dialectica [Phil. 12]
104 * CASE, John. Summa veterum interpretum in vniuersam dialecticam Aristotelis.

105 * CASSANDER, Georgius. Tabulæ præceptionū dialecticarum, quæ quam breuissimè & planissimè artis methodum complectuntur . . .
                         AUCT
AUCT gives the edition as 'Paris, 1549'. BM has an edition printed the previous year.

106   CENSORINUS. Censorini liber de die natali, per Eliam Vinetum . . . emendatus . . .
4° Poitiers, house of Marnesius, 1568.   AUCT

107   CHAPPUSIUS, Nicolaus. Nicolai Chappusij de mente & memoria libellus vtilissimus . . .
4° [Paris, J. Badius, 1515?]   EUL

Ciceronis philosophia [Phil. 29]
108 * CICERO, Marcus Tullius. Philosophia. There were numerous collections of Cicero's philosophy, usually printed in two or more parts, each part often being in two volumes. There is no telling if Drummond had all of a collection, or only one book of the whole. A common arrangement was to print in part one the *Academica*, *Tusculanae disputationes*, *De natura deorum*, *De divinatione*, *De fato*, *De legibus*, *De universitate*, and in part two *De officiis*, *Cato maior*, *Lælius*, *Paradoxa Stoicorum*.

109 * CICERO, Marcus Tullius. Somnium Scipionis Christiani.   AUCT
The *Somnium* with Macrobius' exposition?

110   CLAVIUS, Christophorus. Computus ecclesiasticus per digitorum articulos mira facilitate traditus. Auctore Christophoro Clauio Bambergensi è Societate Iesu.
16° Mainz, B. Lipp, 1599.   EUL

111   CLEOMEDES. Cleomedis circularis inspectionis meterorum libri duo. Georgio valla Placentino interprete.
4° Paris, T. Richard, 1547.   EUL

112   COELESTINUS, Claudius. De his quę mundo mirabiliter eueniunt: vbi de sensuum erroribus, & potentijs animę, ac de influentijs cælorum . . . opusculum. De mirabili potestate artis et naturae, vbi de philosophorum lapide, F. Rogerij Bachonis Anglici, libellus. [*Ed.* O. Finé.]
4° Paris, S. de Colines, 1542.   EUL

113   CONTARINI, Nicolò. De perfectione rerum libri sex.
4° Venice, G. B. Somasco, 1576.   EUL

114   COSMOGRAPHIA. Cosmographię introductio: cum quibusdam geometrię ac astronomię principijs ad eam rem necessarijs. Insuper quattuor Americi Vespucij nauigationes. Vniuersalis cosmographię descriptio tam in solido ꝗ plano, eis etiam insertis quę Ptholomęo ignota, a nuperis reperta sunt. [*Ed.* M. Hylacomylus or Waldsee-Mueller.]
4° Strasburg, J. Grueninger, 1509.   EUL

115   CRANSTON, William. Dialecticae compendium . . . Nunc per eundem tertiò auctum & recognitum.
4° Paris, J. Loys, 1545.   EUL

Iridis celestis et coronæ descrip. demerlieri [Phil. 43]
116 * DEMERLIERIUS, Joannes. Iridis coelestis, et coronæ breuis descriptio.

Quadrati Geometrici vsus Demerlieri [Phil. 42]
117 * DEMERLIERIUS, Joannes. Quadrati geometrici vsus, geometricis demonstrationibus illustratus.

Dicsoni dialogus de memoria [Phil. 17]
118 * DICSONUS, Alexander. A. D. Arelii Thamus; sive de memoriæ virtute consideratio prima.

Dionysius afer de situ orbis [Phil. 24]
119 * DIONYSIUS, *Periegetes*. De situ orbis.

120   DOVIATUS, Gulielmus. Guilielmi Douiatii . . . dialogi duo, de tempore, déque animi perturbationibus.
4° Paris, S. Nivelle, 1583.   EUL

Scholia Rami in Euclidem &c [Phil. 28]
121   EUCLID. ? Euclides elementorum libri quindecim. [*Ed.* Petrus Ramus.]
Or Ramus' *Geometria* (see Ong, pp. 369–72)?

122   DREBBEL, Cornelius. Cornelii Drebbel Alcmariensis tractatus de natura elementorum, qua ratione ventos, pluuias, fulgura & tonitrua parturiant, &c. In linguam Latinam translatus & in lucem emissus à Iohanne Ernesto Burggrauio.

8° Frankfort, C. Rotelius for W. Fitzer, 1628.
EUL

123   DUCHESNE, Léger, *pseud.* [*i.e.* Adrien Turnèbe?] Leodegarii a Quercu animaduersiones in Rullianos Petri Rami commentarios . . .
4° Paris, M. de Vascosan, 1553.   EUL
Turnèbe, according to Ong, used Léger Duchesne's name as a pseudonym in his attack on Ramus. Alternatively, as Ong admits, the work may have been written by Duchesne himself. See Ong, p. 292. Bought in Paris, 1608.

124   DUCHESNE, Léger, *pseud.* [Adrien Turnèbe.] Leodegarii a Quercu responsio ad Audomari Talaei admonitionem.
4° Paris, M. de Vascosan, 1556.   EUL
Turnèbe's rejoinder (under Léger Duchesne's name) to Ramus' reply to Turnèbe's *Disputatio* attacking Ramus' handling of Cicero's *De fato.* Ramus conducted his side of the controversy under Omer Talon's name. See Ong, p. 293.

125   FABRICIUS. Hieronymus. Hieronymi FabricI ab Aquapendente . . . de locutione et eius instrumentis liber a Ioanne Vrsino editus.
4° Venice, G. Alberti for G. B. and A. Meietti, 1601.   EUL

Fernelle [List E]
126   FERNELIUS, Joannes. Joannis Fernelii Ambiani, vniuersa medicina, tribus & viginti libris absoluta, ab ipso quidem authore ante obitum diligenter recognita, et quatuor libris nunquam ante editis, ad praxim tamen perquam necessariis, aucta. Postea autem studio et diligentia Gul. Plantii Cenomani postremum elimata, et in librum therapeutices septimum doctissimis scholiis illustrata. Editio postrema.
2° Lyons, for A. Marsilij, 1578.   DUL

127   FERRERIO, Giovanni. Academica de animorum immortalitate, ex sexto M. T. Ciceronis de Republica libro, enarratio . . .
4° Paris, M. de Vascosan, 1539.   EUL

128   FERRERIO, Giovanni. Auditum visu præstare, contra vulgatum Aristotelis placitum, academica Iohannis Ferrerii Pedemōtani disertatio.
4° Paris, M. de Vascosan, 1539.   EUL

129   FERRERIO, Giovanni. De vera cometæ significatione, contra astrologorum omnium vanitatem libellus . . .
4° Paris, M. de Vascosan, 1540.   EUL

Marsilii ficini libri de vita [Phil. 51]
130* FICINO, Marsiglio. De triplici vita.

131   FREIGIUS, Joannes Thomas. Joannis Thomae Freigii quaestiones oeconomicae et

politicae, cum aliis quibusdam (ejusdem argumenti) doctorum virorum commentationibus . . .
12° Basle, 1580.   SALE
Present location unknown.

Gemma phrisii arithmetica [Phil. 15]
132* GEMMA, Reinerus, *Frisius.* Arithmeticæ practicæ methodus facilis . . .

133* GEPHYRANDER, Thomas. Quadratura Circulis nova, perspicua, expedita . . .   HEND

134   GESNER, Conrad. Conradi Gesneri de rerum fossilium, lapidum et gemmarum maximè, figuris & similitudinibus liber : non solùm medicis, sed omnibus rerum naturæ ac philologiæ studiosis, vtilis & iucundus futurus.
8° Zurich, [house of Gesner,] 1565.   EUL

135   GESNER, Conrad. Historia plantarum et vires ex Dioscoride, Paulo Aegineta, Theophrasto, Plinio, & recētioribus Græcis, iuxta elementorū ordinē . . . Adiecta ad marginē nomenclatura, qua singulas herbas officinæ, herbarij, & vulgus Gallicum efferre solent.
8° Paris, O. Petit [the first], 1541.   EUL
The colophon gives the printer as Jean Loys.

136   [GEUSS, Wolffius.] Methodus curandorum morborum mathematica : qua morborum depellendorum ex astrorum concordanti influxu ratio certa & euidens ostenditur. Cui & locorum hylegialium, & thematum cœlestium structura adiecta. Nunc primum publici iuris facta.
4° Frankfort, W. Richter for A. Humm, 1613. EUL
With two insets : both tables, one planetary, one zodiacal.

137   HEIDFELDIUS, Johannes. Sphinx philosophica, promens et proponens erudita ac arguta ęnigmata sive scrupos, ex variis tum sacris tum profanis authoribus comportatos . . .
8° Herborn, C. Corvinus, 1600.   EUL

138   HIPPOCRATES. [*Supposititious work.*] Iacobi Scutellarii medici Parmensis in librum Hippocratis de natura humana, commentarius. Nunc primum in lucem editus. [With the text.]
4° Parma, S. Viotti, 1568.   EUL

Hunnei dialectica [Phil. 13]
139* HUNNÆUS, Augustinus. Dialectica, seu generalia logices præcepta omnia, quæcunque ex toto Aristotelis Organo, philosophiæ tironibus ad ediscendum proponi consueverunt.

140   JOHN XXI, *Pope* [Pedro Julião Rebello]. Textus summula ⅃ magistri petri hyspani.
16° [Paris,] G. Mittelhus, 1492.   EUL
Not found in Proctor, Goff, or other bibliographies. *Colophon reads :* Petri hyspani sūmulaᵱ

liber dyaletice, exaratū̄p Georgiū̄ mittelhuss
.i.p.2. mēss octob'.
Collation: [a⁸] b-ʃ⁸ s⁸ t-v⁸ u⁸ x-z⁸ &⁸ ꝑ⁴, 212
unnumbered leaves. 88 × 55 mm., 17 lines to the
page.

141 JORDANUS, *Nemorarius*. Iordani opusculum de ponderositate Nicolai Tartaleae studio
correctum, nouis' que figuris auctum.
4° Venice, C.T. de' Navò, 1565.   EUL
And: 'Esperienze fatte da Nicolo Tartalea.'

142 KLEINFELDIUS, Nicolaus. Nicolai Klein-
feldii Gedanensis declamatio philosophica de
immortalitate animæ.
16° Leyden, C.Raphelengius, 1598.   EUL

143 KLEINFELDIUS, Nicolaus. Nicolai Klein-
feldii Gedanensis pathologia secundum genus.
Hoc est de morbis eorumque causis & differentijs.
Lib. I. De symptomatibus eorumque causis &
differentijs. Lib. II.
16° Leyden, C.Raphelengius, 1598.   EUL

Astrolabii [Phil. 47]
144 KOEBEL, Jacob. Astrolabii declaratio,
eiusdemque usus mire iucundus, non modò
astrologis, medicis, geographis, cæterisque literarum cultoribus multum utilis ac necessarius:
uerùm etiam mechanicis quibusdam opificibus
non parum commodus: à Iacobo Kœbelio facilio-
ribus formulis nuper aucta, longéque euidentior
edita. Cui accessit isagogicon in astrologiam
iudiciariam.
8° Paris, G.Cavellat, 1552.   EUL
With an inset and woodcuts.

145 KORNMANN, Heinrich. Templum naturæ
historicum . . . in quo, de natura et miraculis
quatuor elementorum; ignis, aeris, aquæ terræ, ita
disseritur . . .
8° Darmstadt, J.J.Porssius, 1611.   EUL

commentaria Stapulensis i̯n æth. [Phil. 50]
146* LE FÈVRE, Jacques, *d'Étaples*. Moralis J.
Fabri Stapulensis in Ethicen [of Aristotle]
introductio . . .

Leuinius lemnius de occultis naturæ [Phil. 18]
147 LEMNIUS, Levinus. De miraculis occultis
naturae libri iv, item de vita cum animi et corporis incolumitate recte instituenda liber unus . . .
8° Antwerp, C.Plantin, 1574.   SALE
Present location unknown. Title wanting.

148* LENS, Arnoldo de. In geometrica elementa
eisagoge.
8° Antwerp, C.Plantin, 1565.   AUCT

149 LEOPOREUS, Gulielmus. Ars memoratiua
. . .
4° [Paris,] J.Badius, 1520.   EUL
Imperfect: all after c8 is wanting.

Libauius in Melanch. dialect. [Phil. 54]
150 LIBAVIUS, Andreas. Dialectica Philippo-
Ramaea ex descriptionibus et commentariis P.
Melanchthonis et P.Rami aliorumque logicorum
. . .
8° Nuremberg, heirs of Gerlach, 1593.   EUL
Title wanting.

defensio Libleri [Phil. 53]
151* ? LIEBLERUS, Georgius. ?
Possibly Drummond's title refers to a work of
Thomas Liebler or Erastus against astrology:
*Defensio libelli Hieronymi Savonarolae de astrologia
divinatrice adversus Christophorum Stathmionem
medicum Coburgensem* which was printed at
Paris, 1569.

Glariani cosmographia [Phil. 9]
152* LORITUS, Henricus, *Glareanus*. ? De
geographia.
Or Loritus' editions of Strabo or Pius II's cosmo-
graphies.

153 LULL, Ramon. Illuminati sacre pagine
ꝓfessoris amplissimi magistri Raymundi Lull. ars
magna, generalis et vltima: quarūcunꝗ artium &
scientiarum ipsius Lull. assecutrix et clauigera:
& ad eas aditum faciliorē prebēs: antehac nusꝗ
arti impressorie emūctius cōmendata: & per
magistrum Bernardum la Vinheta artis illius fidelis-
simū interpretē elimata. Una cum figuris . . .
4° Lyons, J.Marechal for S.Vincent, 1517.   EUL

Theoremata metaphisicorum Martini [Phil. 39]
154* ?MARTIN,James. ?Partitiones et quaestiones.
Or Cornelius Martinus' *Metaphysica commentatio?*

155 MARTIN, James. Iacobi Martini Scoti . . . de
prima simplicium, & concretorum corporum
generatione disputatio, in qua Aristotelis, Galeni
& aliorum sententia de simplici & absoluta
generatione, deꝗ elementis, quatenus ad genera-
tionem desiderentur, proponitur . . .
8° Cambridge, T.Thomas, 1584.   EUL
STC 17524

156 MĀ SHĀ ALLĀH, *Al-Misrī*. De elementis et
orbibus coelestibus, liber antiquus ac eruditus
Messahalæ laudatissimi inter Arabes astrologi. Cui
adiectum est scriptum cuiusdam Hebræi de Eris
seu interuallis regnorum, & de diuersis gentium
annis ac mensibus. Item ijsdem de rebus: scriptum
cuiusdam Saraceni, continens preterea
precepta ad usum tabularum astronomicarum
utilissima. Quæ omnia . . . dicauit Ioachimus
Hellerus . . .

4° Nuremberg, J. vom Berg and V. Neuber, 1549.
         EUL

Mercurii Morsthemii de astrologia [Phil. 37]
157* MERCURIUS, Joannes, *Morsshemius.*
Explicatio gravis . . . de præsignificationibus atq;
iudiciis astrologicis . . .

158 MUHAMMAD, *Al-Baghdādi.* De super-
ficierum diuisionibus liber Machometo Bagdedino
ascriptus nunc primum Ioannis Dee Londinensis,
& Federici Commandini Vrbinatis opera in lucem
editus. Federici Commandini de eadem re libellus.
4° Pesaro, H. Concordia, 1570.   EUL

159 NEANDER, Michael, *of Sorau, ed.* Orbis
terræ diuisio compendiaria et plana in partes et
regiones suas præcipuas, veteres & nouas: in
vsum studiosæ iuuentutis, in schola Ilfeldensi . . .
Accessit etiam chronicorum omniũ ætatum, gentium
& temporum compendium. [In 2 parts.]
8° Wittenberg, J. Apel, 1594.   EUL

Offusius de diuina astrorum facultate
[Phil. 34]
160* OFFUSIUS, Jofrancus. De divina astrorum
facultate, in larvatam astrologiam.

161 OLEVIANUS, Gaspar. Fundamenta dialecticæ breuiter consignata è prælectionibus . . .
8° Frankfort, A. Wechel, 1581.   EUL
With an inset.

Institutiones Pacii in dialecticum [Phil. 10]
162* PACIUS, Julius. Institutiones logicae quibus
non solum universa Organi Aristotelici sententia
. . . continetur; sed etiam syllogismi hypothetici,
et methodi, quorum expositio in Organo desi-
deratur . . . explicantur.

decisiones physionomiæ Abbani [Phil. 21]
163 PETRUS, *de Abano.* Decisiones physio-
nomiae . . . [*Ed.* M. A. Biondo.]
8° Venice, Comin da Trino, 1548.   EUL
Bought in Paris, 1607.

Philo de mundo [Phil. 36]
164* PHILO, *Judæus.* De mundo.

Alexandri Piccolominei sphera [Phil. 6]
165* PICCOLOMINI, Alessandro, *Abp.* A.
Picolhominei de sphaera libri quatuor ex Italico
in Latinum sermonem conversi.

Commentarium Francisci Piccolomenei in libros
Ar. de anima de ortu et interitu tex latino
[List K]
166* PICCOLOMINI, Francesco. Commentarii
duo: prior, in libros Aristotelis de ortu et interitu: alter, in tres libros ejusdem de anima. [With
the text.]
Also as Phil. 1.

logica Piccolominei [Phil. 11]
167* PICCOLOMINI, Francesco. ? Discursus ad
universam logicam attinens.

Franc. Piccolominei æthicæ quest. [Phil. 8]
168* PICCOLOMINI, Francesco. Ethica.
Also in List G.

opera platonis [Phil. 46]
169 PLATO. Omnia diuini Platonis opera trãla-
tione Marsilii Ficini, emendatione et ad Graecum
codicem collatione Simonis Grynæi . . .
2° Basle, H. Froben and N. Episcopius, 1551.   PR
Bought in Paris, 1607. An earlier edition of the
same work (2° Paris, 1518) now in DUL, may
have also been in Drummond's library: it is
signed 'Gui. Drummond' but the signature is
probably that of Drummond's son.

170 PLATO. [*Supposititious work.*] Platonis
axiochus, siue de morte. Ioachino Perionio Benedictino Cormœriaceno interprete.
4° Paris, T. Richard, 1555.   EUL
Colophon has 1558.

171 PLETIUS, Nicolaus. Compendium de victus
ratione pro anni et aetatis partibus instituenda, ac
de alimentorum facultatibus . . .
8° Paris, widow of C. Chevallon, 1538.   EUL
Title wanting.

Pomponatius de incantationibus [Phil. 30]
172 POMPONATIUS, Petrus. Petri Pomponatii
Mantuani de naturalium effectum causis; siue, de
incantationibus, opus . . . [*Ed. with* scholia *by*
G. Gratarolus.]
8°? Basle, H. Petri, 1556.   SALE
Given in sale catalogue as a 12°. Present location
unknown.

Meteora Pontani [List K]
173* PONTANUS, Joannes Jovianus. Joannis
Joviani Pontani liber de meteoris . . .

Pontanus de rebus cœlestibus [Phil. 22]
174* PONTANUS, Joannes Jovianus. De rebus
cœlestibus.

Simonis Portii liber de dolore [Phil. 23]
175* PORTIUS, Simon. De dolore liber.

176* PRATIS, Jason A. J. a Pratis . . . de pariēte
& partu liber, obstetricibus, puerperis nutricibusꝗ
utilissimus . . .   AUCT
Edition not traced. AUCT has 1525.

177 PTOLEMAEUS, Claudius. Cla. Ptolemæi
inerrantium stellarum significationes per Nicolaum
Leonicum è græco translatæ. XII. Romanorum
menses in ueteribus monumentis Romæ reperti
Sex priorum mensium digestio ex sex Ouidij

Fastorum libris excerpta.
8° Antwerp, J. Grapheus, 1527.   EUL

Tacælus in dialect. Rami [Phil. 45]
178* RAMUS, Petrus. P. Rami dialecticæ libri
duo, A. Talaei prælectionibus illustrati.

*Petri Rami scholia in omnes liberales artes
excepta mathematica* [List K]
179* RAMUS, Petrus. P. Rami scholae in liberales
artes . . .
Contains Ramus' lectures on grammar, rhetoric,
logic, physics and metaphysics, and some of his
orations (see Ong, pp. 431–2). The lectures on
mathematics were listed in the table of contents
but did not appear. Or 179* = 180.*

scholia Rami in omnia ar. opera [Phil. 5]
180* RAMUS, Petrus. ? Scholarum dialecticarum
seu animadversionum in Organum Aristotelis
libri viginti. Recens emendati per Ioannem Piscatorem . . .
Ramus did not edit Aristotle's works; this edition
of his attack on Aristotelian dialectic may be the
work referred to by Drummond. See Ong, p. 65.
Or 180=179.

Geometria Ryff [Phil. 16]
181* RYFF, Petrus. Quæstiones geometricæ in
Euclidis.

Clauius in spheram [Phil. 26]
182* SACRO BOSCO, Joannes de. Christophori
Clauii . . . In sphæram Ioannis de Sacro Bosco
commentarius . . .

183 SARZOZUS, Franciscus. In aequatorem
planetarum libri duo.
2° Paris, S. de Colines, 1526.   EUL
Title wanting.

184 SCHENKELIUS, Lambertus Thomas. Gazo-
phylacium artis memoriæ, in quo duobus libris,
omnia et singula ea quæ ad absolutam hujus
cognitionem inseruiunt, recondita habentur . . .
His accesserunt de eadem arte memoriæ adhuc 3.
opuscula: quorum 1. Ioannis Austriaci, 2. Hieronymi Marafioti, 3. Ioh: Sp[angenbergii] Herd-
[essiani] . . .
8° Strasburg, A. Bertram, 1510 [= 1610].   EUL

185 SCHREVELIUS, Theodorus. Theod.
Schrevelii Ἀλεξίκακον sive de patientia libri IV.
12° Leyden, by J. Cornelius at the house of J.
Maire, 1623.   EUL

186 SCRIBONIUS, Gulielmus Adolphus. Idea
medicinæ secundum logicas leges informandæ et
describendæ. Cui accessit de inspectione vrinarum,
contra eos, qui ex qualibet urina de quolibet
morbo judicare volunt: item de hydrope, de

podagra & dysenteria, physiologia cursoria . . .
8° Lemgow, K. Growthe, 1584.   EUL

Naturales questiones senicæ [Phil. 32]
187* SENECA, Lucius Annæus. Naturales
quæstiones.

188 SETON, John. Dialectica. Ioannis Setoni
Cantabrigiensis, annotationibus Petri Carteri, vt
clarissimis, ita breuissimis explicata. Huic accessit,
ob artium ingenuarum inter se cognationem,
Gulielmi Buclæi arithmetica.
8° London, T. Marsh, 1574.   EUL
STC 22252

Zieglerus de solidæ sphæræ constructione
[Phil. 20]
189 SPHAERA. Sphaerae atque astrorum cœle-
stium ratio, natura, & motus: ad totius mundi
fabricationis cognitione fundamenta.
4° [Basle,] J. Walder, 1536.   EUL
In Greek and Latin. Contains the following works:
Jacobus Ziegler, *De solidæ sphæræ constructione*;
Proclus, *De sphæræ* (with Ziegler's scholia);
De canonica per sphæram operatione; Berosus,
Hemicyclium; Aratus, *De siderum natura & motu*
(with a commentary by Theon of Alexandria);
C. Ptolemy, *Planisphærium*; and Jordanus (Nemo-
rarius), *Planisphærium*. Bought by Drummond in
Paris, 1607, and given to EUL by Adam Sinclair
in 1622.

opera Talei [Phil. 35]
190* TALON, Omer. Audomari Talaei quem Petri
Rami Theseum dicere iure possis Opera Socra-
ticae methodicaeque philosophiae studiosis per-
necessaria . . .
This collection continued the *Rhetorica*, Talon's
lectures on Cicero's *Lucullus, Paradoxa, Topica,
De partitione oratoria,* on Aristotle's *Ethica* and
on Porphyry. Drummond's copy may have been
one of the smaller editions which omitted the
Rhetorica. See Ong, pp. 485–8.

De vnica methodo Tempellus [Phil. 44]
191 TEMPLE, William. Pro Mildapetti de vnica
methodo defensione contra Diplodophilum, commentatio Gulielmi Tempelli, é regio collegio
Cantabrigiensi. Huc accessit nonnullarum é
physicis & ethicis quæstionum explicatio uná cum
epistola de Rami dialectica ad Joannem Piscatorem
Argentinensem.
8° Frankfort, heirs of A. Wechel, 1584.   EUL
Mildapettus = Temple; Diplodophilus =
E. Digby. Bought in Paris, 1608.

Titilmanii dialectica [Phil. 38]
192* TITELMAN, Franciscus. Compendium
dialecticae . . ad libros logicorum Arist. admodum
utile . . . recognitum . . .

Titilmanii compendium philos. [Phil. 32]
193* TITELMAN, Franciscus. F. Titelmanni
naturalis philosophiae compendium, sive de
consideratione rerum naturalium libri XII.

*Toleti commentaria in logicam Aris. 1. 2. libros
acromaticos et de generat. et corrup. 3 in libros
de anima* [List K]
194 TOLETUS, Franciscus, *Card.* D. Francisci
Toleti, societatis Iesu, omnia quae hucusque
extant opera . . .
8° Lyons, S. De La Porte, 1587.   EUL
Incomplete: all after n6 is wanting. Also as
Phil. 7.

Toleti dialectica [Phil. 19]
195* TOLETUS, Franciscus, *Card.* Introductionis
in dialecticam Aristotelis libri V, cum Porphyrii
quinque vocibus et Aristotelis categoriis [Severino
Boetio interprete].
This is probably the work meant by Drummond's
title, though it may have been Toletus' more
detailed commentary on Aristotelian logic.
Also in List G.

196 TOMMAI, Petrus, *Ravennas.* Foenix Domini
Petri Ravennatis memoriae magistri.
8° Venice, P. dei Nicolini da Sabbio for M. Sessa,
1533.   EUL

cutheberti Tonstialii de arte supputandi
[Phil. 25]
197* TUNSTALL, Cuthbert, *Bp.* De arte supputandi libri quatuor.

Adriani turnebi disputatio de fato [Phil. 33]
198 TURNÈBE, Adrien. Ad. Turnebi disputatio
ad lib. Ciceronis de fato, aduersus quendam qui
non solum logicus esse, uerumetiam dialecticus
haberi uult.
4° Paris, M. de Vascosan, 1556.   EUL
A piece in the controversy between Turnèbe and
Ramus over Ramus' commentary on Cicero's *De
fato.*
See Ong, p. 293. Bought in Paris, 1607.

199 VUELPIUS, Henricus. Libellus de minutiis
physicis, & practicis astronomicæ arithmeticæ
regulis . . .
4° Cologne, J. Gymnich, 1544.   EUL

Waseri arithmetica [Phil. 49]
200* WASERUS, Caspar. Institutio arithmeticæ.
Accessit tractatus de quadrato geometricorum
figuris æneis.
See Draud, p. 1318.

201 WILLET, Andrew. De animae natura et
viribus quæstiones quædam, partim ex Aristo-
telicis scriptis decerptæ: partim ex vera philosophia, id est, rationis thesauris, deprompta, in

vsum Cantabrigiensium . . .
8° Cambridge, T. Thomas, 1585.   EUL
STC 25674

*Commentarium Iacobi Zaba. in 8 libros acro-
maticos, de ortu et interitu, et 4 meteorologicorum
Ar.* [List K]
202* ZABARELLA, Giacomo, *the Elder.* J. Z.
. . . in libros Aristotelis physicorum commentarii
. . .
An edition with commentaries on the *De ortu
et interitu* and the *Meteorologica.*
Also as Phil. 2.

Zabarella in log. [Phil. 3]
203* ZABARELLA, Giacomo, *the Elder.* Opera
logica.

LAW

Alciatus de duello [Jur. 3]
204 ALCIATUS, Andreas. Andreæ Alciati
iurecons. clariss. de singulari certamine liber.
Eiusdem consilium in materia duelli, exceptum ex
libro quinto responsorum.
8° Lyons, A. Vincent, 1543.   EUL

lexicon Iuris Nebricensis [Jur. 8]
205 ANTONIO, *de Lebrixa.* Lexicon iuris ciuilis
. . .
8° Paris, O. Petit, 1549.   EUL
Bought in Paris, 1607.

apelli Tyrocinia iuris [Jur. 24]
206* APELLUS, Joannes. Tyrocinia iuris distinctionibus repetita.
Draud has an edition: Basle, 1580. Draud, p. 739.

207 ARNAULD, Antoine. Actio habita . . . olim
verò reginæ regum matri à consiliis & generali
causarum cognitione. Pro academia Parisiensi
actrice. Contra Iesuitas reos. Ex XII. & XIII.
mens. Iulii an M.D.XCV. Præterea litteræ regis de
homicidio in ipsum attentato. & consultum iudica-
tum parlamenti aduersus Ioan. Castel. discipulum
Iesuitam. Ex idiomate Gallico syncerè translata.
8° Paris, 1595.   EUL

lexicon Iuris Brissonii [Jur. 9]
208* BRISSON, Barnabé. Barnabae Brissonii . . .
Lexicon juris, sive de Verborum quae ad jus
pertinent significatione libri XIX, cum appendice
praetermissarum quarundam vocum et parergῶν
libro singulari . . .

budei pandecta iuris [Jur. 20]
209 BUDÉ, Guillaume. Annotationes . . . in
quattuor et viginti pandectarum libros . . . Accura-
tius nitidiusꝗ ab Iodoco Badio Ascensio nuper
impressæ.
2° [Paris,] J. Badius, 1524.   EUL

cherodoti paratitla institutionum [Jur. 10]
210* CHEIRODOTUS, Joannes. Paratitla in 4.
libr institut. iuris.
Draud has an edition: Basle, 1605. Draud, p. 800.

paratitla digest. Cuiacii [Jur. 19]
211* CUJACIUS, Jacobus. Paratitla in libros quinquaginta digestorum seu pandectarum imperatoris
Iustiniani.

Historia Iuris ciuilis Riualii [Jur. 14]
212* DU RIVAIL, Aymar. A. Rivallii civilis
Historiæ Juris . . .
The first editions were printed in the early sixteenth century. The work was re-printed in the
collection *Tractatus universi juris*, 1584.

213 FRANCE. Henry II, *King*. Commentarius
ad edictum Henrici secundi contra paruas datas &
abusus curiæ Romanæ . . . [June, 1550; and other
edicts, with the text, by Charles Du Moulin].
4° Lyons, A. Vincent, 1552.   EUL

Paradoxa Iuris ciuilis [Jur. 16]
214* GRANGERIANUS, Petrus. Paradoxa iuris
ciuilis.
Draud has an edition: Lyons, 1581. Draud, p. 765.

215 GRATIANUS, *the Canonist*. Decretum
Gratiani: seu verius, decretorum canonicorū
collectanea, ab ipso auctore Gratiano primùm
inscripta, concordia discordantium canonum: ex
diuite illa scriptorum ecclesiasticorum, summorum
pontificum, conciliorúmque oecumenicorum
supellectile, eiusdem Gratiani labore concinnata, &
in suas classes digesta. Præfixa sunt ab Antonio
Demochare Sorbonicæ Academiæ collega, singulis
ferè distinctionibus & causarum quæstionibus
παρατιτλα quædam, summam totius rei succinctè
complectentia . . .
2° Antwerp, heirs of J. Steels and P. Nuyts at the
house of C. Plantin, 1573.   EUL
With *Censura in glossas iuris canonici. Ex archetypo
Romano*. And *Mararita decreti, seu tabula Mar-
tiniana, edita per fratrem Martinum ordinis prædicatorum, domini Papæ pœnitentiarium & capellanum.*
The printer of the main work is given as Theodorus Lindanus, while the colophon proper reads
by J. Withagius for C. Plantin, 1572.

Procheoria titulorum pand. [Jur. 23]
216 HOPPER, Joachim. Προθεωρια, siue dispositio titulorum pandectarum iuris ciuilis . . .
prælectionibus collecta, nunc primum in tabulas
digesta, per Ottonem ab Hoeuel.
4° Cologne, heirs of A. Birckmann, 1564.   EUL
Bought in Bourges, 1608.

Hortensius in l. pacta [Jur. 22]
217 HORTENSIUS, Aegidius. Ægidii Hortensii
Anetensis, I.C. in L. pacta conuenta. lxxij. D. de

contrahenda emptione. Ad haec in titulum inte-
grum singulásque leges D. de præscriptis verbis &
infactum actionibus, commentarij . . .
4° Lyons, B. Honorat, 1587.   EUL
Bought in Bourges, 1608.

partitiones Iuris Hottamanii [Jur. 6]
218* HOTMAN, François. F. Hotomani . . . Partitiones iuris civilis elementariæ. Particula universæ
historiæ ab eodem auctore conscripta quæ ad Jus
civile pertinet.
Repeated [in error?], Jur. 13.

Hottomanus in institutiones [Jur. 12]
219* HOTMAN, François. F. H. . . . vetus-
renovatus commentarius in quatuor libros institutionum iuris civilis.

220 JAMETIUS, Franciscus. Francisci Iametii
iurisconsulti commentarius in xliiij. leges sub tit.
de regul. iur. pandect. . . .
8° Paris, O. Petit, 1549.   EUL

corpus Iuris ciuilis [Jur. 1]
221* JUSTINIAN I, *Emperor of the East*. Corpus
iuris civilis.

acurtius [Jur. 5]
222* JUSTINIAN I, *Emperor of the East*. ? Institutiones. [With the commentary of Accursius
the Glossator.]
Or Accursius' commentary on the whole *Corpus
iuris civilis.*

223 JUSTINIAN I, *Emperor of the East*. In-
stitutiones imperiales nouiter impresse . . . [*Ed.*
J. Chappuis.]
4° Lyons, J. Huguetan, 1516.   EUL
The colophon gives the printer as Gilbert De
Villiers.

Institutiones Crispini [Jur. 11]
224* JUSTINIAN I, *Emperor of the East*. Imp.
Caes. Justiniani Institutionum lib. IIII., adnota-
tionibus . . . illustrati . . . Studio et opera J.
Crispini Atre. . . .

Notata Ant. Mercatoris [Jur. 21]
225* JUSTINIAN I, *Emperor of the East*. Dn. N.
Iustiniani . . . Institutionum sive Elementorum . . .
lib. IIII emendatissimi. In eosdem libros Jacobi
Cujacij posteriores notæ . . .
Cujas used the pseudonym Antonius Mercator.

Theophilus [Jur. 2]
226* JUSTINIAN I, *Emperor of the East*. Institutionum juris civilis libri quatuor, olim a
Theophilo antecessore in graecum e latino . . .
translati . . . e graeco in latinum . . . conversi . . .

227   LA MOTHE LE VAYER, Felix de. Legatus seu de legatione legatorumque priuilegiis officio ac munere libellus . . .
4° Paris, M. de Roigny, 1579.   EUL

Obseruationum legalium libri decem [Jur. 4]
228* OBSERVATIONES.
Not identified.

229   PAOLA, *Servita* [Pietro Sarpi]. De iurisdictione serenissimæ reipublicæ Venetae in mare Adriaticum epistola Francisci de Ingenuiis, Germani, ad Liberium Vincentium, Hollandum, aduersus Ioh. Baptistam Valenzolam, Hispanum, et Laurentium Motinum, Romanum; qui iurisdictionem illam non pridem impugnare ausi sunt.
4° Freistadt, 1619.   EUL

Iulii pauli sententiæ cum com. cuiacii
[Jur. 15]
230* PAULUS, Julius. Iulij Pauli receptarum sententiarum ad filium, libri V. In eosdem I. Cuiacij interpretationes.

Reuardus ad leges 12 tabularum [Jur. 17]
231* RÆVARDUS, Jacobus. J. Rævardi . . . ad leges duodecim tabularum liber singularis . . .

232   RAYMUNDUS, Joannes. Epistolarum legalium, in quibus varii iuris articuli continentur, libri tres . . . è corpore iuris collectæ . . .
8° Lyons, G. Rouille, 1549.   EUL
Bought in Bourges, 1608.

sententiæ communes Iuris [Jur. 7]
233* SENTENTIA. Sententiæ sive loci communes utriusque juris serie alphabetica digesti . . . Hisce adjecimus legum flosculos selectissimos . . .

Sudorii disputationes ciuiles [Jur. 18]
234   SUDORIUS, Nicolaus. Nicolai Sudorii consiliarii regii, et praesidis inquisitionis, disputationum ciuilium liber. In quo iuris ciuilis quæstiones complures, difficiles atque obscuræ, accuratè tractantur.
4° Paris, F. Morel [the first], 1578.   EUL
Bought in Paris, 1607.

235   TASSARA, Antonius. Antonii Tassarae notarii pat. auth. compendium in notariorum siue tabellionum excessus, errores atque peccata : naturalibus, theologicis, & legalibus rationibus exornatum : & abipsomet auctore nouissimè a multis mendis repugnatum : & xv. alijs capitibus locupletatum.
8° Frankfort, N. Bassée, 1590.   EUL

236   TIRAQUELLUS, Andreas. Andreae Tiraquelli Fontenaii apud Pictones suppraefecti commentarii, in L. si vnquam. C. de reuo. dona. Nuper enmedati, necnon accentibus diligenter

illustrati.
8° Lyons, G. Rouille, 1547.   EUL

237   WELWOOD, William. Iuris diuini Iudaeorum, ac iuris ciuilis Romanorum parallela ; siue vtriusque è suis vndequaque sedibus ad verbum transcripti ocularis collatio.
4° Leyden, F. Raphelengius, 1594.   EUL

POETRY

238   ABERNETHY, Adam. Ecloga regalis de auspicatissimo matrimonio lectissimorum principum, Caroli Stuarti Magnæ Britaniæ, Hiberniæ, &c. regis, et Henricæ Mariæ Burboniæ . . .
4° Paris, P. Des Hayes, 1625.   EUL

239   ADAMSON, John. Musarum votum & vaticinium. Kalend. Ianuarij. 1620.
4° Edinburgh, A. Hart, 1620.   EUL
STC 137

240* ADAMSON, John. Στοιχείωσις eloquiorum dei.
12° Edinburgh, heirs of A. Hart, 1627.   AUCT
STC 138

241   AMERBACHIUS, Vitus. Variorum carminum viti Amerpachii, nonnullorum que aliorum liber.
8° Basle, J. Oporinus, 1550.   EUL

242   ANDRELINUS, Publius Faustus. P. Fausti andrelini Foroliuiensis hecatodistichon Iohanne Vatello castigatore, et paraphraste.
8° Paris, widow of M. de la Porte, 1549.   EUL

Arati phainomina C. Germanici [Poe. 30]
243* ARATUS, *of Soli*. Phaenomena. [*Tr.* Germanicus Caesar.]

244   ARENA, Antonius de. Antonius Arena Prouincialis, de bragardissima villa de Soleriis, ad suos compagnones studiantes qui sunt de persona friantes, bassas dansas in gallanti stilo bisognatas : & de nouo per ipsum correctas, & ioliter augmentatas, cum guerra Romana totum ad longum sine require : & cum guerra Neapolitana : & cum reuolta Gennuensi : & guerra Auenionensi : & epistola ad falotissimam garsam pro passando lo tempus alegramentum mandat. Leges dansandi sunt hic, quas fecit Arena . . .
8° Lyons, P. Rigaud, 1605.   EUL

Montani Hymni [Poe. 35]
245   ARIAS MONTANUS, Benedictus. Benedicti Ar. Montani hymni et secula. [*Ed.* P. de Valentia.]
16° Antwerp, widow of C. Plantin and J. Mourentorff, 1593.   EUL
And *Ecclesiastes. Humanarum rerum actionumque*

summa, Salomone colligente subducta, et carminibus decantata: B. Aria Montano interprete...

246* AUSONIUS, Decimus Magnus. Opera.
                                                    AUCT

247 AYTON, *Sir* Robert. Basia: siue strena cal. Ian. ad Iacobum Hayum equitem illustrissimum.
4° London, M. Bradwood, 1605.   EUL
STC² 1014.5

248* BAERLE, Kasper van. Britannia triumphans, siue in inaugurationem serenissimi, potentissimi, inuictissimi principis, Caroli I ... poemation.
2° Leyden, 1626.   AUCT

249* BAERLE, Kasper van. Ad illustrissimum principem Fredericum Henricum, principem Auraicum, comitem Nassoviae ... gratulatio panegyrica ...
2° Leyden, G. Basson, 1625.   AUCT

Gilb. blancherii pleiades [Poe. 31]
250 BANCHERELLUS, Gilbertus. Gilberti Bancherelli Pleiades.
8° Limoges, J. Blanchet, 1596.   EUL
Bought in Paris, 1607.

251 BARCLAY, John. Ioannis Barclaii poematum libri duo.
4° London, J. Bill, 1615.   EUL
STC 1387

252 BENCIUS, Franciscus. Francisci Bencii ab Aqua pente, e Societate Iesu, carminum libri quatuor eiusdem Ergastus et Philotimus, dramata.
8° Ingolstadt, D. Sartorius, 1592.   EUL

epigrammata beze [Poe. 28]
253* BÈZE, Théodore de. Poemata.
Bèze's epigrams do not ever seem to have been printed alone; they formed the second half of his *Poemata*, and a part of the more inclusive *Poemata varia*. See Frédéric Gardy, *Bibliographie des œuvres ... de Théodore de Bèze* (Geneva, 1960), pp. 1–14. Possibly Drummond's *Poemata* was incomplete.

254 BÈZE, Théodore de. Epicedia, quae clarissimi aliquot viri, et D. Theodoro Bezae charissimi: sicut & illis ipse Beza viuus charissimus, & mortuus est honoratissimus: scripserunt in ipsius obitum.
4° Geneva, J. Chouet, 1606.   EUL
Hebrew, Greek and Latin verses by various authors.

255 BIZARI, Pietro. Petri Bizzari poematum libri ii.
8° Venice, P. Manuzio, 1565.   EUL
Part of *Petri Bizzari varia opuscula.*

Veneres Blienburgicæ [Poe. 47]
256 BLYENBURGIUS, Damascus. Veneres Blyenburgicæ, siue amorum hortus ...
8° Dordrecht, I. Canin for D. Episcopius, 1600.
Bought in Paris, 1607.   EUL

Boetius de consolat. [Poe. 39]
257* BOETHIUS, Anicius Manlius Torquatus Severinus. De consolatione philosophiae libri v.

258 BORBONIUS, Nicolaus. In Francisci Valesii regis obitum, inq; Henrici eius filij regis aduentū, dialogus ... Item alia quædam eiusdem authoris lectu non iniucunda.
4° Paris, M. de Vascosan, 1547.   EUL

259 BORBONIUS, Nicolaus. Nicolai Borbonii Vandoperani Lingonensis, nugarum libri octo. Ab autore recens aucti et recogniti.
8° Basle, heirs of A. Cratander, 1540. EUL

Bodius [Poe. 49]
260* BOYD, Mark Alexander. M. Alexandri Bodii epistolæ heroides, et hymni ... Addita est eiusdem literularum prima curia.

Narragonia Iacobi philomusi [Poe. 51]
261* BRANT, Sebastian. Stultifera nauis. [*Tr.* Jacob Locher, *Philomusus.*]

Bullengeri poemata [Poe. 24]
262* ? BULLINGER, Ulrich. ? De rebus gestis Mosis libri nouem carmine heroico.
Draud lists two editions, p. 1511.

263 CALPURNIUS, Titus Julius, *Siculus.* Buccolica calphu ⟨rnii⟩ sine commento.
4° [Paris,] F. Baligault, [c. 1500].   EUL
A later issue of Pellechet 3171. Title mutilated.

264 CAMBRIDGE UNIVERSITY. Academiae cantabrigiensis lachrymæ tumulo nobilissimi equitis, D. Philippi Sidneij sacratæ per Alexandrum Neuillum.
4° London, J. Windet for T. Chard, 1587. EUL
STC 4473
Verses in Latin, Greek and Hebrew by various authors.

265 CAMBRIDGE UNIVERSITY. Lacrymæ cantabrigienses: in obitum serenissimæ reginæ Annæ ...
4° Cambridge, C. Legge, 1619.   EUL
STC 4489
With an inset 'In obitum sereniss. Reginæ Annæ ænigmata quædam cabalistica,' being anagrammatic verses in Latin, with some additional matter in Greek and Hebrew. The Hebrew is not printed, but in MS.

266   CHALMERS, George. Sylua Leochaeo suo sacra : siue Lycidae desiderium.
4° Paris, J. La que Hay, 1620.   EUL

267   [CHEEKE, William.] Anagrammata, et chron-anagrammata regia, nunc primum in hâc formâ in lucem emissa.
8° London, W. Stansby, 1613.   EUL
STC 5107

268   CORDUS, Euricius. Opera poetica Euricii Cordi . . . scriptoris omnium festiuissimi ac disertissimi, quæcunq: usquam prodierunt, in unum corpus collecta, et ad postremam autoris recognitionem diligentissime elaborata . . .
8° Frankfort, heirs of C. Egenolff, 1564.   EUL

269   CRAIG, George. Specimen epigrammatum Iacobo primo Britanniarum regi dicatum . . .
8° London, M. F[lesher], 1624.   EUL
STC 5961

270   CRAIG, *Sir* Thomas. Ad sereniss. et potentiss. principem Iacobum sextum e sua Scotia decedentem paræneticon.
4° [Edinburgh,] R. Waldegraue, 1603.   EUL
STC 5968

271   [CRAIG, *Sir* Thomas.] Ad serenissimum Britanniarum principem Henricum, è Scotia discedentem propempticon.
4° Edinburgh, R. Charteris, 1603.   EUL
STC 5969

272   CRAIG, *Sir* Thomas. Serenissimi, & inuictissimi principis, Iacobi Britanniarum et Galliarum regis, στεφανοφορία.
4° [Edinburgh,] R. Charteris, 1603.   EUL
STC 5971

273* CROCUS, Cornelius. Comoedia sacra, cui titulus Ioseph, ad Christianæ iuuentutis institutionem . . .
8° Antwerp, J. Grapheus for J. Steels, 1536. AUCT

274   DAMMAN, Hadrian. Schediasmata Hadr. Dammanis a Bisterueld Gandauensis. I. De nuptiis serenissimi potentissimique Scot. regis Iacobi vi. et serenissimae virginis Annae Friderici ii Daniae, Norduegiae et C. regis F. II. De tempestate, que sponsam regiam nauigantem repulit. III. In aetheos elegia. IV. In regis nauigationem Danicam emblema. V. De coronatione reginæ Scotorum Annae. VI. De introitu eius in primariam regni vrbem Edinburgum.
4° Edinburgh, R. Waldegraue, 1590.   EUL
STC 6217

275   DANEAU, Lambert. Geographicæ poeticæ, id est, vniuersæ terræ descriptionis ex optimis ac vetustissimis quibusque Latinis poetis libri quatuor : quorum, primus, Europam : secundus, Africam : tertius, Asiam : quartus, mare vniuersum, et maris insulas continet . . .
8° [Geneva,] J. Stoer, 1580.   EUL

276   DANSKIN, Henry. De remoris quibus impeditus in sacri ministerii munere capessendo . . . cunctabundus fuerit. H. D. carmen ad amplissimum et reuerendissimum in Christo patrem, Georgium archiepiscopum Andreapolitanum . . .
4° [Edinburgh, A. Hart, 1613?]   EUL
STC² 6267.5

277   DEMPSTER, Thomas. Epithalamion in nuptiis generosissimorum Iacobi Comitis Perthani, Domini Drommondi, Baronis Stobhalliæ, &c. & Isabellae, unicæ Roberti Comitis Wintonij, Domini Setonii &c. filiȩ.
4° Edinburgh, R. Charteris, 1608.   EUL
STC 6580

278* DEMPSTER, Thomas. Musca recidiua. Strena kal. Ian . . .   AUCT

279   DOUSA, Janus, *the Younger*. Iani Dousæ filii poemata : olim à patre collecta ; nunc ab amicis edita.
16° Leyden, A. Clouquius, 1607.   EUL

Guilelmi Blancii poemata [Poe. 5]
280* DU BLANC, Guillaume, *Bp.* Poemata Guilielmi Blanci jun.

281   DUCHAT, Louis François le. L. Francis. Ducatii Trecaei praeludiorum. Lib. iii.
8° Paris, J. Caveiller, 1554.   EUL

282   DUNBAR, Joannes. Ioannis Dunbari Megalobritanni doctoris medici, et philosophi Daphnæum doctorale in Apollinis, et Peneiae nuptiis, siue consensus nobilissimæ, & florentissimæ vniuersitatis Patauinæ . . . Cum amicorum syncharmatis.
4° Padua, G. B. de Martino, 1618.   EUL
At the end are verses in Greek, Latin, Italian, French and English.

283   ECHLIN, John. De regno Angliae, Franciæ, Hiberniæ ad serenissimum et inuictiss. Iacobum 6. Scotorum regem vltrò delato. Panegyricon.
4° [Edinburgh,] R. Waldegraue, 1603.   EUL
STC 7481

284   EDINBURGH UNIVERSITY. Νοστωδια. In serenissimi, potentissimi, et inuictissimi monarchae, Iacobi Magnæ Britanniæ, Franciæ & Hiberniæ regis, fidei defensoris, &c. felicem in Scotiam reditum, academiæ Edinburgensis congratulatio.
4° Edinburgh, A. Hart, 1617.   EUL
And *Epibaterion* by Adam King.
STC 7487

Epigrammata et poemata vetera [Poe. 11]
285* EPIGRAMMATA. Epigrammata et poemata vetera. [Ed. P. Pithou.]

Sacrarum heroidum liber [Poe. 34]
286* ESPENCE, Claude d'. Cl. Espencaei . . . Sacrarum heroidum liber . . .

Fabricius de re poet. [Poe. 12]
287 FABRICIUS, Georgius, *Chemnicensis.* Georgii Fabricii Chemnicensis de re poetica libri septem . . .
16° Paris, J. de Marnef and the widow of G. Cavellat, 1584.   BM

288 FORCATULUS, Stephanus. Elegia . . . de pace inter Henricum Galliæ, & Philippum Hispaniæ reges facta veris tempore M.D.LIX.
4° Toulouse, G. Boudeville, 1559.   EUL

289 FRISCHLIN, Nicodemus. Priscianus vapulans. Nicodemi Frischlini Alemani comoedia lepida, faceta & vtilis, in quo demonstrantur solœcismi & barbarismi, qui superioribus seculis omnia artium & doctrinarum studia, quasi diluuio quodam inundarunt: scripta in laudem huius seculi.
8° Strasburg, B. Jobin, 1580.   EUL
With 'Epicedion de obitu, Iacobi Frischlini . . .' and an address to the rector and senate of the university of Tubingen, and 'Epigrammata'.

290 FUNGERUS, Joannes. Sylua carminum, in qua varia epigrammata et epitaphia doctorum ac illustrium virorum patriæ continentur . . .
8° Leyden, C. Plantin, 1585.   EUL

291 GIRARD, Jean. Stichostratia epigrammatôn centuriae quinque . . .
4° Lyons, M. Bonhomme, 1552.   EUL

292 GORDON, John. Antitortobellarminus, siue refutatio calumniarum, mendaciorum, et imposturarum Laico-Cardinalis Bellarmini, contra iura omnium regum, et sinceram, illibatamque famam, serenissimi, potentissimi, piissimique principis, Iacobi . . .
4° London, 1610.   EUL
STC 12054

293 GORDON, John. Antitortobellarminus . . .
4° London, 1610.   EUL
STC 12054
Another copy. Unsigned.

294 GORDON, John. Elizabethae reginæ manes de religione et regno ad Iacobum magnum, Britanniarum regem . . .
4° London, for T. Man, 1604.   EUL
STC 12057

Gratius de venatione [Poe. 9]
295* GRATIUS, *Faliscus.* De venatione.

296 GREGORY, *of Nazianzus,* St. D. Gregorii Naziazeni aduersus mulieres ambitiosius se adornantes & excolentes, carmen satyricum . . . [Tr. F. Morel.]
4° Paris, F. Morel [the second], 1600.   EUL

297 GWINNE, Matthew. Vertumnus siue annus recurrens Oxonii, xxix Augusti, anno. 1605. Coram Iacobo rege, Henrico principe proceribus. A Joannensibus in scena recitatus ab vno scriptus, phrasi comica prope tragicis Jenariis.
4° London, N. Okes for E. Blount, 1607.   EUL
STC 12555. Greg. L.6.

Franc. Hiemi poemata [Poe. 7]
298* HAEMUS, Franciscus, *Insulensis.* Poemata quædam.

299 HAGEN, Godefridus van der. Miscellanea poemata.
4° Middelburg, S. Moulert, 1619.   EUL
With 'Epitaphia': verses in Latin and English by several authors, including Drummond.

300 HARVEY, Richard. Ricardi Harveii; ephemeron, siue pæan, in gratiam perpurgatæ, reformatæcɋ dialecticæ.
8° London, R. Waldegraue, 1583.   EUL
STC 12912

301 HAY, Archibald. Ad illustriss. tit. S. Stephani in monte cœlio Cardinalem, D. Dauidem Betoun, primatem Scotiæ, Archiepiscopū S. Andreæ, Episco. Meripocensem, de foelici accessione dignitatis cardinalitiæ, gratulatorius panegyricus Archibaldi Hayi.
4° Paris, G. de Gourmont, 1540.   EUL

Dan. Hynsii Auriacus [Poe. 44]
302 HEINSIUS, Daniel. Danielis Heinsii Auriacus, siue libertas saucia. Accedunt eiusdem iambi partim morales, partim ad amicos, partim amicorum causâ scripti.
4° Leyden, A. Clouquius, 1602.   EUL
Bought in Paris, 1608.

danielis Hysii poemata [Poe. 43]
303* HEINSIUS, Daniel. Dan. Heinsii poematum nova editio, auctior emendatiorque . . .
There were at least three editions before 1611.

304 HOMER. Homeri Odyssea aduerbum translata, Andrea Diuo Iustinopolitano interprete. Eiusdem Batrachomyomachia, .i. ranarum & murium pugna, Aldo Manutio interprete. Eiusdem hymni deorum xxxii. Georgio Dartona Cretense interprete.
8° Paris, C. Wechel, 1538.   EUL
The second volume of a two volume edition.

305 HOPE, *Sir* Thomas. In serenissimum
inuictissimumq. monarcham, Carolum Dei gratia
Scotiæ, Angliæ, Franciæ & Hiberniæ regem,
fideique Christianæ vindicem acerrimum carmen
seculare . . .
4° Edinburgh, heirs of A. Hart, 1626. EUL
STC 13766

306 HUME, David. Daphn-Amaryllis.
4° London, R. Field, 1605. EUL
STC 13949

Dauidis Humii poemata [Poe. 53]
307 HUME, David. Dauidis Humii Theagrii
lusus poetici, in tres partes distincti.
4° London, R. Field, 1605. EUL
STC 13950

308* HUNTER, A. Epithalamium, in nuptias
illustris ac generosiss. D. Philippi comitis Hoenloo,
Langebergiæ domini, militum Hollandiæ &
Zelandiæ vicetribuni generalis, &c. & illustris
D. Mariæ, inclyti illius Guilielmi Auriaci principis
& Nassouiæ comitis filiæ, Buranae dominæ, &c.
4° Leyden, F. Raphelengius, 1595. AUCT
Copy in EUL.

309* HUTTEN, Ulrich von. Ars versificatoria . . .
8° Paris, R. Estienne [the first], 1532. AUCT
Copy in EUL.

310 ILLUSTRIUM. Illustrium aliquot Ger-
manorum carminum liber. De immanissima
summéq; miseranda Christianorum laniena ab
impijs & crudelissimis Galliæ tyrannis, Lutetiæ
Parisiorum, Lugduni item alijsque eiusdem regni
locis truculentissimè sceleratissiméq; patrata . . .
Vna cum epiceijs et epithafijs . . .
4° Vilna, 1573. EUL
Imperfect. Brunet wonders whether this work
really was printed in Vilna, but his doubts are not
sustained by Wierzbowski (see *Bibliographia
Polonica*, II, 133).

Iacobi pontani poetic. institutionum lib. [Poe. 8]
311* JACOBUS [SPANMUELLER], *Pontanus.*
Poeticarum institutionum libri iii.

312* JAMES I, *King*. Epicedium Jacobi Regis.
Not identified. AUCT

313 JOHNSTON, Arthur. Elegiae duae: vna ad
episcopum Abredonensem, de fratris obitu:
altera de pace rupta inter Scotos & Gallos.
4° Aberdeen, E. Raban, 1628. EUL
STC 14709

314 JOHNSTON, Arthur. Nicrina ad heroas
Anglos.
8° Heidelberg [London, W. Stansby], 1620. EUL
STC² 14713.5

315 JOHNSTON, John. Cantica sacra noui testamenti lyrico carmine reddita . . .
8° Saumur, T. Portæus, 1611. EUL

316 JOHNSTON, John. Heroes ex omni historia
Scotica lectissimi.
4° Leyden, C. Guyotius for A. Hart, 1603. EUL
STC 14786
See also Addenda in Proof, p. 232.

317 JOHNSTON, John. Iambi sacri, gemmulas
consolationum ex s. scriptura excerptas com-
plectentes . . .
8° Saumur, T. Portæus, 1611. EUL

Ihonstoni inscriptiones regum [Poe. 50]
318* JOHNSTON, John. Inscriptiones historicæ
regum Scotorum . . . Præfixus est Gathelus, siue
de gentis origine. Fragmentum A. Meluini. Additæ
sunt icones omnium regum . . . Stuartorum in ære
sculptæ.
Probably the edition printed in Amsterdam for
A. Hart in 1602. See also Addenda in Proof, p. 232.

319 JOHNSTON, John. Sidera veteris æui siue
heoes [*i.e.* heroes] fide et factis illustres in veteri
testamento, carmine heroico expressi . . . Eiusdem
eteosticha. Et lemmata.
8° Saumur, T. Portæus, 1611. EUL

Iuuenalis [Poe. 38]
320* JUVENALIS, Decimus Junius. Satyræ.
A different edition to Pro. 74 [527].

321* KINLOCH, David. D.K. . . . de hominis
procreatione, anatome, ac morbis internis priores
libri duo heroico carmine donati.
4° Paris, J. Perier, 1596. AUCT

322 LECTIUS, Jacobus. Iac. Lectii I.C. Μακαριτης,
siue, in suo bonorumque omnium luctu, ex
venerandi patris D. Theodori Bezæ ἀπουσια
suscepto, consolatio . . . Accessêre elegantissima
quorundam epicedia non priùs edita.
8° Geneva, P. de la Rouiere, 1606. EUL

323 LEECH, John. Ioannis Leochaei Scoti,
musæ priores, siue poematum pars prior.
8° London [J. Beale?], 1620. EUL
STC 15366

324 LEECH, John. Iani maliferj strena calendis
Ianuarij anno Dom. 1617.
4° Edinburgh, T. Finlason, 1617. EUL
STC 15368

325 LEECH, John. Iani sperantis strena calendis
Januarii anno Dom. 1617.
4° Edinburgh, T. Finlason, 1617. EUL
STC 15369
Given to Drummond by the author.

326   LEECH, John. Iano bifronti strena, siue cornua. Calendis Ianuarii. 1622 . . .
4° St Andrews, E. Raban, 1622.   EUL
STC 15370

327   LEECH, John. Ioannis Leochæi, strenae : calendis Ianuarij. anno Dom. M.DC.XXVI . . .
4° London, B. Alsop and T. Forcet, 1626.   EUL
STC² 15370.5

328   LEECH, John. Iohan. Leochæi nemesis poetica.
4° Edinburgh, A. Hart, 1617.   EUL
STC 15372

329   LEECH, John. Nemo calendis Maii. anno Dom. 1617 . . .
4° Edinburgh, T. Finlason, 1617.   EUL
STC 15373
Given to Drummond by the author.

poemata Bellaii et Hospitalii [Poe. 20]
330* L'HÔPITAL, Michel de. ? De Meti urbe capta . . . In reditum ejusdem ducis Joach. Bellaius.

Lucanus [Poe. 14]
331   LUCANUS, Marcus Annaeus. M. Annei Lucani Cordubensis præstantissimi po⟨etæ?⟩ historici, bellum ciuile pharsalicum nuperrime sedula ⟨reco⟩gnitum opera omnibus prope mendulis abstersis: cui⟨us?⟩ singulorū librorū iniciis litteratissimi viri Sulpicii verulani argumenta preponuntur cum quibusdam annotaciunculis passim in margine pro auditorum vsu coaditis a Magistro Nicolao Chappusoto. Addidit præterea suis in locis Lodouicus Thiboust ānotationes quasdā . . .
4° Paris, J. Petit [the first], 1506.   EUL
Title and last leaf mutilated.

332   LUCRETIUS CARUS, Titus. .T. Lucretii Cari de rerum natura libri .vi. [*Ed.* Petrus Candidus, with commentary.]
8° Florence, F. Giunta, 1512.   EUL

Loudiuici Malachianensis pia carmina [Poe. 4]
333* LUDOVICUS, *a Sancto Malachia.* F. Ludovici a S. Malachia, Monachi Fuliensis ex ordine Cisterciensi piorum carminum libri quinque.

334   LYCOPHRON. Lycophronis Cassandra iambico carmine ac stilo vetere translata per Iosephum Scaligerum Iuli F. Eadem græca, cum versione soluta Gulielmi Canteri, separatim edita.
4° [Heidelberg, H. Commelinus?] 1590.   EUL

335   MELISSUS, Paulus, *pseud.* [Paul Schede.] Melissi schediasmata poetica. Secundo edita multo auctiora. [In 3 parts.]
8° Paris, A. Sittart, 1586.   EUL

336   MELVILLE, Andrew. Principis Scoti-Britannorum natalia.
4° Edinburgh, R. Waldegraue, 1594.   EUL
STC 17807

337   MELVILLE, Andrew. Στεφανισκιον. Ad Scotiae regem, habitum in coronatione reginae. 17 Maij. 1590.
4° Edinburgh, R. Waldegraue, 1590.   EUL
STC 17809

Olympiæ flauie poem. [Poe. 46]
338   MORATA, Olympia Fulvia. Olympiae Fuluiae Moratae mulieris omnium eruditissimae Latina et Græca, quæ haberi potuerunt, monumenta, eáq; plané diuina, cum eruditorum de ipsa iudicijs & laudibus. Hippolytæ Taurellæ elegia elegantissima.
8° Basle, P. Perna, 1558.   EUL
In Latin and Greek. Also in List G.

Mureti Iuuinilia [Poe. 33]
339* MURET, Marc Antoine. M. A. Mureti Juvenilia.

Metaphrasis Naupactiados [Poe. 52]
340   MURRAY, Thomas. Naupactiados, siue Lepantiados Iacobi Magni, Britanniarum, Franciæ, & Hiberniæ regis, fidei verè Christianæ vindicis, & assertoris verè Christianissimi. Metaphrasis poetica authore Thoma Morauio Scoto. Huic adtexta sunt paucula quædam ejusdem Thomæ Morauii schediasmata.
4° London, J. Norton, 1604.   EUL
STC 18298

341   NANQUIER, Simon. De lubrico temporis curriculo, deque hominis miseria opusculum, necnon de funere Christianissimi regis Caroli octaui, cū commētario familiari.
8° Paris, widow of M. de La Porte, 1549.   EUL

342   OPPIAN. O.A. de piscatu libri v, L. Lippio interprete. De venatione libri iv, ita conuersi (ab Adr. Turnebo) . . .
4° Paris, G. Morel, 1555.   FOLG
Bound with two works of Oppian both bearing Drummond's signature.

343   OPPIAN. O. de venatione libri iiii, J. Bodino Andegauensi interprete . . . His accessit commentarius . . . ejusdem interpretis.
4° Paris, M. de Vascosan, 1555.   FOLG
Bound with the Greek text.

Ouidius [Poe. 39]
344   OVIDIUS NASO, Publius. [Opera. 3 vols.]
8° [Lyons, B. de Gabiano, c. 1506.]   EUL
The second Lyons counterfeit of the Aldine edition of 1502.
Containing: 1. *Ouidii Metamorphoseon libri XV.*

And *P. Ouidij Nasonis vita ex eius ipsius libris ab Aldo. M.R. collecta.*
2. *Publii Ouidii Nasonis Heroidum epistolae. Auli Sabini epistolæ tres. P.O.N. elegiarum. Libri tres. De arte amandi. Libri tres. De remedio amoris. Libri duo. In Ibin. Liber unus. Ad Liuium epistola de morte Drusi. De nuce. De medicamine faciei.*
3. *Publii Ouidii Nasonis, quae hoc in libello continentur. Fastorum, libri. VI. De tristibus. libri. V. De Ponto. libri. IIII.*
See Baudrier, VII, 13–14 for a detailed description of this edition.
On the third volume, in Drummond's hand: 'Il mondo, sol di strage, e d'horror theatro immondo.'

345   OVIDIUS NASO, Publius. Pub. Ouidii Nasonis heroidum epistolæ. Epistola prima.
4° Paris, D. Du Pré, 1571.   EUL

epigrammata oudoeni [Poe. 15]
346* OWEN, John. Epigrammatum libri tres.
Drummond must have owned one of the editions printed in 1607, either the original three books (as above) or the supplement, since he made his library catalogue in 1611, before any other editions were printed.

347   OWEN, John. Epigrammatum Ioannis Owen Cambro-Britanni, Oxoniensis, collegij B. Mariae, (quod vulgò Novum vocant) nuper socij, quæ hactenus prodierunt. Libri decem. Editio quarta Londinensis.
12° London, N. Okes for S. Waterson, 1612. EUL
STC 18988
The ten books are divided in four parts (3, 1, 3, 3) each with a title-page. The general title (quoted above) is at the end. The first and second parts were printed by John Legatt. The editions of the parts vary in numeration.

348   OXFORD UNIVERSITY. Academiæ Oxoniensis funebria sacra. Æternæ memoriæ serenissimæ reginæ Annæ potentissimi monarchæ Iacobi . . . sponsæ, dicata.
4° Oxford, J. Lichfield and J. Short, 1619.   EUL
STC 19024
In Latin, Greek and Hebrew.

349   PALINGENIUS, Marcellus, *pseud.* [Pietro Angelo Manzolli.] Marcelli Palingenii Stellati poetae doctissimi zodiacus vitæ, hoc est, de hominis vita, studio, ac moribus optimè instituendis libri xii . . .
8° [Venice?] 1569.   EUL

poemata palladii Sorani [Poe. 21]
350* PALLADIUS, Domicus, *Soranus.* ? Domici Palladii Sorani epigrammaton libelli. Libellus elegiarum. Genethliacon urbis Romæ . . .

procelii Basinii Trebani poemata [Poe. 10]
351   PANDONI, Giovanni Antonio de', *Porcellius.* Trium poetarum elegantissimorum, Porcelij, Basinij, & Trebani opuscula, nunc primùm diligentia eruditissimi viri Christophori Preudhomme Barroducani in lucem ædita.
8° Paris, S. de Colines, 1539.   EUL
Bought in Paris, 1607.

Pantalionus [Poe. 13]
352* PANTALEON, Henricus. ?
Draud lists a comedy in verse by this author among the *Libri poetici.* Draud, p. 1526.

poemata pascasii [Poe. 27]
353* PASQUIER, Étienne. Poemata.

Nihil passeratii [Poe. 48]
354* PASSERAT, Jean. Nihil.

persius [Poe 38]
355* PERSIUS FLACCUS, Aulus. Satyrae.
A different edition to Pro. 40 (563); perhaps a school text printed with Juvenal.

Petrarchæ africa epist [Poe. 1]
356* PETRARCHA, Francesco. Africa. Epistolæ.

Hymni pici Merandulæ [Poe. 19]
357   PICO DELLA MIRANDOLA, Giovanni Francesco. Ioannis Francisci Pici Mirandulani principis: cōcordiæꝗ comitis hymni heroici tres ad sāctissimam Trinitatem: ad Christum: & ad Virginem Mariam: una cū commentariis luculentiss. ad Io. Thomam filiū.
2° Milan, A. Minutianus, 1507.   EUL

Sudorii pindarus [Poe. 29]
358* PINDAR. Pindari opera omnia . . . latino carmine reddita per Nicolaum Sudorium . . .

Plauti com. [Poe. 45]
359   PLAUTUS, Titus Maccius. Ex Plauti comoediis. xx. quarum carmina magna ex parte in mensum restituta sunt M.D.XXII. . . . [*Ed.* F. Asulanus.]
4° Venice, A. Manuzio and A. Torresano, 1522.   EUL

Iouiani Pontani poemata [Poe. 6]
360   PONTANUS, Joannes Jovianus. Ioan. Iouiani Pontani carminum . . . pars prima (–secunda).
8° Basle, A. Cratander, 1531.   SALE
Bought in Paris, 1607. Present location unknown.

Ioh. Posthii poemata [Poe. 32]
361   POSTHIUS, Joannes. Iohannis Posthii Germershemii parergorum poeticorum pars prima . . . Eiusdem Posthii parergorum pars altera, nunc recens edita cum adoptiuis.

8° [Heidelberg,] H. Commelinus, 1595.   EUL
Bought in Paris, 1608.

362   PUTEANUS, Erycius. Eryci Puteani Musarum ferculum: carmina eius selecta.
8° Louvain, H. van Haesten, 1622.   EUL

363   QUIN, Walter. Sertum poeticum, in honorem Iacobi Sexti serenissimi, ac potentissimi Scotorum regis . . .
4° Edinburgh, R. Waldegraue, 1600.   EUL
STC 20567

364   ROLLOCK, Hercules. Panegyris de pace in Gallia constituenda.
8° Poitiers, house of Bouchet, 1576.   EUL

Grenerii poemata [Poe. 23]
365   RONSARD, Pierre de. Hymnus Calaidis et Zethæ, e Gallico Petri Ronsardi Latine expressus à Iacobo Grenerio Parisiensi. Versibus Gallicis è regione Latinorum appositis. Adiecta sunt aliquot eiusdem Grenerii præludia poëtica.
4° Paris, L'Huillier, 1586.   EUL

366   ST ANDREWS UNIVERSITY. Antiquissimae celeberrimæque academiæ Andreanæ χαριστηρια. In aduentum augustissimi serenissimique Iacobi primi Magnæ Britanniæ, Franciæ & Hiberniæ monarchæ, fidei defensoris, &c.
4° Edinburgh, A. Hart, 1617.   EUL
STC 21553

Samarthani filii poemata [Poe. 18]
367   SAINTE-MARTHE, Abel de. Abelii Sammarthani Scæuolæ fil. poemata.
8° Paris, M. Patisson, 1597.   EUL
Bought in Paris, 1607.

Macronii Salmini poe. [Poe. 22]
368   SALMONIUS, Joannes, *called Macrinus.* Salmonii Macrini . . . elegiarum, epigrammatum, & odarum, libri tres.
4° Paris, A. Augereau, 1534.   EUL
Bought in Paris, 1607.

Edoardi Dumonii Berisithias [Poe. 3]
369* SALUSTE DU BARTAS, Guillaume de. Ioannis Edoardi Du Monin . . . beresithias, siue mundi creatio, ex Gallico G. Salustij Du Bartas heptamero expressa . . .

Salusti Hebdomas Lermei [Poe. 37]
370   SALUSTE DU BARTAS, Guillaume de. Domini Guillelmi Salustii Bartassii, poetarum nostri seculi facilè principis Hebdomas. Opus Gallicum à Gabriel de Lermeo nobili Volca, Latinitate donatum. Noua & repurgata editio.
12° [Geneva,] G. Carterius, 1596.   EUL

371   SANDS, Patrick. Memoriæ sacrum sacratissimi monarchæ Iacobi sexti-primi Magnæ Britanniæ, Franciæ & Hiberniæ regis.
4° [London, B. Norton and J. Bill, 1625?]   EUL
STC² 21712.5
Unsigned.

372   SANNAZARO, Jacopo. Iacobi Sannazarii opera omnia.
16° Lyons, J. Pillehotte, 1603.   NLS
Bought in Edinburgh, 1610.

373   SCALIGER, Julius Cæsar. Iulii Cæsaris Scaligeri viri clarissimi poemata in duas partes diuisa. Pleraque omnia in publicum iam primum prodeunt: reliqua vero quam ante emendatius edita sunt. Sophoclis Aiax Lorarius stylo tragico a Iosepho Scaligero Iulii F. translatus. Eiusdem epigrammata quaedam, tum Græca tum Latina, cum quibusdam e Græco versis.
8° [Heidelberg,] 1574.   EUL
In the fly leaves of this book are some Latin poems (by Melville and others) written in the hand of Andrew Melville.

374   SCALIGER, Joseph Juste. Iosephi Scaligeri Iul. Cæs. f. poemata omnia, ex museio Petri Scriuerii.
16° [Leyden,] house of Plantin and Raphelengius, 1615.   EUL

375   SCOT, John. In serenissimi et inuictissimi regis Iacobi sexti, e Scotia sua decessum, hodœporicon, per Ioannem Scotum adolescentem, omnium bonarum artium cognitione, pro ætate cumulatissimum. Adiecta insuper D. Ioannis Scoti, à Scottistaruet, patruelis schediasmata miscellanea.
4° Edinburgh, A. Hart, 1619.   EUL
STC 21856

376   SECUNDUS, Joannes. Ioannis Secundi Hagiensis opera. Nunc primum in lucem edita.
8° Utrecht, H. Borculous, [15]41.   EUL

Sereni Samonici carmina [Poe. 25]
377   SERENUS SAMMONICUS, Quintus. Quinti Sereni Sammonici poetæ & medici clarissimi, de re medica siue morborum curationibus liber tum elegans tum humanæ saluti perquàm utilis, & diligenter emendatus. Gabrielis Humelbergij Rauenspurgensis, medici, in Q. Sereni librum medicinalem, commentarij.
4° Zurich, [C. Froschauer,] 1540.   EUL
Bought in Paris, 1608.

378   SIGÆA, Aloisia [*afterwards* Cuevas, Aloisia de]. Syntra . . . Tumulus eiusdem ab Andrea Resendio, & Claudio Monsello concinnatus.
4° Paris, D. Du Pré, 1566.   EUL

Silius Italicus [Poe. 41]
379* SILIUS ITALICUS, Caius. Punica.

380 SIMON, Marcus. Parentalia piis manibus
Friderici secundi, Daniæ & Norvuegiæ regis,
honorificentissima semper memoria celebrandi,
consecrata . . .
4° Wittenberg, Z. Krafft, 1589.   EUL

Statii papinii opera [Poe. 40]
381* STATIUS, Publius Papinius. Opera.

Marullus cum socii [Poe. 42]
382* TARCHANIOTA MARULLUS, Michael.
Poetæ tres elegantissimi, emendati et aucti. M.
Marullus, H. Angerianus, J. Secundus. [*Ed. B.*
Albinus.]

Terentius [Poe. 38]
383* TERENTIUS, Publius. Comoediae.

384* THEODULUS, *of Athens.* Liber theodoli
cum commento [by Odo Picardus?].   HEND

385 THORIUS, Raphael. Hymnus tabaci.
4° Leyden, I. Elzevier, 1625.   EUL

386 TILENUS, Daniel. Paraenesis ad Scotos,
Geneuensis disciplinæ zelotas.
8° London, W. Stansby for N. Butter, 1620. EUL
STC 24070

387 TORRENTIUS, Lævinus, *Bp.* Læuini Tor-
rentii V.C. poemata.
16° Antwerp, C. Plantin, 1579.   EUL

poetæ Italici duo. vol. [Poe. 16]
388 TOSCANUS, Joannes Matthæus, *ed.* Carmina
illustrium poetarum Italorum. Io. Matthæus
Toscanus conquisiuit, recensuit, bonam partem
nunc primum publicauit. Tomus primus
[—secundus].
16° Paris, G. Gourbin, 1576, 1577.   EUL
Bought in Paris, 1607.

poemata Hadriani Turnebi [Poe. 17]
389* TURNÈBE, Adrien. Poemata.

poemata vidæ [Poe. 2]
390* VIDA, Marcus Hieronymus, *Bp.* Poemata
omnia.

Virgilius aldi [Poe. 26]
391 VIRGILIUS MARO, Publius. Virgilius,
post omnes omnium editiones accurate emendatus.
8° Venice, sons of A. Manuzio, 1545.   EUL
Bought in Paris, 1607.

Commentaria in Vergilium [List F]
392* VIRGILIUS MARO, Publius. ? Vergilii
opera quotquot extant omnia, cum commentariis

[of Donatus, Probus, Pomponius, Vives *et al.*].
See Draud, pp. 1604–5.

393 VIRGILIUS MARO, Publius. P. Virgilii
Maronis Georgicorum lib. IIII. Enarrationibus,
quæ commentarij loco esse possunt, illustrati a
Federico Ceruto Veronensi.
8° Verona, A. Tamo, 1598.   EUL

Vrientii epigraṁata [Poe. 36]
394* VRIENTIUS, Maximilianus. M.V. Gaudensis
epigrammatum libri ix.

395 VULTEIUS, Joannes. Ioannis Vulteii
Remensis epigrammatum libri iiii. Eiusdem xenia.
8° Lyons, J. Barbou for M. Parmantier, 1537. EUL

396 ZEVECOTE, Jacob van. Iacobi Zevecotii
poematum editio noua . . .
12° Leyden, P. Muller for A. Clouquius, 1625.
                                         EUL

397 ZIEGLER, Hieronymus. Christi vinea.
Drama sacrum, ex Mathæi cap. xx argumento
sumpto. Hieronymo Zieglero Rotenburgensi
autore. Eiusdem Ophiletes, drama aliud comico-
tragicum, ex eodem Matthæi Euangelio desump-
tum.
8° Basle, house of Oporinus, 1551.   EUL

PROSE

Achilles statius [Pro. 85]
398* ACHILLES TATIUS. De Clitophontis &
Leucippes amoribus libri viii. Lat. facti a L.A.
Cruceio.
8° Cambridge, J. Legate, [1589?]   AUCT
STC 89

399* Entry cancelled.

Paulus Æmilius commentaria Cæsaris [Pro. 34]
400* ÆMILIUS, Paulus. ?
Not identified. An edition of Caesar's Commentaries?

Politica Albani spinasati [Pro. 60]
401* ALBANUS, *Spinasatus.* Albani Spinasati
Aquitani IC. politicorum libri duo, ex recensione
Ioach. Cluten.
Draud gives a Strasburg edition, no date. Draud,
p. 1226.

Mirabilia Romæ Albertini [Pro. 4]
402 ALBERTINI, Francesco degli. Mirabilia
Rome. Opusculū de mirabilibus nouæ et veteris
urbis Romæ editū a F.A.F.
4° Lyons, J. Marion for R. Morin, 1520.   DUL

Alexandri ab Alexandro Genia. dierum [Pro. 33]
403 * ALEXANDRO, Alexander ab. Genialium dierum libri sex.

404 [ANDREÆ, Johann Valentin.] Turbo, siue moleste et frustra per cuncta diuagans ingenium. In theatrum productum.
12° Helicone, iuxta parnassum [Strasburg?], 1616.
EUL

405 ANTONY, *Prior of Crato.* Explanatio veri ac legitimi iuris, quo serenissimus Lusitaniæ rex Antonius eius nominus primus nititur, ad bellum Philippo regi Castellæ pro regni recuperatione inferendum. Vna cum historica quadam enarratione rerum eo nomine gestarum vsque ad annum M.D. LXXXIII.
4° Leyden, C. Plantin, 1585.   EUL
With an inset: 'Tabula genealogica præsenti opusculo conueniens.'

Apuleius [Pro. 88]
406 * APULEIUS, Lucius. ? Asinus aureus.

407 ARISTOTLE. Aristotelis politica ab Iacobo Lodoico Strebæo ... conuersa.
4° Paris, M. de Vascosan, 1542.   PR
Also signed 'Alexander' (Sir William Alexander).

Regii prolegomina politica [Pro. 59]
408 * ? ARISTOTLE. Politica. [*Ed.* Ludovicus Regius.]
Draud has an edition of Paris, 1578. Draud, p. 1230.

409 ARNAUDUS, Andreas *and* GUIRANDUS, Petrus. Arnaudi atque Guirandi ioci. In quibus lepos, & festiuitas maxime existit ex tribus exornationibus.
12° Venice, J. Boatius, 1609.   EUL

410 B., C. Iusti Lipsi defensio postuma. C.B. amico benè merenti posuit.
16° Antwerp, J. Mourentorff at the house of Plantin, 1609.   EUL

411 * BACON, Francis, *Viscount St. Albans.* F. Baconi De sapientia veterum liber.
12° London, R. Barker, 1609.   AUCT
STC 1127

412 BADUELLUS, Claudius. Annotationes in M.T. Ciceronis pro Milone et pro Marcello orationes, quibus adjunctae sunt ejusdem orationes aliquot.
8° Lyons, [S. Gryphe,] 1552.   EUL
Title and all before o2 wanting.

413 BARCLAY, John. Epistola Iohannis Barclaii. Ad amicum suum Iohan. Flaminium.
8° Lyons, P.G., 1616.   EUL

414 BARCLAY, William M.D. Guil. Barclayi ... iudicium de certamine G. Eglisemmii cum G. Buchanano, pro dignitate paraphraseos psalmi ciiii ... Adjecta sunt, Eglisemmii ipsum iudicium ... ejusdem psalmi elegans paraphrasis Thomae Rhaedi.
8° London, G. Eld, 1620.   EUL
STC 1404

415 BARNAUD, Nicholas. Nicolai Barnaudi ... commentariolum in ænigmaticum quoddam epitaphium, Bononiæ studiorum, ante multa secula marmoreo lapidi insculptum. Huic additi sunt processus chæmici non pauci.
8° Leyden, T. Basson, 1597.   EUL

Bembi opuscula [Pro. 11]
416 BEMBO, Pietro. Petri Bembi opuscula aliquot ...
8° Lyons, house of Gryphe, 1532.   EUL

417 BENCIUS, Franciscus. Francisci Bencii ab Aqua pendente, e Societate Iesu, orationes & carmina. Quæ partim nunquam antehac, partim Germania nunc primum in lecem prodierunt ... His demum subiuncta est eiusdem de stylo & scriptione disputatio.
8° Ingolstadt, D. Sartorius, 1592.   EUL

noua noui orbis descriptio [List G]
418 BENZONI, Girolamo. Nouae noui orbis historiæ, id est, rerum ab Hispanis in India Occidentali hactenus gestarum, & acerbo illorum in eas gentes dominatu, libri tres, Vrbani Caluetonis opera industriàque ex Italicis Hieronymi Benzonis Mediolanensis, qui eas terras XIIII. annorum peregrinatione obijt, commentarijs descripti, Latini facti, ac perpetuis notis, argumentis & locupleti memorabilium rerum accessione, illustrati. His ab eodem adiuncta est, de Gallorum in Floridam expeditione, & insigni Hispanorum in eos sæuitiæ exemplo, breuis historia.
8° [Geneva,] E. Vignon, 1578.   EUL

Beroaldi opera [Pro. 51]
419 * BEROALDUS, Philippus. Philippi Beroaldi opera. Orationes multifariae a P. Beroaldo editae recognitaeque cum appendicula aliarum quoque oratiūcularum ...

420 BEURHUSIUS, Fredericus. Analysis epistolarum et euangeliorum dominicalium scholastica. Ad Rameæ logicæ rationes, pro domestica præcipuè repetitione, nonnihil accommodata ...
8° Erfurt, J. Pistor, 1588.   EUL
Leaves o7 and o8 are uncut.

Besius de Repub. [Pro. 35]
421 BIESIUS, Nicolaus. De republica libri quatuor, quibus vniuersa de moribus philosophia continetur.
4° Antwerp, M. Nuytes, 1556.   HUL

Blacvidii apologia regum [Pro. 26]
422* BLACKWOOD, Adam. Aduersus Georgii
Buchanani dialogum, de iure regni apud Scotos,
pro regibus apologia.

Boccacius de Casibus illustrium vir. [Pro. 28]
423* BOCCACCIO, Giovanni. De casibus illustrium virorum libri nouem.

Boccacii genologia deorum [Pro. 57]
424 BOCCACCIO, Giovanni. Genealogiae
Ioannis Boccatii: cum demonstrationibus in
formis arborū designatis. Eiusdē de mōtibus &
syluis. de fontibus: lacubus: & fluminibus. Ac
etiā de stagnis & paludibus: necnon & de mari-
bus: seu diuersis maris nominibus.
2° Venice, A. de Zanni, 1511.   NLS
Bought in Paris, 1607.

425 BOETHIUS, Anicius Manlius Torquatus
Severinus, [*Supposititious work.*] [*Begin.*] In diui.
Seuerini Boetij de scolarium disciplina commentarium feliciter incipit.
2°[Lyons, G. Le Roy,] 1486   BM
Printed with Boethius' *De consolatione philosophiae*
but in this case separated from the main work. For
a detailed description see the *British Museum
Catalogue of Books printed in the XVth century*,
VIII, 238-9. Bought in Bourges, 1608. On the
last printed page Drummond has a note on the
invention of printing.

426 BOETHIUS, Hector. Episcoporum Murthla-
ceñ. & Aberdoneñ. . . . vitæ.
4° [Paris,] J. Badius, 1522.   EUL

427 BOETHIUS, Hector. Scotorum historiæ a
prima gentis origine, cum aliarum & rerum &
gentium illustratione non vulgari . . .
2° [Paris,] J. Badius, [1526].   SALE
Present location unknown.
'Enriched throughout with numerous MS. Notes
by Drummond, of Hawthornden.'

poggii florentini opera [Pro. 10]
428* BRACCIOLINI, Poggio. Poggij Florentini
. . . opera . . .

Brussonii memorabilia [Pro. 93]
429* BRUSONIUS, Lucius Domitius. Rerum
memorabilium, insignium sententiarum, historiarum, miraculorum, apophthegmatum,
exemplorum, facetiarumque, etc., libri vii.

chronica Buchanani [List G]
430* BUCHANAN, George. Rerum Scoticarum
historia.

Budeus de contemptu rerum fort. [Pro. 32]
431 BUDÉ, Guillaume. Gulielmi Budæi Parisiensis, de contemptu rerum fortuitarum libri tres:

cum breui & erudita eorundem expositione.
4° [Paris, J. Badius,] 1528.   EUL

philologia budei [Pro. 44]
432 BUDÉ, Guillaume. De philologia libri .ii.
2° [Paris,] J. Badius, 1532.   EUL
Bought in Paris, 1607.

433 BUDÉ, Guillaume. De studio literarum
recte et commode instituendo . . .
2° [Paris,] J. Badius, 1532.   EUL

Budeus de transitu Hellinismi [Pro. 31]
434 BUDÉ, Guillaume, G. Budæi . . . de transitu
Hellenismi ad Christianismum, libri tres.
2° Paris, R. Estienne [the first], 1535.   EUL
Bought in Paris, 1607.

435* BUSBECQ, Ogier Ghislain de. De re mili-
tari aduersus Turcas instituenda consilium.
Edition not traced.   AUCT
AUCT has 'Bardi Pomeranæ [i.e. Bardt], 1594.'

436 CAESAR, Caius Julius. C. Iulii Caesaris
rerum ab se gestarum commentarii. De bello
Gallico libri VIII. De bello ciuili Pompeiano libri
III. De bello Alexandrino liber I. De bello Africo
liber I. De bello Hispaniensi liber I. Omnia
collatis uetustis exemplaribus tam scriptis quàm
impressis accuratè emendata. Pictura totius
Galliæ, pontis in Rheno, Auarici, Alexiæ, Vxello-
duni, Massiliæ, per Iucundum Veronensem, ex
descriptione Cæsaris. Veterum Galliæ locorum,
populorum, urbium, montium, ac fluuiorum
breuis descriptio. Eutropii epitome belli Gallici
ex Suetonii Tranquilli monumentis quæ deside-
rantur.
2° Paris, M. de Vascosan and J. de Roigny, 1543.
          EUL

Dictionarium Calepini septem linguarum
[List K]
437* CALEPINUS, Ambrosius. Dictionarium
septem linguarum.
Also Pro. 73.

Chronica carionis [Pro. 81]
438* CARION, Johann. Chronica.

439 CARMICHAEL, James. Grammaticæ
Latinae, de etymologia, liber secundus, ex
vetustissimis artis, et linguae auctoribus, de-
promtus, ea methodo quam senatus literatorum,
regia auctoritate, Sterlingi habitus, Scoticæ iuuen-
tuti facillimam censuit . . .
4° Cambridge, T. Thomas, 1587.   EUL
STC 4660

Loud. carionis emendationum liber [Pro. 38]
440 CARRIO, Ludovicus. Lud. Carrionis
emendationum et obseruationum liber primus . . .

4° Paris, G. Beys, 1583.   EUL
Wanting the second book. Bought in Paris, 1607.

441* CASTIGLIONE, Ippolita. Hippolitæ
Taurellæ . . . Epistola ad maritum suum Baltha-
sarem Castilionem apud Leonem X. Ponti. Rom.
oratorem. 1558.   AUCT

442 CHARPENTIER, Jacques. Ia. Carpentarii
. . . contra importunas Rami actiones, senatus
decreto nuper confirmati oratio, habita initio
professionis, in auditorio regio anno 1566. calend.
April.
8° Paris, G. Buon, 1566.   EUL

443 CHARPENTIER, Jacques. Ia. Carpentarii
. . . oratio. Quam in auditorio regio, cum inter-
pretationem sphæræ & logici organi aggrederetur,
de sua professione habuit, contra quorundam
calumnias . . .
8° Paris, G. Gourbin, 1567.   EUL
All after B4 is wanting.

Carpentarii orationes contra Ramum [Pro. 18]
444 CHARPENTIER, Jacques. Ia. Carpentarii
. . . orationes tres: pro iure professionis suę,
in senatu ex tempore habitæ, contra importunas
Rami actiones.
8° Paris, G. Buon, 1566.   EUL

445 CHÉRADAME, Jean. Ioannis Cheradami
alphabetum linguae sanctae, mystico intellectu
refertum.
8° Paris, G. de Gourmont, 1532.   EUL

446 CHACON, Pedro. Petrus Ciacconius Tole-
tanus de triclinio. siue, de modo conuiuandi apud
priscos Romanos, & de conuiuiorum apparatu.
Accedit Fuluii Vrsini appendix . . .
8° [Heidelberg, J. Commelin,] 1590.   EUL

447 CHION. Chionis Matridis F. Platonici
philosophi epistola apologetica ad Clearchum
Ponti principem. Ex interpretatione Fed. Morelli
. . .
4° Paris, F. Morel [the second], 1600.   EUL

448 CICERO, Marcus Tullius. [*Begin.*] M.
Tulii Ciceronis ad M. Brutum liber. [*End.*]
M.T. Ciceronis. Ad. M. Brutū paradoxa finiūt
feliciter.
8° [Paris,] P. Pigouchet, [*c.* 1500].   EUL
Pellechet 3768.

Ciceronis epist. ad Atticum [Pro. 87]
449* CICERO, Marcus Tullius. M. Tullii
Ciceronis epistolae ad T. Pomponium Atticum.

Rami agraria [Pro. 47]
450 CICERO, Marcus Tullius. M. Tullij Ciceronis
de lege agraria contra P. Seruilium Rullum trib-

unumplebis orationes tres, Petri Rami . . .
prælectionibus illustratæ.
4° Paris, L. Grandin at A. Wechel's, 1561.   EUL
Colophon reads 1562. See Ong. p. 161, for a
detailed description. Bought in Paris, 1607.

451 CICERO, Marcus Tullius. M.T. Ciceronis
epistola duodecima, ad L. Luceium Q.F. Ex
quinto libro epistolarum familiarium.
4° Paris, D. Du Pré, 1569.   EUL

epistolæ ciceronis famil. latin Gall. [Pro. 14]
452* CICERO, Marcus Tullius. M. Tul. Ciceronis
epistolarum familiarium liber II. Item, aliquot
epistolæ selectæ ex cæteris libris, cum Latina et
Gallica interpretatione, Maturino Corderio authore.

Commentarius in part. orat. cic. [Pro. 80]
453* CICERO, Marcus Tullius. Partitiones
oratoriæ.
Possible commentators include Valla, Strebæus
and Majoragius (Conti).

sententiæ Ciceronis [Pro. 90]
454* CICERO, Marcus Tullius. Sententiae
Ciceronis.
Edited by Petrus Lagnerius? Vautrollier printed
an edition in Edinburgh in 1584 (STC 5319).

454.5* COCCIUS, Marcus Antonius, *Sabellicus*.
Orationes. 1607.   PR
Copy, reported as Drummond's, at Hawthornden
Castle.

oratio patricii Cocburnii [Pro. 97]
455* COCKBURN, Patrick. Oratio . . . de utilitate
et excellentia verbi Dei.

456* COLLIBUS, Hippolytus à. Harpocrates,
siue de rectâ silendi ratione. (Descriptio silentii
Cælio Calcagino autore.)
8° Leyden, house of Commelin, 1603.   AUCT

columella de re rustica [Pro. 43]
457* COLUMELLA, Lucius Junius Moderatus.
De re rustica.

458* COMMELIN, Jerome. Catalogus librorum
qus vel excudit vel quorum exempla ad fe recepit.
8° Heidelberg, heirs of J. Commelin, 1599.
     AUCT
A catalogue listing the stock of books printed
by Commelin, his wholesale stock from other
printers, and the Greek and Latin manuscripts
in his private library. See Graham Pollard and
Albert Ehrman, *The distribution of books by
catalogue* (Cambridge, 1965), p. 58.

compendium chronicorum aug. fr. [List K]
459* COMPENDIUM.
Not identified.

Compendium historicum [Pro. 95]
460* COMPENDIUM.
Not identified. Probably the *Compendium historicum petri senensis* entered on List G, also not identified.

supplementum linguæ latinæ constantini [Pro. 46]
461* CONSTANTINUS, Robertus. Supplementum linguæ Latinæ, seu dictionarium abstrusorum vocabulorum . . .

Antiparadoxon Antonii Maioragii [Pro. 12]
462 CONTI, Antonio Maria de, *Majoragio*. M. Antonii Maioragii antiparadoxon libri sex. In quibus M. Tullij Ciceronis omnia paradoxa refelluntur.
8° Lyons, S. Gryphe, 1546.   EUL
Bought in Paris, 1607.

463 CONTI, Antonio Maria de, *Majoragio*. M. Antonii Maioragii decisiones xxv. Quibus M. Tullium Ciceronem ab omnibus Cælij Calcagnini criminationibus liberat.
8° Lyons, S. Gryphe, 1544.   EUL

464 CORRADUS, Sebastianus. Sebastiani Corradi in M. T. Ciceronis epistolas ad Atticum. σχολια, nuper correcta, & aucta.
8° Venice, G. Scoto, 1549.   EUL
Bought in Paris, 1608.

465 CORTÈS, Hernando. De insulis nuper inuentis Ferdinandi Cortesii ad Carolum V. Rom. imperatorem narrationes, cum alio quodam Petri Martyris ad Clementem VII. pontificem maximum consimilis argumenti libello. His accesserunt epistolæ duæ, de felicissimo apud Indos euangelij incremento, quas superioribus hisce diebus quidam fratres Mino. ab India in Hispaniam transmiserunt. Item epitome de inuentis nuper Indiæ populis idolatris . . . [*Tr.* P. Savorgnanus.]
2° Cologne, M. von Neuss for A. Birckman, 1532.   EUL
Wanting all gathering 'L' (6 leaves?) Of Cortes' dispatches, only two and three are here (the first was lost or suppressed before it reached Charles v, the fifth only discovered in the nineteenth century, while the fourth, being only first printed in 1526, was not included in this translation).

oratio Crithonii in mortem Ronsardi [Pro. 65]
466* CRITTONIUS, Georgius. Georg. Crittonii laudatio funebris, habita in exequiis Petri Ronsardi . . . cui præponuntur eisudem Ronsardi carmina . . .

Q Curtius [Pro. 20]
467* CURTIUS RUFUS, Quintus. De rebus gestis Alexandri Magni.

Daretis phrgii historia [Pro. 17]
468* DARES, *Phrygius, pseud.* De excidio Troiae.

469 DE. De verbis anomalis commentarius . . . Prioribus editionibus accessit ingens verborum numerus, cùm ex alijs scriptoribus, tum ex Homero & alijs poetis. [Attributed to Filippo Venuti.]
8° Paris, G. Morel, 1558.   EUL

470 DES MASURES, Louis. Ludouici Masurii Neruii Babylon: siue Babylonicæ tyrannidis euersio, Gallicè ante aliquot annos in lucem edita, nunc primùm verò ab authore ipso in Latinum conuersa.
4° Geneva, F. Perrin, 1569.   EUL

Grammatica magna Dispaut. [Pro. 29]
471* DESPAUTERIUS, Joannes. ? Ioannis Despauterii Niniuitæ, grammaticæ institutionis libri septem.
Or perhaps *I.D. commentarii grammatici.*

dictionarium latino Gallicum [Pro. 21]
472* DICTIONARIUM.
Not identical with Robert Estienne's dictionary, since a different price. Draud has a possibility: *Dictionarium Latino Gallicum iam recens post omnium editiones excusum*, Antwerp, 1598. Draud, p. 1346.

473 DINOTHUS, Richardus. Richardii Dinothi aduersaria historica in centurias, quinquagenarias, decurias, & ἀτακτους digesta.
4° Basle, P. Perna, 1581.   EUL

diogenes laertius [Pro. 23]
474* DIOGENES, *Laertius*. De vita et moribus philosophorum libri decem.

Dionis Nicei rerum Romanarum Xiphilino authore [Pro. 66]
475* DION CASSIUS. Dionis rerum Romanarum a Pompeio Magno ad Alexandrum Mamææ filium epitome, Joanne Xiphilino authore, et G. Blanco interprete.
Also in List E.

476 DONALDSON, Walter. Lacrymæ tumulo nunquam satis laudati herois Henrici-Friderici Stuarti, Walliæ principis . . .
8° Sedan, J. Jannon, 1613.   EUL

477 DU TILLET, Jean, *Bp*. Io. Tilii chronicon de regibus Francorum, a Faramundo vsque ad Franciscum primum. Cui deinceps adiunximus quæ à Francisco primo usque ad Henricum II. gesta sunt.
8° Paris, house of Vascosan, 1551.   EUL

oratio eucharistica G. du Val [Pro. 67]
478* Du Val, Guillaume. Oratio eucharistica habita in scholarum regiarum ingressu nonis decemb. anno Dom. 1606.

479 Elverus, Hieronymus. H.E. . . . deambulationes vernæ; quibus ruralis philosophia ad vnguem discutitur . . . [*Ed.* M. Gurttnerus.]
8° Frankfort, J.F. Weiss, 1620.   PR

480 Elvidius. Stanislaus, *pseud.* [Joachimus Camerarius.] Ornatissimi cuiusdam viri [Gui Du Faur], de rebus Gallicis, ad Stanislaum Eluidium, epistola.
4° Paris, F. Morel [the first], 1573.   EUL

481 Epistolae. Epistolæ regum, principum, rerumpublicarum ac sapientum virorum: ex antiquis & recentioribus, tam Græcis, quàm Latinis historijs & annalibus collectæ. [Compiled by G. Donzellini.]
8° Basle, J. Foillet for L. Zetzner of Strasburg, 1593.   EUL

Epistolæ amatore gallice [List K]
481.5* Epistolae.
Not identified.

adagia Erasmi [Pro. 89]
482* Erasmus, Desiderius. Adagia.

Apologia Erasmi aduersus monachos [Pro. 101]
483* Erasmus, Desiderius. D. Erasmi apologia adversus articulos aliquot per monachos quosdam in Hispaniis, exhibitos.

Bellum per Erasmum Rothe. [Pro. 100]
484* Erasmus, Desiderius. Bellum.
Part of the *Adagia*, but often printed separately.

Colloquia Erasmi [Pro. 96]
485* Erasmus, Desiderius. Colloquia.

Erasmus de institutione principis [Pro. 99]
486* Erasmus, Desiderius. Institutio principis Christiani.

encomium Moriæ [Pro. 82]
487* Erasmus, Desiderius. Moriæ encomium.

epistola Stephani [Pro. 70]
488 Estienne, Henri, *le Grand.* Henrici Stephani epistola, qua ad multas multorum amicorum respondet, de suæ typographiæ statu, nominatimque de suo thesauro linguae Graecae . . . Index librorum qui ex officina eiusdem Henrici Stephani hactenus prodierunt.
8° [Geneva,] H. Estienne [the first], 1569.   EUL
Bought in Bourges, 160[8?]

Dictionarium Step. Gallicum [Pro. 13]
489* Estienne, Robert, *the Elder.* Dictionarium Latino-gallicum . . .

490 Estienne, Robert, *the Elder.* Gallicae grāmatices libellus, Latinè conscriptus in gratiam peregrinorum qui eam linguam addiscere cupiunt.
8° Paris, R. Estienne [the first], 1569.   EUL

Eutropius [List E]
491* Eutropius, Flavius. Eutropii breuiarium historiæ Romanæ.

491.5* Fern. Fern [?] de regno Siciliae
                             HEND
Not identified.

492 Ferrerio, Giovanni. Cicero, poeta etiā elegans, nedū ineptus fuisse, contra vulgatam grammatistarum opinionem asseritur . . .
4° Paris, M. de Vascosan, 1540.   EUL

Florus de gestis Rom. [Pro. 79]
493* Florus, Publius Annius. L. Iulii Flori de gestis Romanorum, historiarum libri iiii.

Foxii Morzelii de regis inst. [Pro. 36]
494* Foxius Morzillus, Sebastianus. S. Foxii Morzilli . . . de regni, regisque institutione libri iii . . .

495 Fulgentius, Fabius Planciades. Enarrationes allegoricae fabularum Fulgentii Planciadis.
4° Paris, J. Laliseau, n.d.   DUL
Pellechet 4935. Bound with Albertini's *Mirabilia Romæ.*

496 Furio Ceriol, Federico. Christophori Varseuicii, equitis Poloni, viriq́; doctissimi de concilio et consiliariis principis liber, ex Friderici F. Ceriole Hispanico in latinum versus, inǳ lucem editus. Item ejusdem Varseuicij liber de legatis & legationibus lectu utilissimus & jucundissimus. Accessit Hippolyti de collibus consiliarius, rem eandem diuersa ratione tamen explicans.
12° Rostock, C. Reusner for L. Albert, 1597.
                             EUL
Colophon has 1598.

P. Gallandii oratio contra Ramum [Pro. 1]
497 Galland, Pierre. P. Gallandii literarum Latinarum professoris regij, contra nouam academiam Petri Rami oratio . . .
4° Paris, house of Vascosan, 1551.   EUL

498 Galland, Pierre *and* Turnèbe, Adrien, *eds.* De agrorum conditionibus, & constitutionibus limitum, Siculi Flacci lib. i. Iulii Frontini lib. i. Aggeni Vrbici lib. ii. Hygeni Gromatici lib. ii. Variorum auctorum ordines finitionum. De iugeribus metiundis. Finium regundorum. Lex

Mamilia. Coloniarum pop. Romani descriptio. Terminorum inscriptiones & formæ. De generibus lineamentorum. De mensuris & ponderibus. Omnia figuris illustrata. [2 parts in 1.]
4° Paris, A. Turnèbe, 1554.   EUL

Gellii noctes atticæ [Pro. 16]
499* GELLIUS, Aulus. Noctes Atticæ.

500   GELLIUS, Joannes, *Scotus*. Programmatis Queuilliani contra Adrianum Behotium Archidiaconum. Apologia . . .
8° La Rochelle, 1605.   EUL

Gemellii orationes [Pro. 62]
501* GEMELLIUS, Petrus. P.G. . . . Orationes duae pro Sorbonicis disputationibus habitæ . . .

502   GILDAS. Opus nouum. Gildas Britannus monachus cui sapientis cognomētū est inditum, de calamitate excidio, & conquestu Britanniæ . . . [*Ed.* Polydore Vergil and R. Ridley.]
8° [Paris? 1525.]   EUL
Formerly STC 11892.

503   [GOLDAST, Melchior.] Processus iuris, ioco-serius, tam lectu festiuus et iucundus, quàm ad vsum fori & praxeos moralis cognitionem vtilis ac necessarius: in quo continentur, I. Bartoli à Saxoferrato IC. Perusini, processus Sathanæ contra D. Virginem coram iudice Iesu . . . II. Iacobi de Ancharano IC. archidiaconi aduersani & canonici Aprutini, processus Luciferi contra Iesum . . . III. Martialis Aruerni IC. cognitoris in senatu regio Parisiensi, aresta amorum, siue processus inter amantes, cum decisionibus parlamenti: adiectis Benedicti Curtii Symphoriani IC. commentariis . . . Nunc primùm in originali sermone Latino collectum & simul editum.
8° Hanau, house of Viller for C. Bierman, 1611. Latin and French.   EUL

504   GRENIER, Jacques. Vita Iacobi Grenerii Poisæi, Parisiensis adolescentis.
4° n.p.d. [not before 1588.]   EUL

505   [GREUENBRUCH, Gerard.] Tragoedia Moscouitica: siue de vita et morte Demetrii, qui nuper apud Ruthenos imperium tenuit, narratio, ex fide dignis scriptis & litteris excerpta.
8° Cologne, G. Greuenbruch, 1608.   EUL

506   GULIELMUS, *Appulus*. Guillielmi Apuliensis rerum in Italia ac regno Neapolitano Normanicarum. Libri quinque. [*Ed.* J. Tiremæus.]
4° Rouen, M. Le Mégissier and T. Mallard, 1582.   EUL

507   GUYETUS, Franciscus. Francisci Guyeti Andregaui hypar. Οὐκ ὄναρ, ἀλλ᾽ ὕπαρ.

4° n.p., [c. 1620].   EUL
Part of a larger work.

508   HADDON, Walter. G. Haddoni . . . lucubrationes passim collectæ, & editæ. Studio & labore Thomæ Hatcheri Cantabrigiensis. (D. Gualteri Haddoni . . . poemata . . .) [In 2 parts.]
4° London, W. Seres, 1567.   EUL
STC 12596

509* HAMILTON, John. Joh. Hamiltonij præludia de defin.
Not identified.   HEND

510   HEGATE, William. Guillielmi Hegati Scoti Glasguensis, recidiuæ Athenæ. Oratio panegerica.
8° [Limoges,] 1599.   EUL

511   HEINSIUS, Daniel. Danielis Heinsii de tragoediæ constitutione liber. In quo inter cætera, tota de hac Aristotelis sententia dilucide explicatur.
8° Leyden, J. Balduinus for L. Elzevier, 1611.   EUL

512   HELVICUS, Christophorus. Chronologia uniuersalis ab origine mundi per quatuor summa imperia, (quas monarchias appellant,) ad præses tempus compendiosè deducta, cum præcipuis synchronismis vitorum celebrium, euentorum & politiarum, seu regnorum cæterorum . . .
4° Giessen, C. Chemlin, 1618.   EUL

Herbarium [Pro. 78]
513* HERBARIUM.
Not identified. Draud gives a list of *Herbaria*, pp. 920–1. Also in List K as *Herbarium antiquium*.

514   HOPKINSON, John. Synopsis Paradisi: siue, Paradisi descriptio, ex variis diuersarum tum linguarum, tum ætatum scriptoribus desumpta; cum chorographica eiusdem tabula . . .
4° Leyden, F. Raphelengius, 1593.   EUL
With a map of Paradise and district.

515   HORAPOLLO. Orus Apollo, de sacris apud Aegyptios notis ac cœlaturis, Latinitate per Io. Mercerum Vticensem donatus, & scholijs, quibus multa loca restituta sunt & enodata, illustratus.
4° Paris, C. Wechel, 1548.   EUL

516   HUME, David. De vnione insulæ Britannicæ tractatus.
4° London, G. Elde, 1605.   EUL
STC 13951

517   HUME, James. Pantaleonis vaticinia. Satyra.
12° Rouen, widow Courant, 1633.   EUL

Iamblichus de Mysteriis ægip. [Pro. 2]
518   IAMBLICHUS, *of Chalcis.* Iamblichus de mysteriis Ægyptiorum.

519   IRLANDUS, Bonaventura. Publicæ lætitiæ nuntiatio ob natum regi & regno delphinum 27. die Septembris 1601. & inde venerationis regum ab insimulatione paganismi adsertio.
8° Limoges, J. Blanchet, 1605.   EUL

Gnomologia platonis Isocratis [Pro. 8]
520* ISOCRATES. Gnomologiae ex omnibus operibus collectae per Hieronymum Vuolfium. See also Plato. Several editions of selections from Plato and Isocrates compiled by H. Wolf were printed in Lyons after 1550; Drummond probably had the *Gnomologiæ* of both authors bound together.

521   JAMES, Thomas. Catalogus librorum bibliothecæ publicæ quam vir ornatissimum Thomas Bodleius eques auratus in academia Oxoniensi nuper instituit; continet autem libros alphabeticè dispositos secundum quatuor facultates: cum quadruplici elencho expositorum S. Scripturæ, Aristotelis, iuris vtriusq; & principum medicinæ, ad vsum almæ academiæ Oxoniensis, auctore Thomæ James ibidem bibliothecario.
4° Oxford, J. Barnes, 1605.   EUL
STC 14449

522   JAMES, Thomas. Ecloga Oxonio-Cantabrigiensis, tributa in libros duos; quorum prior continet catalogum confusum librorum manuscriptorum in illustrissimis bibliothecis, duarum florentissimarum academiarum, Oxoniæ & Cantabrigiæ. Posterior, catalogum eorundem distinctum & dispositum secundum quatuor facultates . . . [In 2 parts.]
4° London, G. Bishop and J. Norton, 1600.   EUL
STC 14453

Acostæ Lusitanis historia orientis [Pro. 52]
523   JESUITS. Rerum a Societate Iesu in Oriente gestarum volumen . . .
8° Cologne, G. Calenius and heirs of J. Quentel, 1574.   EUL
With the commentary of Manuel Acosta.

opera Iosephi [Pro. 41]
524* JOSEPHUS, Flavius. Opera.

Flaui Iosephi vita [Pro. 69]
525   JOSEPHUS, Flavius. Flauii Iosephi templi quondam Hierosolymitani è prima ephemeride sacerdotis, dein toparchæ & archistrategi vtriusq; Galilææ vita, per Godefridum Tilmannum Cartusiæ Parisiensis monachum è Græcis versa primùm, & excusa typis.
8° Paris, M. Fezandat, 1548.   EUL
Bought in Paris, 1607.

526   JUSTUS, Pascasius. Pascasii Iusti . . . alea, siue de curanda ludendi in pecuniam cupiditate libri ii. . . .
4° Basle, J. Oporinus, 1561.   EUL

In Iuuenalem commentarius Badii Mancinelli [Pro. 74]
527   JUVENALIS, Decimus Junius. Decij Iunij Iuuenalis satyræ sexdecem ab Antonio Mancinello expositæ; cum Iodoci Badii Ascensii familiari earundem explanatione.
4° [Lyons,] J. Clein, [1498?]   EUL
All after x4 is wanting.

528   LALAMANTIUS, Johannes. Exterarum fere omnium et præcipuarum gentium anni ratio, & cum Romano collatio: rara & exquisita rerum scitu dignissimarum cognitione, ac diuersi generis auctorum explicatione referta.
8° [Geneva,] 1571.   EUL

Leonicus de varia hist. [Pro. 9]
529   LEONICUS THOMÆUS, Nicolaus. N. Leonici Thomæi de varia historia libri tres nuper in lucem editi . . .
4° Basle, H. Froben and N. Episcopius, 1531.
     CH CH
Leonici opera [Pro. 61]
530* LEONICUS THOMÆUS, Nicolaus. Opuscula. Or his *Dialogi*?

vita budei [Pro. 44]
531   LE ROY, Louis. G. Budæi viri clariss. vita . . .
4° Paris, J. de Roigny, 1540.   EUL
Bought in Paris, 1607.

Lynacer de emendat. [Pro. 3]
532   LINACRE, Thomas. Thomae Linacri Britanni de emendata structura Latini sermonis libri sex. Emendatiores.
8° Paris, R. Estienne [the first], 1550.   EUL
Bought in Paris, 1607.

533   LINACRE, Thomas. Rudimenta grāmatices Thomæ Linacri, ex Anglico sermone in Latinum versa, interprete Georgio Buchanano Scoto.
8° Paris, R. Estienne [the first], 1550.   EUL

534   LIPSIUS, Justus. Iusti LipsI Louanium: siue opidi et academiæ eius descriptio. Libri tres.
4° Antwerp, J. Mourentorff at the house of Plantin, 1605.   EUL

535   LIPSIUS, Justus. Iusti LipsI . . . oratio in calumniam . . .
4° London, F. Kingston, 1615.   EUL
STC 15700

M

536* LLWYD, Humphrey. Commentarioli
Britannicae descriptionis fragmentum.
8° Cologne, J. Birckmann, 1572.   AUCT

epistolæ longolii [Pro. 48]
537 LONGOLIUS, Christophorus. Christophori
Longolii orationes duæ pro defensione sua ab læsę
maiestatis crimine, longe exactiori q̄ ante iudicio
perscriptæ, atꝗ ex ipsius authoris sententia in
lucem editæ. Oratio vna ad Luterianos. Eiusdem
epistolarum libri quatuor. Epistolarū Bēbi &
Sadoleti liber vnꝰ. Quibus omnibꝰ præponetur
ipsius Lōgolii vita perdocte atꝗ eleganter ab
ipsius amicissimo quodam exarata.
8° Paris, J. Badius, 1526.   EUL
Bought in Paris, 1607.

538* LORITUS, Henricus, *Glareanus*. De ratione
syllabarum brevis isagoge .. De figuris cōpendiosa
lucubratio, ex probatissimis authoribus, præsertim
Diomede. Item elegiæ quaedam.   AUCT
Edition not traced.
AUCT has 'Freiburg, 1534'.

Collectanea Manlii [Pro. 92]
539* MANLIUS, Joannes. Locorum communium
collectanea: a J. Manlio per multos annos, pleraꝗ
tum ex lectionibus D. P. Melanchthonis, tum ex
aliorum doctissimorum virorū relationibus excerpta, & nuper in ordinem ab eodem redacta
. . .

540 MANUTIUS, Aldus Pius. Aldi Manutii
Romani institutionum grammaticarum libri duo,
per Petrum Homphæū Cochemensem, summa
cura in compendium redacti, atꝗ iam tertiùm
recogniti. In locum libri tertii successit epitome,
complectens fermè summam eorum, quæ in
libello sunt Erasmi de constructione octo partium
orationis, eiusdem Petri Homphaei opera.
8° Cologne, P. Horst, 1550.   EUL

epistolæ Manutii [Pro. 49]
541* MANUZIO, Paolo. Epistolae.

542 MARLIANUS, Joannes Bartholomaeus.
Consulum, dictatorum censorumꝗue Romanorum
series vnà cum ipsorum triumphis quae marmori-
bus scalpta in foro reperta est, atque in capitolium
translata.
8° Rome, 1549.   EUL

543 [MEIER, Georg.] Tabulæ de schematibus
et tropis Petri Mosellani. In rhetorica Philippi
Melanchthonis. In Erasmi Roterodami libellum
de duplici copia.
8° Paris, R. Estienne [the first], 1539.   EUL

Pomponeus Mela de sita orbis [Pro. 91]
544 MELA, Pomponius. Pomponij Mele scriptoris luculentissimi maxima cura recogniti cosmographia. [*Ed.* P. Phoenix.]
4° [Paris,] J. Seurre at the house of J. Petit [the
first], 1513.   EUL

545 MENSA. Mensa philosophica optime custos
valitudinis studiosis juuenibus apparata: nō min⁹
sententiarū grauitate cōducibilis: ꝗ facetiarū
enarratione delectabilis.
8° Paris, J. de Harsy, 1530.   EUL

Historia Meruli Alexandrini [Pro. 27]
546 MERULA, Georgius. [*Begin.* πlr] Othoni
Vicecomiti summae spei adolescenti Alexander
Minutianus salutem cum foelicitate. [alr] Georgii
Merulae Alexandrini antiquitatis vicecomitum
liber primus (–decimus). *Ed.* A. Minutianus.
2° [Milan, G. Le Signerre for A. Minutianus,
1497?]   EUL
Proctor 6074, Hain 11095.

547 MIGNAULT, Claude. De liberali adoles-
centum institutione in academia Parisiensi.
Declamationes contrariæ, quarum summa quæstio
est, an sit commodius adolescentes extra gymnasia,
quàm in gymnasiis ipsis institui . . .
8° Paris, J. Richer, 1575.   EUL

orationes 3 claud. Minois [Pro. 54]
548 MIGNAULT, Claude. De re literaria orationes tres, habita in academia Parisiensi . . .
8° Paris, J. Richer, 1576.   EUL
Bought in Paris, 1607.

eutopia Mori [Pro. 86]
549 MORE, *Sir* Thomas, *St.* Illustris viri Thomæ
Mori regni Britanniarum cancellarii, de optimo
reipublicæ statu, deque noua insula Vtopia, libri
duo . . .
12° Frankfort, J. Sauer for P. Kopff, 1601.   EUL

550 MORESINUS, Thomas. Papatus, seu de-
prauatae religionis origo et incrementum . . .
8° Edinburgh, R. Waldegraue, 1594.   EUL
STC 18102

551 MORUS, Hubertus. Oratoriae definitiones
ex optimis quibusque rhetoribus, maximè ex
Aristotele, Cicerone, & Fabio in gratiam rudio-
rum collectæ, recèns auctæ & recognitæ. . . .
Tertia editio.
4° Paris, D. Du Pré, 1571.   EUL

Mureti epistolæ [Pro. 72]
552* MURET, Marc Antoine. Epistolae.

Consilium Historiæ vniuersitatis scribendæ
[Pro. 56]
553* MYLAEUS, Christophorus. Consilium
historiae universitatis scribendae . . .

554 OPSOPŒUS, Vincentius. De arte bibendi libri tres, autore Vincentio Obsopœo Germano. Quibus adiunximus de arte iocandi libros quatuor, Matthiæ Delij Hamburgensis, cum luculenta in eosdem præfatione.
8° Frankfort, heirs of C. Egenolff for A. Lonicer, J. Cnipius and P. Steinmeyer, 1578.   EUL

Oratio de valens [Pro. 58]
555* ORATIO.
Not identified.

Orationes diuers. ad duces Venetorum [Pro. 5]
556* ORATIONES.
Not identified.

in epistolas ouidii commentarius [Pro. 75b]
557 OVIDIUS NASO, Publius. [*Begin.* πlv] Antonii Volsci Priuernatis ad Ludouicum Diaedum . . . [π2v] Ouidii vita per Antonium Volscum. [alr] Publii Ouidii Nasonis epistolarum heroidum liber primus. [ilr] Georgii Alexandrini in Sapphus epistolam interprætatio incipit. [klv] P. Ouidii Nasonis de Pulice opusculum icipit. [k2r] P. Ouidii Nasōis de Philomēa liber icipit. [k3r] Publii. Ouidii. Nasonis de remedio amoris. [15v] Publii Ouidii Nasōis de medicamine faciei libellus. [17r] Publii Ouiddii nasonis de nuce libellus.
2° Venice, B. de Tortis, 1481.   EUL
Hain *12213.

in epistolas ouidii commentarius [Pro. 75a]
558 OVIDIUS NASO, Publius. Epistole Ouidij cum commento. Epistole Heroides Publij Ouidij Nasonis dilgenti castgatione exculte, aptissimisꝗ figuris ornate: commentantibus Antonio Volsco, Vbertino Cresentinate, & A. Iano Parrhasio, necnon Iodoco Badio Ascensio. Liber seu epistola Sapphus cum enarrationibus Domitij Calderini Veronensis primarij interpretis, Georgij Merule Alexandrini, et ipsius Iodoci Badij Ascensij. Liber in ibin cum diligentissimis interpretationibus Domitij Calderini, Christophori zaroti, cunꝗ perꝗ familiari Iodoci Badij Ascensij expositione . . . Ouidij vita a Petro Crinito in de poetis latinis descripta.
4° Lyons, B. Bounyn, 1536.   EUL
Bought in Bourges, 1607.

Commentarius Erasmi in nucem ouidii [Pro. 98]
559* OVIDUS NASO, Publius. [*Supposititious work.*] Commentarius Erasmi Roterdami in nucem Ouidij.

flores doctorum [Pro. 83]
560* PALMER, Thomas, *Hibernicus.* Flores doctorum.

561 PARADISUS, Paulus. Pauli Paradisi de modo legendi hæbraicè, dialogus.
8° Paris, J. Gormont, 1534.   EUL

562 PARIS [SORBONNE]. Proœmium reformandæ Parisiensis academiæ, ad regem. 1562.
8° [Paris,] 1562.   EUL

Persius cum commentariis Murmelii [Pro. 40]
563 PERSIUS FLACCUS, Aulus. Auli Persii Flacci satyræ sex . . . [*Com.* J. Murmellius and H. Buschius.]
4° Paris, C. Wechel, 1538.   EUL

564 PETRONIUS ARBITER, Titus. Petronii Arbitri satyricon; cum notis et obseruationibus variorum. Editio noua. [*Ed.* J. a Wower.]
16° Leyden, F. Raphelengius, 1596.   TC

Philon de vita Moseos [Pro. 37]
565* PHILO, *Judæus.* Philonis Judæi de vita Mosis lib. iii, A. Turnebo interprete.

peloti Institutio linguæ gallicæ [Pro. 53]
566* PILLOT, Jean. Gallicae linguae institutio, latino sermone conscripta . . .

Æneæ Sil Asiæ Europ. desc. [Pro. 7]
567* PIUS II, *Pope* [Enea Silvio Piccolomini]. Asiae Europæ que, elegantissima descriptio . . .

Comentaria Æneæ Siluii de consilio Basiliæ Celibrato [Pro. 64]
568 PIUS II, *Pope* [Enea Silvio Piccolomini]. Commentariorum Aeneae Syluii Piccolominei Senensis, de concilio Basileæ celebrato libri duo, olim quidem scripti, nunc uero primum impressi . . . Cum multis aliis nunquam antehac impressis . . .
2° [Basle, A. Cratander? 1524?]   EUL
Wanting the last page of the text. Bought in Paris, 1607.
On the title-page Drummond wrote 'Veritas odium parit'.

Æneæ siluii epistolæ [Pro. 6]
569* PIUS II, *Pope* [Enea Silvio Piccolomini]. Epistolæ.

Gnomologia platonis Isocratis [Pro. 8]
570* PLATO. Divini Platonis gnomologia. See also Isocrates. Several editions of selections from Plato and Isocrates compiled by H. Wolf were printed in Lyons after 1550; Drummond probably had the *Gnomologiæ* of both authors bound together.

571 PLINIUS CÆCILIUS SECUNDUS, Caius. C. Plinii Cæc. Sec. epist. lib. IX. Eiusdem & Traiani imp. epist. amœbææ. Eiusdem Pl. & Pacati, Mamertini, Nazarii, panegyrici. Item, Claudiani panegyrici: adiunctæ sunt Isaaci Casauboni notæ in epist . . .
16° [Geneva,] P. Estienne, 1611.   DUL
The edition of 1599 (itself a copy of Henri

Estienne's 1591 edition) with a new title-page.
See Renouard, *Estienne*, I, 197, 195.

epitome plutarchi [List F]
572 * PLUTARCH. Epitome vitarum Plutarchi . . .

Plutarchi vitæ [Pro. 55]
573 * PLUTARCH. Vitae parallelae.

Pomponeus Letus de magist. Rom. [Pro. 94]
574 * POMPONIUS LAETUS, Julius. De Romanorum magistratibus.

opera Io. Iouiani Pontani [Pro. 30]
575 * PONTANUS, Joannes Jovianus. Ioannis Iouiani Pontani . . . Opera . . .

576   PONTE, Petrus de. Petri pōtani Cacci Brugensis sequunda pars artis grammaticæ : vndecim dirempta libris. de triplici recte loquendi modo : grammatico. Oratorio. Et poetico . . .
4° Paris, D. Roce, (1515).   E U L

577   POSTEL, Guillaume. De originibus, seu, de varia et potissimum orbi Latino ad hanc diem incognita, aut incōsyderata historia, quū totius Orientis, tum maximè Tartarorum, Persarum, Turcarum, & omnium Abrahami & noachi alumnorum origines, & mysteria Brachmanum retegente . . .
8° Basle, J. Oporinus, (1553).   E U L

Quintiliani Instit. orat. [Pro. 19]
578   QUINTILIANUS, Marcus Fabius. M. Fabii Quintiliani institutionum oratoriarum libri duodecim . . .
8° Lyons, A. Gryphe, 1585.   P R
Bought in Paris, 1607.

Rami epistolæ et declamat. [Pro. 84]
579 * RAMUS, Petrus. ? Petri Rami professoris regii, et Audomari Talaei collectaneae praefationes, epistolae, orationes . . .
See Ong, p. 448.

epitheta textoris [Pro. 25]
580 * RAVISIUS, Johannes, *Textor*. Epithetorum . . . opus absolutissimum.

officina Textoris [Pro. 24]
581 * RAVISIUS, Johannes, *Textor*. J. Rauisii . . . officina, partim historia partim poeticis referta disciplinis.

582   REYNARD THE FOX. Speculum vitæ aulicæ. De admirabili fallacia et astutia vulpeculæ Reinikes libri quatuor, nunc primum ex idiomate Germanico latinitate donati, adiectis elegantissimis iconibus, veras omnium apologorum animaliumq́; species ad viuum adumbrantibus, auctore Hartmanno Schoppero . . .
12° Frankfort, N. Bassée, 1584.   E U L

Eumudus Richerus de arte figurarum [Pro. 22]
583   RICHER, Edmond. Emundi Richerii de arte figurarum et causis eloquentiæ. Opus, non pueris modò compendiosiùs, & faciliùs erudiendis, sed poetis, atque oratoribus imitandis, & Sacris Scripturis interpretandis necessarium.
8° Paris, P. Pautonnier, 1605.   E U L
Bought in Paris, 1607.

584   ROBERTELLO, Francesco. Francisci Robertelli Vtinensis de artificio dicendi . . . liber. Eiusdem tabulae oratoriae in or. Cic. qua gratias agit senatui post reditum. In or. pro Milone. In or. pro Cn. Plancio. [In 3 parts.]
4° Bologna, A. Benacci, 1567.   E U L

Ronsardi vita [Pro. 68]
585 * RONSARD, Pierre de.
Not identified. A translation of Claude Binet's life ?

Vitruuii Roscii gram̄attica [Pro. 50]
586   ROSCIUS, Vitruvius. L. Vitruuii Roscii Parmensis libetius primus, secundus, et tertius : vel grammaticarum quaestionum libri tres.
8° Genoa, A. Bellone, 1547.   E U L
Bought in Paris, 1608.

587   RUSSELL, John. Verba Ioann. Russelli iureconsulti pro senatu populoque Edinburgensi habita, ad serenissimam Scotorum reginam Annam, dum Edinburgum ingreditur 19. Maij. an. 1590.
4° Edinburgh, R. Waldegraue, 1590.   E U L
STC 21459

588   RUTHERFORD, John. Commentariorum de arte disserendi libri quatuor . . .
4° [London, T. Vautrollier ?] For H. Charteris, Edinburgh, 1577.   E U L
STC 21463

Salustius [List K]
589 * SALLUSTIUS CRISPUS, Caius. Opera.

Gasparis Sardi epistolæ [Pro. 71]
590   SARDI, Gasparo. Gasparis Sardi Ferrariensis epistolarum liber, varia reconditáque historiarum cognitione refertus. Eiusdem de triplici philosophia commentariolus.
8° Florence, L. Torrentino, 1549.   E U L

591   SELDEN, John. Analecton Anglobritannicon libri duo. Quibus ea maxime, quæ ad ciuilem illius, quæ iam Anglia dicitur, Magnæ Britanniæ partis antiquitus administrationem, res domi publicas, sacras, prophanas, statusque catastrophas vsq; ad Normanni aduentum attinent, ex antiquis simul & neotericis depromta, temporum iuxta seriem digesta historice & arctissime componuntur . . .
4° Frankfort, house of Palthenius, 1615.   E U L

Senecæ Medea Meraulomantii [Pro. 63]
592 SENECA, Lucius Annæus. Medea L. Annei
Senecæ tragoedia septima. Petri Miraulmontii
Ambiani interpretatione illustrata.
4° Paris, D. Du Pré, 1571.   EUL
Bought in Paris, 1607.

Sigonius de regno Italiæ [List G]
593* SIGONIO, Carolo. De regno Italiæ libri
viginti.

594 SIMSON, Archibald. Hieroglyphica animalium terrestrium volatilium, natatilium, reptilium,
insectorum, vegetiuorum, metallorum, lapidum:
&c. Quæ in scripturis Sacris inueniuntur; &
plurimorum aliorum, cum eorum interpretationibus, ob theologiæ studiosos.
4° Edinburgh, T. Finlason, 1622–24.   EUL
STC 22567. All after 'insectorum' wanting.

595 SOAREZ, Cyprianus. De arte rhetorica libri
tres ex Aristotele, Cicerone & Quintiliano præ-
cipue deprompti.
8° [Paris? T. Brumen? 1584?]   EUL
Wanting the title-page and all the first gathering.
The lay-out is almost identical with Brumen's
edition of 1573.

Solinus cum scholiis [Pro. 42]
596* SOLINUS, Caius Julius. C. Julii Solini
Polyhistor, de memorabilibus mundi opus.
An edition with *scholia*.

597 STATORIUS, Petrus. In clarissimi viri D:
Ioannis a Lasko Poloniæ Baronis obitū, funebris
oratio . . .
8° Pinczow, D. Lancicius, 1560.   EUL

598* STELLA, Joannes. De vitis ac gestis summorum pontificum ad Julium II.   HEND

599 STRADA, Famianus. R.P. Famiani Stradæ
Romani, e Societate Iesu, prolusiones academicæ,
seu orationes variæ, ad facultatem oratoriam,
historicam, poeticam spectantes. Editio tertia.
8° Cologne, J. Kinckius, 1625.   EUL

Suetonius Tranquillus [Pro. 77]
600 SUETONIUS TRANQUILLUS, Caius.
[*Begin, after five lines of Ausonius.*] C. Suetonii
Tranquilli de vita .XII. Caesarum liber primus
(–duodecimus) . . .
2° [Treviso, J. Rubeus,] 1480.   EUL
Proctor 6494, Hain *15119.

601 SULPICIUS, Joannes, *Verulanus*. Gram-
matice Sulpitiana cum textu Ascēsiano recognito
et aucto. Cui recentius hec addita sunt. Textus in
regulas sulpitianas de cōstructiōe. Regule com-
pendiose de orthographia.
4° Paris, J. Petit [the first], 1505.   EUL

Synesius de insomniis [Pro. 39]
602 SYNESIUS, *of Cyrene, Bp. of Ptolemais*.
Synesii Cyrenæi Ptolemaidis Episcopi de insomniis
libellus, ab Antonio Pichonio gymnasiarcha
scholarum diui Martini Turonensis, e Græco in
latinum conuersus.
8° Tours, R. Siffleau, 1571.   EUL
Bought in Paris, 1607.

603 THEMISTOR, Joannes, *Scotus*. Ioannis
Themistoris Scoti, ad discipulos suos in nobili
academia Montana arti disserendi operam
nauantes, dialogus de argumentatione.
4° Paris, P. Calvarin, 1554.   EUL

604 THUCYDIDES. Thucydidis Atheniensis
historiographi de bello Peloponnensium Atheni-
ensiumque libri VIII. Laurentio Valla interprete:
& nunc à Conrado Heresbachio ad græcum
exemplar diligentissime recogniti.
2° Cologne, E. Cervicornus, 1527.   EUL
And *Ex Marcellino Graeco Thucydidis Atheniensis
historici clarissimi vita, Bartholomaeo Parthenio
Benacensi interprete.*

605* TRICASSO, Patricio. Tricassi . . . Enarratio
pulcherrima principiorum chyromantiæ . . . Ejusdem Tricassi . . . opus chyromanticum absolutissimum . . .
4° Nuremberg, J. vom Berg and U. Neuber,
1560.   AUCT

Iustinus Aurelius victor [Pro. 15]
606* TROGUS POMPEIUS. Justini ex Trogi
Pompeii historiis externis libri xliii. Hic accessit,
ex Sexto Aurelio Victore de vita & moribus
Romanorum Imperatorum epitome . . .

607 URSINUS, Fulvius. Virgilius collatione
scriptorum Graecorum illustratus . . .
8° Antwerp, C. Plantin, 1567.   EUL

608 VULTEIUS, Joannes. Oratio funebris, à Io.
Minutio Tholosae habita.
8° Lyons, J. Barbou for M. Parmentier, 1537. EUL

609 WAKE, Isaac. Rex Platonicus: siue, de
potentissimi principis Iacobi Britanniarum regis,
ad illustrissimam academiam Oxoniensem, aduentu,
Aug. 27. an. 1605 . . . narratio. Editio tertia.
12° Oxford, J. Barnes, 1615.   EUL
STC 24940

610* WAUCHOPE, George. G. Vauchopii de
veteri populo Romano tractatus.
12° Caen, widow of J. Le Bas, 1595.   AUCT
Copy in EUL

611* WELWOOD, William. Guilielmi Velvod de
aqua in altum per fistulas plumbeas facile expri-
menda apologia demonstratiua.

4° Edinburgh, A. Arbuthnet, 1582.   AUCT
STC 25239
Copy in EUL.

612 ZAMOYSKI, Jan, *Chancellor of Poland.*
Ioan. Sarij Zamoscij . . . oratio : qua Henric.
Valesium regem renunciat.
4° Paris, F. Morel [the first], 1573.   EUL
Bought in Paris, 1607.

❋ GREEK BOOKS ❋

æschinis epistolæ [Gk. 28]
613* AESCHINES, *pseud.* Ἐπιστολαι Αἰσχινου . . .

aeschili tragediæ [Gk. 27]
614* AESCHYLUS. Αἰσχυλου τραγῳδιαι Ζ΄.
Æschyli tragœdiæ VII.

Anacreon H. Stephani [Gk. 9]
615* ANACREON. Ἀνακρεοντος και ἀλλων τινων
λυρικων ποιητων μελη. Anacreontis et aliorum
lyricorum aliquot pöetarum odæ. In easdem Henr.
Stephani observationes. Eædem Latinæ. (Anacreontis . . . odæ, ab Helia Andrea Latinæ factæ.) [In
2 parts.] Drummond may have had the earlier
(1554) Estienne edition.

616 APOLLONIUS, *Rhodius.* Ἀπολλωνιου του
Ῥοδιου Ἀργοναυτικων βιβλια δ΄. Apollonii Rhodii
Argonauticων libri IIII. Scholia vetusta in eosdem
libros, quæ palmam inter alia omnia in alios poetas
scripta, obtinere existimantur. Cum annotationibus
Henrici Stephani : ex quibus, quantam in hanc
editionem contulerit diligentiam, cognosci poterit.
4° [Geneva,] H. Estienne [the second], 1574. EUL

Aratus cum commentariis Hieronis [Gk. 2]
617* ARATUS. ? Phænomena.
Commentator unidentified.
A mistake for Hyginus?

618 ARISTEAS. Aristeae, de legis diuinæ ex
Hebraica lingua in Graecam translatione, per
septuaginta interpretes, Ptolemæi Philadelphi
Aegyptiorum regis studio ac liberalitate Hiero-
solyma accersitos, absoluta, historia nunc primùm
Græcè edita . . . Cum conuersione Latina, autore
Matthia Garbitio. [*Ed.* Simon Schardius. In 2
parts.]
8° Basle, J. Oporinus, [1561].   EUL

*Commentarium Iulii Pacii cum textu græco in
organon Arist.* [List K]
619* ARISTOTLE. Ἀριστοτελους ὀργανον. Aristotelis . . . Organum . . . Iul. Pacius recensuit . . .
emendauit ; e græca in latinam linguam conuertit
. . . Accessit eiusdem Pacii in vniuersum Organum
commentarius analyticus . . . [In 2 vols.]

620 ARISTOTLE. Ἀμμωνιου του Ἑρμειου εἰς τας
πεντε φωνας του Πορφυριου ὑπομνημα. Ammonii
Hermiæ in quinque voces Porphyrii commentaria.
[*Ed.* J. B. Felicianus. In 3 vols.]
8° Venice, by the brothers Nicolini da Sabbio
for M. Sessa, 1545.   EUL
And Ἀμμωνιου . . . εἰς τας του Ἀριστοτελους
κατηγοριας ὑπομνημα. *Ammonii . . . in Aristotelis
prædicamenta commentaria.* And Ἀμμωνιου του
Ἑρμειου εἰς το του Ἀριστοτελους περι ἑρμηνειας
ὑπομνημα. *Ammonii Hermiæ in librum Aristotelis de
interpretatione commentaria.*
With the texts of Aristotle and Porphyry. The
three volumes in EUL had a common owner
(16th cent.) and though only 1 and 3 were
included in the *Drummond Collection* by David
Laing, it is most probable that all three were
owned by Drummond. His signature is on the
first volume.

Aristotelis acromatica [Gk. 19]
621* ARISTOTLE. Ἀριστοτελους φυσικης ἀκροασεως
βιβλια θ΄. Aristotelis Naturalis auscultationis
libri octo.

commentarius paci in 8 phy. Ar. [List K]
622* ARISTOTLE. Ἀριστοτελους φυσικης ἀκροασεως
βιβλια θ. Aristotelis . . . Naturalis auscultationis
libri VIII. Iul. Pacius . . . cum græcis . . . codicibus
. . . contulit, latina interpretatione auxit, commentariis . . . illustrauit.

Aristotelis de mundo cælo [Gk. 30]
623* ARISTOTLE. De cœlo et mundo libri quatuor.

ethica aristotelis [Gk. 29]
624* ARISTOTLE. Ἀριστοτελους ἠθικων Νικομαχειων βιβλια δεκα. Aristotelis de moribus ad Nicomachum libri decem.

testamentum crispini [Gk. 13]
625* BIBLE. New Testament. Της Καινης Διαθηκης ἁπαντα ... Nouum Iesu Christi Domini nostri Testamentum. Additis summis rerum & sententiarum, quæ singulis capitibus continentur: variis item lectionibus mutuisque testimoniis, quæ laborem in legendo ac conferendo magnopere subleuabunt. [*Ed.* J. Crespin.]

testamentum H. Stephani [Gk. 26]
626* BIBLE. New Testament. Ἡ Καινη Διαθηκη. Nouum Testamentum. Obscuriorum vocum & quorūdam loquendi generum accuratas partim suas partim aliorum interpretationes margini adscripsit Henr. Stephanus.

catechesis H. Stephani [Gk. 11]
627* CALVIN, Jean. Στοιχειωσις της Χριστιανων πιστεως, ἡ Κατηχισμός. Rudimenta fidei christianæ, sive cathechismus ... [*Tr.* H. Estienne.]
Possible editions in Greek alone, or in Greek and Latin.

628 CHION. Ἡ του Χιωνος Πλατωνικου προς τον Κλεαρχον ἐπιστολη ἀπολογητικη.
4° Paris, F. Morel [the second], 1595.   EUL

629 CHRYSOLORAS, Emmanuel. Erotemata chrysolorae. Ἐρωτηματα του Χρυσολωρα. De formatione temporum ex libro chalcondylae. Περι σχηματισμου των χρονων ἐκ των Χαλκονδυλου. Quartus gazae de constructione. Το τεταρτον του γαζη περι συνταξεως. De anomalis verbis. Περι ανωμαλων ῥηματων. De encliticis. Περι ἐγκλιτικων. Sententiae monostichi ex varijs poetis. Γνωμαι μονοστιχοι ἐκ διαφορων ποιητων.   [*Ed.* Demetrio Duncas.]
4° Logroño [in compluti academia], Arnao Guillén de Brocar, 1514.   EUL
The first two works are in Greek and Latin, the others in Greek only. Theodorus Gaza is the grammarian referred to.

630 CICERO, Marcus Tullius. Μαρκου Τυλλιου Κικερωνος Κατων, ἡ περι γηρως. Ἑρμηνεια Θεοδωρου. Mar. Tul. Ciceronis de senectute. Traductio Theodori.
8° Paris, C. Wechel, 1536.   EUL

catichesis Cyrilli [Gk. 5]
631* CYRIL, *Saint, Patriarch of Jerusalem.* Του ἁγιου Κυριλλου ... κατηχησεις Sancti. Cyrilli ... catecheses.

Dionysius affer cum scholiaste [Gk. 7]
632 DIONYSIUS, *Perigetes.* Διονυσιου Ἀλεξανδρεως της οἰκουμενης περιηγησις, ὑπομνηματισθεισα ὑπο του Εὐσταθιου ... Dionysii Alexandrini de situ orbis libellus, Eustathii Thessalonicensis archiepiscopi commentariis illustratus.
4° Paris, R. Estienne [the first], 1547.   EUL
Bought in Paris, 1607, and given to EUL by Joseph Johnston in 1622.

Epigraṁata Græca [Gk. 15]
633* Epigrammatum Græcorum annotationibus J. Brodæi, necnon V. Obsopæi, et Græcis scholiis illustratorum libri VII. Accesserunt H. Stephani in quosdam anthologiæ epigrammatum locos annotationes ...

Eunapius de vitis philosophorum [Gk. 12]
634 EUNAPIUS. Εὐναπιου ... βιοι φιλοσοφων και σοφιστων. E. bibliotheca Ioan. Sambuci Pannonij Tirnauiensis. (Eunapius Sardianus, de vitis philosophorum et sophistarum: nunc primum Græcè & Latinè editus, interprete Hadriano Iunio Hornano. Cum indice & Græci exemplaris castigatione.) [In 2 parts.]
8° Antwerp, C. Plantin, 1568.   EUL
Bought in Bourges, 1608.

635 GREEK ANTHOLOGY. Omnium horarum opsonia. Amoeniori lectione, grataque iucunditate festiue simul & grauiter exposita ac disposita, in moralia. Satyrica & cauillatoria. Epitaphia. Imagines ac statuas. Anathematica seu dedicatoria & amatoria. Prout cuiusque humori ac palato conueniunt degustanda ...
8° Frankfort, I.-I. Porsio, 1614.   BUL
A re-issue under a new title of the edition of 1602, which according to Brunet was edited by Hier. Megisier. Brunet, I, 311. This anthology is based on the abridgement by Maximus Planudes of the collection made by the Byzantine scholar Constantine Cephalas, particularly the *Cycle* of epigrams gathered and written by Agathias. The preface is signed by Vincentius Opsopoeus. In Greek and Latin. With a poem by Conrad Celtis.

Nazianceni καταγυνεικων [Gk. 6]
636 GREGORY, *of Nazianzus, St.* Ἐπος ἁγιου Γρηγοριου του Ναζιανζηνου του θεολογου κατα γυναικων καλλωπιζομενων. Carmen diui Gregorii Nazianzeni cognomento theologi aduersus mulieres ambitiosius se adornantes & fucantes.
4° Paris, E. Prévosteau, 1588.   EUL

637 GREGORY, *of Nazianzus, St.* Sententiae et regulæ vitæ ex Gregorii Nazanzeni scriptis collectæ. Eiusdem iambi aliquot, nunc primùm in lucem editi: per Ioannem Sambucum Pannonium.
8° Antwerp, C. Plantin, 1568.   EUL

Heliodorus [Gk. 21]
638* HELIODORUS. Ἡλιοδωρου Αἰθιοπικης ἱστοριας βιβλια δεκα. Heliodori Historiæ Æthiopicæ libri decem . . .

Herodianus [Gr. 20]
639 HERODIAN. Ἡρωδιανου Ἱστοριων βιβλια η΄. Herodiani Histor. lib. VIII. cum Angeli Politani interpretatione, et hujus partim supplemento, partim examine H. Stephani: utroque margini adscripto. Ejusdem H. Stephani emendationes quorundam Græci contextus locorum . . . Historiarum (Zosimi) Herodianicas subsequentium libri duo, nunc primum Græci editi. [In 2 parts, with the Latin version of J. Leunclavius.] 4° [Geneva,] H. Estienne [the second], 1581. Present location unknown.   SALE

640 HIPPOCRATES. [*Supposititious works.*] Julii Cæsaris Scaligeri, de insomniis commentarius in librum Hippocratis: denuò nitori suo restitutus, & in lucem editus, cum indice rerum & verborum locupletissimo. Accessit in fine Aristotelis de somno & vigilia, insomniis & divinatione libellus. 8° Giessen, house of Chemlin, 1610.   EUL Greek and Latin.

Homeri Ilias [Gk. 22]
641* HOMER. Ὁμηρου Ἰλιας. Homeri Ilias, id est, de rebus ad Trojam gestis.

642 HORATIUS FLACCUS, Quintus. Q. Horatii Flacci carmen seculare. A Fed. Morello profess. & interpr. reg. Græcè eod. genere carm. expressum. 4° Paris, F. Morel [the second], 1600.   EUL And *In Dianam et Apollinem ode*. Greek and Latin.

643 IGNATIUS, St., Bp. Ἐπιστολαι. 8° Paris, G. Morel, 1558.   EUL Title and first seven leaves wanting.

Isocratis orationes [List K]
644* ISOCRATES. Isocratis orationes.

645 JOHN, Chrysostom, St. Ιωαννου του Χρυσοστομου, περι του μη καταφρονειν της του θεου ἐκκλησιας και των μυστηριων. Io. Chrysostomi, de non contemnenda Dei ecclesia, & mysteriis. 8° Paris, J. Bienné, 1570.   EUL

Iuliani de cæsaribus oratio [Gk. 31]
646* JULIANUS, Flavius Claudius, *Emperor.* Ἰουλιανου αὐτοκρατορος περι Καισαρων λογος. Iuliani imperatoris de Cæsaribus sermo. C. Cantoclari . . . studio atque opera in lucem editus, & ab eodem Latinus factus.

647 JUSTINIAN I, *Emperor of the East.* Ἰνστιτουτα Θεοφιλου Ἀντικενσωρος. Institutiones iuris ciuilis in Graecam linguam per Theophilum

Antecessorem olim traductæ, ac fusissimè planissiméque explicatæ, superioribus diebus cura & studio Viglii Zuichemi Phrysij primùm in lucem æditæ . . . 8° Paris, C. Wechel, 1534.   EUL The work described as *Theophilus* (Jur. 2)?

648 LAUREMBERGIUS, Petrus. Ἀνωνυμου εἰσαγωγη ἀνατομικη. Cum interpretatione doctissima, excellentissimi philosophi aci medic, Petri Laurembergi. Nunc primum in lucem edita auspicijs ac sumptibus Ioachimi Morsi. 4° Leyden, 1618.   EUL Greek and Latin.

Luciani dialogi minores [List K]
649* LUCIAN, *of Samosata.* Dialogi aliquot. Also as Gk. 35.

650 LUCIAN, *of Samosata.* Λουκιανου Σαμοσατεως Προμηθευς ἡ Καυκασος. Luciani Samosatensis Prometheus vel Caucasus. 4° Paris, E. Prévosteau, 1587.   EUL

651* MARTINBOS, Nicolaus a. Græcæ grammatices rudimenta.   AUCT Edition not traced. AUCT has 'Paris, 1544'.

Moscopulus [Gk. 33]
652 MOSCHOPOULOS, Emanuel. Του σοφωτατου και λογιωτατου Μανουηλου του Μοσχοπουλου περι σχεδων. Manuelis Moschopuli de ratione examinandæ orationis libellus. 4° Paris, R. Estienne [the first], 1545.   EUL Bought in Paris, 1607, and given to the library in 1623 by William Brown.

Nicetæ historia [Gk. 17]
653 NICETAS, *Acominatus, Choniates.* Nicetæ Acominati Choniatæ . . . Imperii Græci historia . . . Itera editio græcolatina, Hieronymo Wolfio . . . interprete . . . 4° [Geneva,] heirs of E. Vignon, 1593.   PR Bought in Paris, 1608.

Nicomachi Gerasineni arithmetica [Gk. 8]
654* NICOMACHUS, Gerasinus. Νικομαχου Γερασινου Ἀριθμητικης βιβλια δυο. Nicomachi . . . Arithmeticæ libri duo . . .

ocellus [Gk. 16]
655 OCELLUS, Lucanus. Ὠκελλος ὁ Λευκανος φιλοσοφος περι της του παντος φυσεως. Ocellus Lucanus philosophus de vniuersi natura, interprete Ludouico Nogarola Com. Veronensi. Eiusdem Nogarolae annotationes in Oceuum & epistola de viris illustribus Italis qui Græcè scripserunt. Editio tertia, collatione exemplarium melior facta. 8° [Heidelberg,] J. Commelin, 1596.   EUL Greek and Latin. Bought in Bourges, 1608.

oppianus [Gk. 14]
656 OPPIAN. Ὀππιανου Ἀναζαρβεως ἁλιευτικων βιβλια ε'. Κυνηγετικων βιβλια δ'. Anazarbei de piscatu libri v. De venatione libri iv.
4° Paris, A. Turnèbe, 1555.   FOLG
Bought in Bourges, 1608. Bound with this book is a Latin translation of the *De Venatione* (343) also bearing Drummond's signature, and Latin translations of the *De Piscatu* and *De Venatione* (342) without Drummond's signature. See Brunet, IV, 195, for a description of all three editions.

orphei arganautica [Gk. 4]
657 ORPHEUS. Orphei poetarum vetustissimi Argonauticῶn opus Græcῦ, cῦ interpretatione Latina incerti autoris, recens addita, & diligētius quàm hactenus emēdata.
4° Basle, A. Cratander, 1523.   EUL
Greek and Latin.

epistolæ Phalaridos [Gk. 3]
658* PHALARIS. Phalaridis . . . Epistolae.
The letters are spurious.

Phile de animantibus [Gk. 25]
659 PHILES, Manuel. Του σοφωτατου Φιλη στιχοι ιαμβικοι περι ζωων ἰδιοτητος μετα προσθηκης I. του Καμεραριαδου. Sapientissimi Phile versus iambici de animalium proprietate, cum auctario Ioach. Camerarii. Exposita eodem metro versuum Latinorum a Gregor. Bersmano Annæbergensi.
8° [Heidelberg,] J. Commelin, 1596.   EUL

Pindarus [Gk. 23] and *Poetæ minores* [Gk. 24]
660* PINDAR. ? Pindari Olympia, Pythia, Nemea, Isthmia. (Cæterorum octo lyricorum carmina, Alcæi, Sapphus, Stesichori, Ibyci, Anacreontis, Bacchylidis, Simonidis, Alcmanis . . .) [In two parts.]
See especially the Estienne editions.

plutarchi apothegmata [Gk. 34]
661* PLUTARCH. Apophthegmata graeca regum et ducum, philosophorum item aliorumque . . . ex Plutarcho et Diogene Laertio. Cum latina interpr. . . .
Possibly the Estienne edition of 1568, from which the above title is taken.

662 PLUTARCH. Πλουταρχου περι παιδαγωγης. Plutarchi de liberis educandis commentarius in certa capita distinctus, perpetua analysi logica & sententiis variorum autorum illustratus . . . [*Ed.* M. Beumler.]
8° Speyer, B. Albinus, 1593.   EUL
Greek and Latin.

663 PLUTARCH. Plutarchi . . . Septem sapientum convivium, G. Plantio Cenomanno . . . interprete: adjecto Græco, ab eodem innumeris emendato locis. Item, de superstitione libellus,

eodem interprete. [3 parts in 1.]
8° Lyons, S. Gryphe, 1552.   MUL
Greek and Latin.

664 PLUTARCH. Πλουταρχου Χαιρωνεως, περι ἀρετης και κακιας.
4° [Paris, c. 1566.]
Two leaves, without a title leaf.   EUL

665 POLYBIUS. Πολυβιου μεγαλοπολιτου, ἱστοριων βιβλια ε'. Polybii historiarum libri quinꝗ, opera Vincentii Obsopœi in lucem editi. Iidem Latini Nicolao Perotto episcopo Sipontino interprete. [In 2 parts.]
2° Hagenau, J. Setzer, 1530.   EUL
Greek and Latin.

666 PSELLUS, Michael Constantine. Του σοφωτατου Ψελλου συνταγμα εὐσυνοπτον εἰς τας τεσσαρας μαθηματικας ἐπιστημας, ἀριθμητικην, μουσικην, γεωμετριαν, και ἀστρονομιαν. Doctissimi Pselli opus dilucidum in quattuor mathematicas disciplinas, arihmeticam, musicam, geometriam, & astronomiam.
8° Paris, J. Bogard, 1545.   EUL
With an inset table at the end showing degrees of consanguinity.

Hieroclis commentarius in aurea carmina Pythagoræ [Gk. 1]
667* PYTHAGORAS. Ἱεροκλεους . . . ὑπομνημα εἰς τα των Πυθαγορειων ἐπη τα χρυσα. Hieroclis . . . Commentarius in aurea Pythagoreorum carmina . . .
Probably with the text, and a Latin translation by J. Curterius.

Greca Grammattica P. Rami [Gk. 10]
668* RAMUS, Petrus. Grammatica Graeca, praecipue quatenus a Latina differt . . .
Most probably one of the later editions including syntax, the Ramists' second part of grammar. See Ong, p. 337.

Dictionarium græcum Iohanis scapulæ e Henrici Stephani [List K]
669* SCAPULA, Joannes. Lexicon graecolatinum nouum.
Scapula, while working for Henri Estienne, extracted his *Lexicon* from Estienne's then unpublished *Thesaurus.* See Renouard, *Estienne*, I, 139. Also as Gk. 18.

670 THEMISTIUS, Euphrada. Θεμιστιου φιλοσοφου . . . λογοι τεσσαρεσκαιδεκα. Themistii philosophi (euphradæ ab eloquētia cognominati) orationes XIIII. Harum sex posteriores, nouæ, cæteræ emendatiores prodeunt. Cum Latina interpretatione.
8° [Geneva,] H. Estienne, 1562.   EUL
The Latin translation did not appear. According to Renouard the words announcing it were

covered with a slip of paper (which is missing in this copy, although the words are partly obliterated). See Renouard, *Estienne*, I, 120–1.

671 VARENNIUS, Joannes. Ioannis Varenii Mechliniensis περι προσῳδιων libellus, antehac nunquam excusus, plané que necessarius. 'Ε. Μοσχοπουλου περι προσῳδιαν. De dialectis Græcis collecta ex Corintho, Ioanne Gram. Plutarcho, Ioan. Philopo. atque aliis eiusdem classis, per Hadrianum Ameriotium, in gratiam illorum qui poëtas Græcos intelligere cupiunt.
8° Paris, A. Wechel, 1566.   EUL

Syntaxis greca [Gk. 32]
672 VARENNIUS, Joannes. Syntaxis linguæ Græcæ, Ioanne Varennio Mechliniensi authore, vna cum annotatiunculis paucis ad præcepta syntaxis Varennianæ, per Ioachimum Camerarium. Renatus autem Guillonius præcepta syntaxεωs

multis in locis repurgauit, multáque in illis annotauit. Accessit prætereà opusculum perutile de passionibus dictionum ex Tryphone grammatico.
8° Paris, D. Du Val, 1576.   EUL

673 XENOPHON. Ξενοφωντος. 'Απολογια Σωκρατους προς τους δικαστας. 'Αγησιλαος. 'Ιερων ἡ τυραννικος. [*Ed.* J. Setzer.]
4° Hagenau, T. Anshelm, 1520.   EUL
Brunet gives an issue dated June, 1520. (Brunet, v, 1495.) This issue is dated July. Bought in Paris, 1607.

674 XENOPHON. Ξενοφωντος Κυρου παιδειας βιβλια τεττara A'.B'.Γ'.Δ'. (—E'.ϛ'.Z'.H'.)
Xenophontis Cyri paediae libri quatuor priores (–quatuor posteriores).
4° Paris, C. Wechel, 1538, 1539.   EUL
Some of the marginal notes are in George Buchanan's hand.

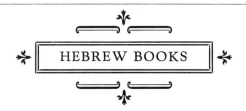

HEBREW BOOKS

675 ABRAHAM BAR HIYYĀ, *han-Nāśi'.* Sphæra mundi, describens figuram terræ dispositionemque orbium cœlestium & motus stellarum, autore Rabi Araham Hispano filio R. Haijæ. Sebast. Munsterus. Quicquid difficile in Hebraismo apud autorem istum inuenitur, explicatum est annotationibus nostris, ne librum nudum tibi lector traderemus.
4° Basle, H. Petri, (1546).   EUL
And *Compendium arithmetices, decerptum ex libro arithmeticarum institutionum magistri Eliæ Orientalis* (Elijah Mizrāhi). The *Sphæra mundi* is annotated by Münster, and the *Compendium arithmetices* by Münster and O. Schreckenfuch.

Biblia [Heb. 2]
676* BIBLE. Biblia Hebraica.

Ionas [Heb. 11]
677 BIBLE. Obadiah *and* Jonah. Abdiæ & Ionæ vaticinia.
4° Paris, M. Le Jeune, 1568.   EUL

Ruth [Heb. 11]
678 BIBLE. Ruth. Historia Ruth.
4° Paris, M. Le Jeune, 1569.   EUL

679 BIBLE. Esther. Libellus Ester.
4° Paris, M. Le Jeune, 1555.   EUL

psalmi hebraicè [Heb. 3]
680* BIBLE. Psalms. Psalterium Dauidis Hebræum.

ecclesiastes hebraice [Heb. 9]
681 BIBLE. Ecclesiastes. Ecclesiastes Salomonis Hebraice.
4° Paris, M. Le Jeune, 1569.   EUL

canticum canticorum [Heb. 11]
682 BIBLE. Song of Solomon. Canticum canticorum Salomonis.
4° Paris, M. Le Jeune, 1574.   EUL

683 BIBLE. Obadiah. Abdias cum commētariis R. Dauid Kimhi, à Francisco Vatablo, Hebraicarū literarū professore regio, summa cura & diligentia recognitis.
4° Paris, R. Estienne [the first], 1540.   EUL

catichesis Tremelii [Heb. 6]
684* CALVIN, Jean. [Rudimenta fidei Christianæ.] ספר הכוך בהוריס (Domini electi initiationis liber) id est (J. Calvini) liber catecheseos juventutis Dei ab Immanuele Tremellio Hebraice versus. Robert Estienne (the first) printed an edition at at Geneva in 1554. See Renouard, *Estienne*, I, 84.

Cantica eruditionis [Heb. 10]
685* Not identified.

claii Grammattica Hebraica [Heb. 4]
686* CLAIUS, Joannes. Elementa linguae Hebræae
pro incipientibus.

Grammatica Hebreæ Iunii [Heb. 8]
687* DU JON, François, *the elder.* F. Junii
grammatica Hebraeae linguae . . .

688 ELIJAH BEN ASHER, hal-Lēvi. Nomenclatura Hebraica autore Helia Leuita Germano
grãmatico, in gratiam omnium tyronum ac studio-
sorum linguæ sanctę.
8° Isny [P. Fagius?], 1542.   EUL
A small vocabulary in Hebrew, Latin and German.

Dictionarium Hæbreum Auenarii [Heb. 1]
689* HABERMANN, Johann. ? סבּר השושים
Hoc est, liber radicum seu lexicon ebraicum . . .

*cathechesis Lutheri Hebraice grece latine
germanice* [List K]
690* LUTHER, Martin. Catechesis minor.
[*Tr.* J. Claius.]

A polyglott edition in Hebrew, Greek, Latin
and German. Also listed as Heb. 5.

691 NATHAN, Isaac Mordecai. Dictionarium
Hebraicum, è concordantijs Hebræis, à M.
Anthonio Reuchlino Latinitate donatis, ea fide &
diligentia excerptum, ut necӡ dictio Hebraica ulla,
necӡ significatio uocabuli (modo in concordantijs
illis contineatur) desideretur. Habentur præterea
in hoc libello: compendium Hebraicæ grammaticæ,
unà cum modo inuestigandi radicem seu thema.
Formula omnium coniugationum, perfectarum &
imperfectarum, adiectis etiam quibusdam anomalis.
Lucas Osiander. D.
8° Basle, S. Koenig, 1569.   EUL
With the signature of Andrew Melville on the
flyleaf.

compendium Grammatticæ Pagnini [Heb. 7]
692* PAGNINUS, Santes. Hebraicarum institutionum libri IIII, Sancte Pagnino Lucensi authore,
ex R. David Kimhi priore parte כוכלול [*com-
plementum*] quam חלק הדקדגק [*pars grammatices*] inscripsit, fere transcripti.

ENGLISH BOOKS

693* ADAMSON, John. Τὰ των μουσων εἰσόδια.
The muses welcome to the high and mightie
prince Iames . . .
2° Edinburgh, T. Finlason, 1618.   AUCT
STC 140–1
Drummond's *Forth Feasting* was included in this
collection, gathered to mark the return of James
to Scotland after an absence of fourteen years
(see Kastner, I, lxx–lxxi).

694* ADAMSON, John. The travellers joy or a
sermon on the third verse of the second chapter
of Solomons Song.
8° London, J. Haviland for H. Bell, 1623. AUCT
STC 143
AUCT has 1622.

The Alcoran of the cordeliers H. Step. [List A]
695* ? ALBERUS, Erasmus.
Not identified. There is no recorded English
translation of the French work of this name,
nor is Henri Estienne known to have been associated with an edition.

696* ALEXANDER, William, *Earl of Stirling.*
An elegie on the death of Prince Henrie.
4° Edinburgh, A. Hart, 1613.   AUCT
STC 340

697 ALEXANDER, William, *Earl of Stirling.*
An encouragement to colonies.
4° London, W. Stansby, 1624.   EUL
STC 341
Between F1 and F2 there is an engraved map
showing the northern colonies of North America.

Menstries Tragedies [Eng. 6]
698 ALEXANDER, William, *Earl of Stirling.*
The monarchicke tragedies. Crœsus, Darius,
The Alexandræan, Iulius Cæsar. Newly enlarged.
4° London, V. Simmes for E. Blount, 1607.
STC 344. Greg 209, 196, 260, 261   NLS
Heavily annotated by Drummond.

699* ALEXANDER, William, *Earl of Stirling.*
The monarchicke tragedies.
8° London, W. Stansby, 1616.   AUCT
STC 345. Greg 209, 196, 260, 261

700* [ALEXANDER, William, *Earl of Stirling.*] A short discourse of the good ends of the higher providence in the late attemptat against his maiesties person.
8° Edinburgh, R. Waldegraue, 1600.   AUCT
STC 348

701* ALEXANDER, William, *Earl of Stirling.* [Supplement to the third book of *The Countesse of Pembrokes Arcadia.*]   AUCT
Alexander's supplement of ten leaves to Sidney's *Arcadia* was printed between 1613 and 1621 as a separate insertion, and was so used in the two editions of 1617 and the 'London' reissue of the Dublin edition of 1621.

Englands Parnassus [Eng. 41]
702* ALLOT, Robert. Englands Parnassus; or the choysest flowers of our moderne poets.
STC 378–80
Also in List F.

the anatomie of sin [Eng. 45]
703* ANATOMY. The anathomie of sinne. (The genealogie of vertue.) [In 2 parts.]
STC 565

Batschelour's banquet [Eng. 35]
704* BACHELOR. The batchelars banquet: or a banquet for batchelars.
STC 6476–7
A translation of *Les quinze joyes de mariage* which is sometimes attributed to Antoine de La Sale (cf. STC 15258). The translator was once thought to be Dekker (cf. STC 6476) and later Robert Allot, but now Robert Tofte is the most likely candidate. Also in List G.

705 BALE, John, *Bp.* The first part of the actes of English votaries, comprehendynge their vnchast practises and examples by all ages . . .
8° London, J. Tysdale, 1560.   EUL
STC 1274
Bought in St Menons, 1612? Drummond's note of purchase is a puzzle: he is not known to have been in France in 1612, nor does this seem a book likely to be bought there.

Mr Henrie Balnauess Book of Iustification [Eng. 36]
706 BALNAVES, Henry. The confession of faith, conteining how the troubled man should seeke refuge at his God . . .
8° Edinburgh, T. Vautrollier, 1584.   EUL
STC 1340
With a dedicatory letter by John Knox. The title and the dedication to 'Alison Sandilands, Lady of Hormistoun', are wanting, but are supplied in MS. Also in List G.

707 BARCLAY, John. Barclay his Argenis: or, the loues of Poliarchus and Argenis: faithfully

translated out of Latine into English, by Kingesmill Long, gent.
2° London, G. P[urslowe] for H. Seile, 1625.
STC 1392   DUL
With the motto, in Drummond's hand: 'Quicquid calcas rosa est'.

The thrid part of the bibil [List K]
708* BIBLE. The third part of the bible.
STC 2130 or 2137
A selection containing Job, Psalms, Proverbs, Ecclesiastes and the Song of Solomon, in the Geneva version.

academia perigrina or moral philosophie in englis & Italians [List K]
709* [BIDPAI.] The morall philosophie of Doni: drawne out of the ancient writers. A work first compiled in the Indian tongue and afterwards reduced into divers other languages: and now lastly englished out of the Italian by Sir Thomas North.
STC 3053–4
Doni was the Italian translator, whose immediate source was Joannes de Capua's Latin version. Also as Eng. 42, and It. 59?

Boetius chronicle [Eng. 43]
710* BOETHIUS, Hector. Heir beginnis the hystory and croniklis of Scotland. [*Tr.* J. Bellenden.]
STC 3203

Strapado for the diuel Richard brathwat [List B]
711* BRATHWAIT, Richard. A strappado for the divell. Epigrams and satyres. [In 2 parts.]
STC 3588

712 BRETON, Nicholas. Pasquils passe, and passeth not. Set downe in three pees.

His ⎰ passe,
     ⎱ precession, and
       prognostication.

8° London, V. S[ims] for J. Smithicke, 1600.
STC 3679   EUL

a post wt packets [List F]
713* BRETON, Nicholas. A poste with a madde packet of letters.
STC 3684

714 BUCK, *Sir* George. Δαφνις πολυστεφανος. An eclog treating of crownes, and of garlandes, and to whom of right they appertaine. Addressed, and consecrated to the kings maiestie . . .
4° London, G. Eld for T. Adams, 1605.   EUL
STC 3996

715 BULLOKAR, William. Bullokars booke at large, for the amendment of orthographie for English speech . . . with . . . a short pamphlet for

all learners, and a primer agreeing to the same . . .
Heerevnto are also ioyned written copies with the
same orthographie.
4° London, H. Denham, 1580.   EUL
STC 4086

716   BUSCHE, Alexander van den. The orator:
handling a hundred seuerall discourses, in the
forme of declamations . . . Written in French . . .
and Englished by L. P[iot, *i.e.* A. Munday].
4° London, A. Islip, 1596.   EUL
STC 4182

Campion the lordes maske [List B]
717*   CAMPION, Thomas. The discription of a
maske, in honour of the Lord Hayes.
STC 4538

718   CANISIUS, Petrus. Ane cathechisme or
schort instruction of Christian religion drauuen
out of the scripturs and ancient doctours . . .
VVith ane kallendar perpetuale . . . vvith dyuers
vthers thingis . . . maid be M. Adame king pro-
fesseur of philosophe and mathematikis, at Paris.
In the end ar adionned certian godlie prayers and
ane schort method vvhairby euery manmay exame
his conscience hovve he has offendet the maiestie
of god or his nichtbour.
8° Paris, P. Hury, 1588.   EUL
STC 4568. A and R 199
Amongst the 'dyuers vthers thingis' is a 'Table of
full sey at all ye costes of Scotland', which is
missing from this copy.

Baldasser castilios curteor [List F]
719*   CASTIGLIONE, Baldassare, *Count.* The
courtyer. Done into Englyshe by T. Hoby.
STC 4778–81

Chapman [List B]
720   CHAPMAN, George. Al fooles a comody,
presented at the Black Fryers, and lately before
his maiestie.
4° London, [G. Eld] for T. Thorpe, 1605.   EUL
STC 4963. Greg 219

721   CHAPMAN, George. Eugenia: or true
nobilities trance; for the most memorable death,
of the thrice noble and religious; William Lord
Russel, &c. Diuided into foure vigils of the night.
4° [London,] 1614.   EUL
STC 4975

722   [CHAPMAN, George?] Tvvo vvise men and
all the rest fooles: or a comicall morall, censuring
the follies of this age, as it hath beene diuerse
times acted.
4° [London,] 1619.   EUL
STC 4991. Greg 361

723   CHURCHYARD, Thomas. A generall
rehearsall of warres, wherein is five hundred
seuerall seruices of land and sea: as sieges,
battailes, skirmiches, and encounters. A thou-
sande gentle mennes names, of the best sort of
warriours. A praise and true honour of soldiours:
a proofe of perfite nobilitie. A triall and first
erection of Heraides: a discourse of calamitie. And
ioyned to the same some tragedies and epitaphes,
as many as was necessarie for this firste booke.
4° [London, E. White, 1579].   EUL
STC 5235

274   CHURCHYARD, Thomas. The mirror of
man, and manners of men.
4° London, A. Hatfield for W. Holme, 1594.
STC 5242   EUL

725   CHURCHYARD, Thomas. A musicall
consort of heauenly harmonie (compounded out
of manie parts of musicke) called Churchyards
charitie. (*And* A praise of poetrie.) [In 2 parts.]
4° London, A. Hatfield for W. Holme, 1595.
STC 5245

church ard [List B]
726   CHURCHYARD, Thomas. A pleasant
discourse of court and wars: with a replication
to them both, and commendation of all those that
truly serue prince and countrie . . .
4° London, A. Hatfield for W. Holme, 1596.
STC 5249   EUL

727   CHURCHYARD, Thomas. A sad and
solemne funerall, of the right honorable sir
Francis Knowles knight.
4° London, A. Hatfield for W. Holme, 1596.
STC 5254   EUL

728   CLERKE, William. The triall of bastardie:
that part of the second part of policie, or maner
of gouernement of the realme of England: so
termed, spirituall, or ecclesiasticall. Annexed at
the end of this treatise, touching the prohibition
of marriage, a table of the Leuitical, English, and
positiue canon catalogues, their concordance and
difference.
4° London, A. Islip, 1594.   EUL
STC 5411
With three insets (the tables mentioned in the
title).

729   COCKBURNE, *Sir* William. Respublica de
decimis.
4° Edinburgh, J. Wreittoun, 1627.   EUL
STC 5460

the Heauen of health [Eng. 46]
730*   COGAN, Thomas. The hauen of health.
STC 5478–5482

ὑπνεροτομαχια [List F]
731* [COLONNA, Francesco.] Hypnerotomachia. The strife of loue in a dreame. [*Tr. R.D., i.e.* Sir R. Dallington.]
STC 5577–8

Coluins parainisis [Eng. 23]
732 COLVILLE, John. The paraenese or admonition of Io. Coluille (laitly returnit to the Catholique Romane religion in vhilk he was baptesit and brocht vp till he had full 14. years of age) vnto his cuntrey men.
8° Paris, E. Prévosteau, 1602.   EUL
STC 5589. A and R 249

ciuil warrs of france [Eng. 39]
733* ? COLYNET, Antony. The true history of the ciuill vvarres of France, betweene the French king Henry the 4, and the leaguers.
STC 5590?
Copy in EUL.

734 C[OVELL], W[illiam]. Polimanteia, or, the meanes lawfull and vnlawfull, to iudge of the fall of a common-wealth, against the friuolous and foolish coniectures of this age. Whereunto is added, a letter from England to her three daughters, Cambridge, Oxford, Innes of Court, and to all the rest of her inhabitants: perswading them to a constant vnitie of what religion soeuer they are . . .
4° Cambridge, J. Legate, 1595.   EUL
STC 5883
And 'Religions speech to Englands children' and 'Loyalties speech to Englands children'.

735 COWPER, William, *Bp.* The Bishop of Galloway his dikaiologie: contayning a iust defence of his former apologie. Against the iniust imputations of Mr. David Hume.
4° London, T. Snodham for J. Budge, 1614.
STC 5915   EUL

736 CROOKE, Samuel. Death subdued, or, the death of death. Begun in a sermon at Denmarke house on Ascension day, May 6. 1619 . . .
12° London, W. J[ones] for E. Weaver, 1619.
STC 6065   EUL

737 CROWLEY, Robert. The confutation of .xiii. articles, whereunto Nicholas Shaxton, late Byshop of Salisburye subscribed . . . whē he recanted in Smithfielde at London at the burning of mestres Anne Askue . . .
8° London, J. Day and W. Seres, [1548].   EUL
STC 6083
Imperfect: wanting all after K6.

Daniels workes [Eng. 10]
738 DANIEL, Samuel. The works of Samuel Daniel newly augmented. [In 3 parts.]

2° London, S. Waterson, 1602.   EUL
STC 6237

739 DARIOT, Claude. A briefe and most easie introduction to the astrologicall iudgement of the starres . . . translated by F. W. gent. And lately renued, and in some places augmented and amended by G[eorge] C[oombe] gentl. Whereunto is annexed a most necessarie table for the finding out of the planetarie and vnequall houre, vnder the lattiude of 52 gr. 30 mi. exactly calculated by the sayde F. W. Also hereunto is added a briefe treatise of mathematicall phisicke . . . Written by the sayd G. C. . . . [In 2 parts.]
4° London, T. Purfoot, 1598.   EUL
STC 6276

Ihon Dauis [List B]
740 DAVIES, John, *of Hereford.* Humours heau'n on earth; with the ciuile warres of death and fortune. As also the triumph of death: or, the picture of the plague, according to the life; as it was in anno Domini. 1603.
8° London, A. I[slip], 1609.   EUL
STC 6331

741* ? DAVIES, *Sir* John. ? Nosce teipsum. This oracle expounded in two elegies.
4° London, R. Field for J. Standish, 1599.   AUCT
STC 6355
This seems the probable work. AUCT has *Know Thy Selfe, Lond.* 1599.

Francis Davison [List B]
742* DAVISON, Francis. A poetical rapsody.
STC 6373–5

Engls. secretarie [List F]
743* DAY, Angel. The English secretorie.
STC 6401–5

Day [List B]
744* DAY, John. ?
Drummond read both *The ile of guls* (STC 6412, Greg 235) and *Law-trickes* (STC 6416, Greg 267).

745 DEKKER, Thomas. Dekker his dreame. In which, being rapt with a poeticall enthusiasme, the great volumes of heauen and hell to him were opened, in which he read many wonderfull things.
4° London, N. Okes, 1620.   EUL
STC 6497

Dekker the honest whore [List B]
746 DEKKER, Thomas. The honest vvhore. With the humours of the patient man, and the longing wife.
8° London, N. Okes for R. Basse, 1616.   EUL
STC 6504. Greg 204

747   DEKKER, Thomas. VVorke for armorours: or, the peace is broken. Open warres likely to happin this yeare 1609: God helpe the poore, the rich can shift.
4° London, for N. Butter, 1609.   EUL
STC 6536

westwar hoe [List B]
748* DEKKER, Thomas, *and* WEBSTER, John. West-ward hoe.
STC 6540. Greg 257

749   DERRICKE, John. The image of Irelande, with a discouerie of vvoodkarne, wherein is moste liuely expressed, the nature, and qualitie of the saied wilde Irishe woodkarne . . . The execrable life, and miserable death of Rorie Roge, that famous archtraitour to God and the croune (otherwise called Rorie Oge) is likewise discribed. Lastlie the commying in of Thyrlaghe Leonaghe the great Oneale of Irelande, with the effecte of his submission, to the right honourable Sir Henry Sidney . . .
4° London, J. Daie, 1581.   EUL
STC 6734
With twelve woodcuts.

the French schoolmaister [List F]
750* DESAINLIENS, Claude. The French schoolemaister, wherein is shewed the pronouncinge of the Frenche tongue.
STC 6748–51

the Italian schoolmaster [Eng. 29]
751* DESAINLIENS, Claude. The Italian schoolemaister: contayning rules, &c.
STC 6759–60

The Desert of Deuotion [List A]
752* DESERT.
Not identified. A translation of Henri Caupain's *Le desert d'deuotion* (Paris, c. 1530)?

753   DONNE, John. The first sermon preached to King Charles, at Saint Iames: 3°. April. 1625.
4° London, A. M[athews] for T. Jones, 1625.   EUL
STC 7040

754   [DONNE, John.] Ignatius his conclaue: or, his inthronisation in a late election in Hell: wherein many things are mingled by way of satyr. Concerning the disposition of Iesuits, the creation of a new Hell, the establishing of a church in the moone. There is also added an apology for Iesuites. All dedicated to the two aduersary angels, which are protectors of the papall consistory, and of the colledge of Sorbon. Translated out of Latine.
12° London, M. F[lesher] for R. More, 1626.   EUL
STC 7028

755   DOUGLAS, Gawin, *Bp.* Heir beginnis ane treatise callit the palice of honour . . .
4° Edinburgh, J. Ros for H. Charteris, 1579.   EUL
STC 7074

756   DRAYTON, Michael. The battaile of Agincourt . . . The miseries of queene Margarite, the infortunate wife, of that most infortunate king Henry the sixt. Nimphidia, the court of Fayrie. The quest of Cinthia. the shepheards Sirena. The moone-calfe. Elegies vpon sundry occasions.
2° London, [A. Mathewes] for W. Lee, 1627.   EUL
STC 7190

Endemion and phebe by M. drayton. [Eng. 15]
757* DRAYTON, Michael. Endimion and Phœbe. Ideas Latmus.
STC 7192

Ideas Miroir [Eng. 16]
758* DRAYTON, Michael. Ideas mirrour. Amours in quatorzains.
STC 7203

759* DRAYTON, Michael. The legend of great Cromwel.
4° London, F. Kingston, sold by J. Flasket, 1607.   AUCT
STC 7204

Dratons oule [Eng. 33]
760* DRAYTON, Michael. The oule.
STC entries for *The oule* are all misleading or incorrect: see Bent Juel-Jensen's bibliography in Drayton's *Works* (Oxford, 1961), V, 282–3.
Copy in EUL

761   DRAYTON, Michael. Poemes lyrick and pastorall.
⎰Odes,
⎱eglogs
the man in the moone . . .
8° London, R. B[radock] for N. L[ing] and J. Flasket, [1606?].   EUL
STC 7217

Dratons works [Eng. 8]
762   DRAYTON, Michael. Poems . . . Newly corrected by the author.
8° London, [V. Sims] for J. Smethwicke, 1608.   EUL
STC 7218

763   DRUMMOND, William, *of Hawthornden.* Flowres of Sion . . . To which is adjoyned his cypresse groue.
4° [Edinburgh, A. Hart,] 1623.   EUL
STC 7249
There are three known issues of this edition, differing in their title-pages (see Kastner, I, lxxii-lxxv). This copy has many corrections pasted in—presumably by Drummond himself—on printed slips. These corrections were in nearly all cases adopted in the second edition

(1630) of *Flowres of Sion*. It must be supposed that Drummond had copies of all his own works. Only those now in EUL are here listed. For a full bibliography see Kastner.

764   DRUMMOND, William, *of Hawthornden*. Flowres of Sion . . . To which is adjoyned his cypresse groue.
4° Edinburgh, J. Hart, 1630.   EUL
STC 7251

765   DRUMMOND, William, *of Hawthornden*. Forth feasting. A panegyricke to the kings most excellent majestie.
4° Edinburgh, A. Hart, 1617.   EUL
STC 7252

765.5   DRUMMOND, William, *of Hawthornden*. In pious memorie of the right worthie and vertuous Euphemia Kyninghame, who in the prime of her youth died the 23. of Iulie, 1616.
S. sh. fol. [n.p.d.]   EUL
STC² 7252.3.
Consisting of the sonnet 'This Beautie faire, which Death in Dust did turne . . .' The sonnet with some slight alteration appeared afterwards in *Flowres of Sion* (1623) dedicated to Jane, Countess of Perth, and in Phillips' editions of the *Poems* and in the *Works* (1711) titled 'On the Death of a Young Lady'.

766   DRUMMOND, William, *of Hawthornden*. Poems . . . The second impression.
4° Edinburgh, A. Hart, 1616.   EUL
STC 7255
Another copy of this issue, bearing Drummond's inscription 'Giuen to the Colledge of king James in Edinbrough by the Author. 1624.', is now in Aberdeen University library (see Kastner, I, lxiv-lxx).

767   DRUMMOND, William, *of Hawthornden*. Teares on the death of Moeliades [Henry, Prince of Wales] . . . The third edition.
4° Edinburgh, A. Hart, 1614.   EUL
STC 7258

768   DRUMMOND, William, *of Hawthornden*. Teares on the death of Moeliades [Henry, Prince of Wales]. The third edition.
4° Edinburgh, A. Hart, 1614.   EUL
STC 7259
Another issue of STC 7258. Two copies.

769   [DRUMMOND, William, *of Hawthornden*.] To the exequies of the honourable, Sᴿ. Antonye Alexander, knight, &c. A pastorall elegie.
4° Edinburgh, G. Anderson, in King James his college, 1638.   EUL
STC² 7259.4
Imperfect, containing only the title and the last leaf.

770   DU CHESNE, Joseph. The sclopotarie of Iosephus Quercetanus, phisition. Or his booke containing the cure of wounds receiued by shot of gunne or such like engines of warre. Whereunto is added his spagericke antidotary of mediocines against the aforesayd wounds. Published into English by Iohn Hester, practitioner in the said spagiricall arte.
4° London, R. Ward for J. Sheldrake, 1590.   EUL
STC 7277

the holie loue of heaunlie wisdome [Eng. 25]
771*   DU VAIR, Guillaume. The holy loue of heauenly wisdome. With many other godly treatises. Tr. Tho. Sto[cker?] Gent.
STC² 7373.4

772   EDMONDES, *Sir* Clement. Observations upon the five first bookes of Cæsars commentaries. [In 2 parts.]
2° [n.p.d.]   DUL
STC 7492
Title wanting.

773*   ELEMENTS. The elements of the beginning of the oracles of God.
8° London, J. Beale, 1619.   AUCT
STC 7569. Press names this work as by 'J. A.'

the castel of Health [List F]
774*   ELYOT, *Sir* Thomas. The castel of helth.
STC 7643–56

775   ENGLAND. *Proclamations*. By the Queene. A true copie of the proclamation lately published by the queenes maiestie, vnder the great seale of England, for the declaring of the sentence, lately giuen against the queene of Scottes . . .
2° London, C. Barker, [1586].   EUL
STC 8160

776   ENGLAND. *Statutes*. Anno primo Edwardi Sexti statutes made in the parliamente begon at Westminster the fowerthe daye of Nouember, in the firste yeare of the reigne of our most dreade souueraine lorde Edward the .vi. . . .
2° [London, R. Tottell, c. 1565.]   EUL
STC² 9421.4. Beale S. 219.
Imprint given as Richard Grafton, 1548.

777   ENGLAND. *Statutes*. Anno secundo et tertio Edouardi Sexti. Actes made in the session of this present parlament, holden vppon prorogation at Westminster, the fourthe daye of Nouember, in the seconde yeare of our moste dread souereigne lord, Edwarde the .vi. . . .
2° London, R. Grafton, 1552.   EUL
STC 9425. Beale S. 225

778   ENGLAND. *Statutes*. Anno. III & IIII. Edwardi Sexti. Actes made in the session of this

present parlament, holden vpon prorogation at Westmynster, the .iiii. daye of Nouembre, in the thirde yere of the reygne of our most dread souereygne lorde Edward the .vi. . . .
2° [London, R. Tottell, 1560?]   EUL
STC² 9430.5. Beale S. 228
Imprint given as Richard Grafton, 1553.

779   ENGLAND. *Statutes.* Anno quinto et sexto Eduardi Sexti. Actes made in the session of this presēt parlamente, holden vpon prorogacion at Westminster, the .xxiii. daye of Ianuarye, in the fyueth yeare of the reygne of our most dradde souereygne lorde, Edwarde the .vi. . . .
2° [London, R. Tottell, 1560?]   EUL
STC² 9437.3. Beale S. 235
Imprint given as Richard Grafton, 1552.

780   ENGLAND. *Statutes.* Anno septimo Edwardi Sexti. Actes made in the parlament holden at Westminster, the first daie of Marche, in the .vii. yere of the reigne of our most redoubted souereine lorde Edwarde the .vi. . . .
2° London, R. Grafton, 1553.   EUL
STC 9440. Beale S. 236.

781   ENGLAND. *Statutes.* Anno Mariæ primo. Actes made in the parlyamente begonne and holden at Westminster the seconde daye of Apryll, in the firste yeare of the raygne of oure moste gratious soueraygne ladye, Marye . . .
2° London, J. Cawood, 1554. [1566?]   EUL
STC 9442. Beale S. 246

782   ENGLAND. *Statutes.* Anno Mariæ primo. Actes made in the parliament begonne and holden at Westminster the .v. daye of October, in the first year of the reigne of our most gratious soueraigne ladye, Mary . . .
2° London, J. Cawood, 1554. [1560?]   EUL
STC 9445. Beale S. 240

783   ENGLAND. *Statutes.* Anno primo et secūdo Philippi & Mariæ. Actes made at a parliament begon and holden at Westminster the .xi day of Nouember in the firste and secōd year of the reigne of our soueraigne lorde and lady, Philippe and Marye . . .
2° London, J. Cawood, 1555. [1558?]   EUL
STC 9448. Beale S. 254 c.

784   ENGLAND. *Statutes.* Anno secundo et tertio Philippi & Mariæ. Actes made at a parlyamente begon and holdē at Westminster the .xxi daye of October, in the seconde and thyrd yeare of the reigne of our soueraygne lorde and ladye, Phylyppe and Marye . . .
2° London, J. Cawood, 1555. [1560?]   EUL
STC 9451. Beale S. 261 a.

785   ENGLAND. *Statutes.* Anno quarto et quinto Philippi & Mariæ. Actes made at a parliament begon and holden at Westminster the .xx day of Ianuary in the fourthe and fifte yeare of the reigne of our soueraigne lorde and lady, Philippe and Marye . . .
2° London, J. Cawood, 1558.   EUL
STC² 9457.5. Beale S. 264.

786   ENGLAND. *Statutes.* Anno primo Reginæ Elizabethe. At the parliament begonne at Westmynster, the xxiij. of Ianuarye in the fyrste yeare of the raygne of oure soueraigne lady, Elizabeth . . .
2° London, R. Jugge and J. Cawood, 1559.   EUL
STC² 9459.5. Beale S. 270

787   ENGLAND. *Statutes.* Anno quinto Reginæ Elizabethe. At the parliament holden at Westmynster, the .xii. of Ianuary, in the fifth yere of the reigne of our soueraigne ladye, Elizabeth . . .
2° London, R. Jugge and J. Cawood, 1563.   EUL
STC² 9463.5. Beale S. 278.

the countrie ferme [Eng. 40]
788 * ESTIENNE, Charles, and LIEBAULT, Jean. Maison rustique, or the countrie farme. [*Tr.* R. Surflet.]
STC 10547–8
Also in List F.

789   FELTHAM, Owen. Resolues diuine, morall, politicall . . .
12° London, for H. Seile, [1623?]   EUL
STC 10755

Golden epistles Gueuarra [Eng. 28]
790 * FENTON, *Sir* Geoffrey. Golden epistles.
STC 10794–6
Most of this anthology was gathered and translated from Antonio de Guevara.

Fitzgefrays Satyres [List B]
791 * FITZGEFFRAY, Henry. Satyres and satyricall epigrams.
STC 10945

792   F[LETCHER], J. The differences, causes, and iudgements of vrine, according to the best writers thereof, both old and new, summarily collected.
8° Cambridge, J. Legat, 1598.   EUL
STC² 11062.5

793   FLORIO, Giovanni. A worlde of wordes, or most copious, and exact dictionarie in Italian and English . . .
2° London, A. Hatfield for E. Blount, 1598.   EUL
STC 11098   EUL

794 FORDE, William. A sermon preached at Constantinople, in the vines of Perah, at the funerall of the vertuous and admired Lady Anne Glouer, sometime wife to the honourable knight Sir Thomas Glouer, and then ambassadour ordinary for his maiesty of Great Britain, in the port of the Great Turke.
4° London, E. Griffen for F. Constable, 1616.
STC 11176   EUL

795 FOWLER, William. An ansvver to the calumnious letter and erroneous propositiouns of an apostat named M. Io. Hammiltoun . . .
4° Edinburgh, R. Lekprewick, 1581.   EUL
STC 11213

796 FOWLER, William. An epitaphe vpon the death of the right honorable, M. Robert Bowes esquire, thesaurer of Barwick . . . ambassadour for the queenes majestie, to the king of Scotland.
S. sh. fol. [Edinburgh,] R. Waldegraue, [1597].
STC 11214   EUL
Bound with Fowler's MS. Triumphs of Petrarch.

797 F[OWLER], W[illiam]. Epitaphe vpon the death of Sir Iohn Seton of Barns knight, ane of the lords of our soueranes priuie counsell and session.
S. sh. fol. [Edinburgh,] n.d.   EUL
STC² 11214.2.
Bound with Fowler's MS. Triumphs of Petrarch.

798 F[OWLER], W[illiam]. A funeral sonet written vpon the death of the honorable, and maist vertuous gentlewoman, Elizabeth Dowglas, spouse to M. Samuell Cobuurne laird of Temple-Hall.
S. sh. fol. [Edinburgh,] R. Waldegraue, n.d.
STC² 11214.4   EUL
Bound with Fowler's MS. Triumphs of Petrarch.

799 FRAUNCE, Abraham. The Countesse of Pembrokes Emanuel. Conteining the natiuity, passion, buriall and resurrection of Christ: together with certaine psalmes of David. All in English hexameters.
4° London, [T. Orwyn] for W. Ponsonby, 1591.
STC 11339   WINC

800 FRAUNCE, Abraham. The Countesse of Pembrokes Yuychurch. Conteining the affectionate life and unfortunate death of Phillis and Amyntas: that in a pastorall; this in a funerall: both in English hexameters.
4° London, T. Orwyn for W. Ponsonby, 1591.
       WINC
STC 11340. The pastorall is translated from Tasso, the funerall from Thomas Watson's Latin *Amynta* (itself a 'distant paraphrase' of Tasso's *Aminta*). And included in the *Yuychurch* is: 'The lamentation of Corydon, for the love of

Alexis, verse for verse out of Latine [Virgil's]. The beginning of Heliodorus his Æthiopical History'.

the french Academia [List G]
801* FRENCH.
Not identified.

french historye [List E]
802* FRENCH.
Not identified.

a rich cabinet [List F]
803* ? GAINSFORD, Thomas. The rich cabinet, furnished with varietie of excellent discriptions . . .
An early edition of STC 11522?

Cornelia of Garner [List B]
804* [GARNIER, Robert.] Cornelia. [*Tr.* Thomas Kyd.]
STC 11622. Greg 116

The Tragedie of Antonie by Countess of Pembrox [Eng. 17]
805 [GARNIER, Robert.] The tragedie of Antonie. Done into englishe by the Countesse of Pembroke.
8° London, P. S[hort] for W. Ponsonby, 1595.
STC 11623. Greg 108   EUL
A variant copy.

confession of faith [List K]
806* GENEVA. The confession of faith used in the English congregation at Geneva.
STC 11724

807 GOMERSALL, Robert. The Leuites reuenge: containing poeticall meditations vpon the 19. and 20. chapters of Iudges.
8° London, for J. Marriott, 1628.   EUL
STC 11992

808* GOMERSALL, Robert. The tragedie of Lodovick Sforza.
8° London, for J. Marriott, 1628.   HEND
STC 11995. Greg 418

809 GORDON, James, of Huntley. A treatise of the written word of God. Composed in Latin, by the reuerend father Iames Gordon Huntley . . . of the society of Iesus. And translated into English, by I. L. of the same society. The first part of the first controuersy.
8° [St. Omer,] 1614.   EUL
STC 13996. A and R 360
Title wanting [title taken from A and R].

810 GORDON, James, of Huntley. A treatise concerning the ground of faith. Written in Latin, by the reuerend father Iames Gordon Huntley of Scotland, doctour of diuinity, of the society

of Iesus. And translated in English, by I. L. of the same society. The second part of the second controuersy.
8° [St. Omer,] 1614.   EUL
STC 13997a. A and R 363

811   GORDON, James, *of Huntley*. A treatise concerning the church. Wherin it is shewed, by the signes, offices, and properties thereof, that the church of Rome (and consequently such particular churches as liue in her communion) is the only true church of Christ . . . translated into English, by I. L. . . . The third part of the second controuersy.
8° [St. Omer,] 1614.   EUL
STC 13997b. A and R 364
This and the previous two works were translated by William Wright (according to A and R).

812*   GORDON, John. ’Ενωτικόν or a sermon of the Union of Great Brittanie.
4° London, for G. Bishop, 1604.   AUCT
STC 12059

813   GORDON, *Sir* Robert, *of Lochinvar*. Encouragements, for such as shall haue intention to bee vnder-takers in the new plantation of Cape Briton, now New Galloway in America, by mee Lochinuar.
4° Edinburgh, J. Wreittoun, 1625.   EUL
STC 12069

814   GOSSON, Stephen. Playes confuted in fiue actions, prouing that they are not to be suffered in a Christian common weale, by the waye both the cauils of Thomas Lodge, and the play of playes, written in their defence, and other obiections of players frendes, are truely set downe and directlye aunsweared . . .
8° London, for T. Gosson, [1582].   EUL
STC 12095

the gouernanss of Verteu [List F]
815*   GOVERNANCE.
Not identified.

The Bread of life [List A]
816*   GRANGER, Thomas. The bread of life, or food of the regenerate. A sermon.
STC 12177

Giacomo di Grassi his art of fencing [Eng. 12]
817*   GRASSI, Giacomo di. G. di Grassi his true arte of defence.
STC 12190

the castel of memorie [List F]
818*   GRATAROLUS, Gulielmus. The castel of memorie.
STC 12191–2

Grayes arithmetique [Eng. 49]
819*   GRAY, Dionis. The store-house of breuitie in woorkes of arithmetike.
STC 12201

Tullies loue by Greene [Eng. 22]
820*   GREENE, Robert. Ciceronis amor, Tullies loue. Wherein is discoursed the prime of Ciceroes youth.
STC 12224–8

Mustapha [List B]
821*   GREVILLE, Fulke, *Baron Brooke*. The tragedy of Mustapha.
STC 12362. Greg 278

the Dial of princes Gueuarra [Eng. 27]
822*   GUEVARA, Antonio de, *Bp*. The diall of princes (with the famous booke of Marcus Aurelius). Englysshed oute of the Frenche by T. North.
STC 12427–9

823   GUILD, William. Issachars asse, braying vnder a double burden. Or, the vniting of churches.
4° Aberdeen, E. Raban, 1622.   EUL
STC 12482

The guyde to the sacrament [List A]
824*   GUIDE.
Not identified.

paris & onone [Eng. 21]
825*   H., T. Oenone and Paris. A poem.
STC² 12578.5
Attributed to Thomas Heywood.

826   HALL, Joseph, *Bp*. Occasionall meditations. By Ios: Exon. Set forth by R. H.
12° London, for N. Butter, 1630.   EUL
STC 12678

827   HAMILTON, John. Ane Catholik and facile traictise, drauin out of the halie scriptures, treulie exponit be the anciêt doctores, to confirme the real and corporell præsence of chrystis pretious bodie and blude in the sacrament of the alter . . .
16° Paris, 1581.   EUL
STC 12729. A and R 370

828   HAYWARD, *Sir* John. Of supremacie in affaires of religion . . .
4° London, J. Bill, 1624.   EUL
STC 13003

the sanctuarie of a troubled soule [Eng. 50]
829*   HAYWARD, *Sir* John. The sanctuarie of a troubled soul.
STC 13004–5

830* HENRY, *Prince of Wales.* Mausoleum; or the choisest flowres of the epitaphs on the death of Prince Henrie.
4° Edinburgh, A. Hart, 1613.   AUCT
STC 13160
Three of the pieces were contributed by Drummond (Kastner, I, xlvii-l).

831* HERACLIUS, *Emperor of the East.* Here begynneth the boke intituled Eracles, and also of Godefrey of Boloyne, the whiche speketh of the conquest of the holy londe of Iherusalem . . . [*Tr.* William Caxton, from the French.]
STC 13175   AUCT

831.5 HEYWOOD, John. Iohn Heywoodes woorkes [i.e. Proverbes and Epigrams].
4° London, F. Kingston, 1598.
STC 13289   PR
Copy, reported as Drummond's, at Hawthornden Castle.

832 HEYWOOD, Thomas. The brazen age, the first act containing, the death of the centaure Nessus, the second, the tragedy of Meleager: the third the tragedy of Iason and Medea. The fourth. Vulcans net. The fifth. The labours and death of Hercules . . .
4° London, N. Okes for S. Rand, 1613.   EUL
STC 13310. Greg 313

833 HEYWOOD, Thomas. The siluer age, including. The loue of Iupiter to Alcmena: the birth of Hercules. And the rape of Proserpine. Concluding, with the arraignement of the moone.
4° London, N. Okes for B. Lightfoote, 1613.
STC 13365. Greg 317   EUL

834 HIERON, Samuel. Certaine vsefull meditations touching death: collected out of St. Pauls words, Phil. 1. 23.
12° London, H. L[ownes] for S. Macham, 1615.
STC² 13392.5   EUL

contents of scripture [Eng. 42]
835* HILL, Robert. The contents of scripture. (The consent of the foure evangelists.) [In 2 parts.]
STC 13478

Pancharis [Eng. 37]
836* HOLLAND, Hugh. Pancharis; the first booke.
STC 13592
Also in List B.

837 HOOKER, Richard. Of the lavves of ecclesiasticall politie. Eyght bookes.
2° London, J. Windet, [1594].   EUL
STC 13712
The first four books. Bound with the fifth book

(London, 1597) which was given to the university library in 1827 by David Laing. It was probably not Drummond's copy.

838 HOWARD, Charles, *Earl of Nottingham.* The royall entertainment of the right honourable the earle of Nottingham, sent ambassador from his maiestie to the king of Spaine. Written by a gentle-man-souldier, who was present with the L. ambassador, this yeere 1605.
4° Edinburgh, R. Charteris, 1605.   EUL
STC 13857a

839 HOWARD, Henry, *Earl of Surrey.* Songes and sonnets, written by the right honorable Lord Henrie Haward late earle of Surrey, and others.
8° London, R. Robinson, 1587.   EUL
STC 13868

840 HUME, Alexander, *Minister of Logie.* Hymnes, or sacred songs, wherein the right vse of poësie may be espied . . . Whereunto are added, the experience of the authors youth, and certain precepts seruing to the practise of sanctification.
4° Edinburgh, R. Waldegraue, 1599.   EUL
STC 13942

841 HUME, Alexander, *Schoolmaster.* A diduction of the true and catholik meaning of our Sauiour his words, this is my bodie, in the institution of his laste supper through the ages of the church from Christ to our owne dayis. Whereunto is annexed a reply to M. William Reynolds in defence of M. Robert Bruce his arguments in this subject: and displaying of M. Iohn Hamiltons ignorance and contradictions: with sundry absurdities following vpon the Romane interpretation of these words.
8° Edinburgh, R. Waldegraue, 1602.   EUL
STC 13945

842* [JACKSON,] Bonaventura, O.F.M. Manuductions to the pallace of trueth. By F.B. Obseruant.
8° Mackline, H. Jaye, 1616.   AUCT
STC² 14296.5. A and R 411

Basilicon δορον [Eng. 24]
843 JAMES I, *King.* βασιλικον Δωρον. Or His Maiesties instructions to his dearest sonne Henry, the prince.
STC 14348–55

844 JAMES I, *King.* A princes looking glasse, or a princes direction, very requisite and necessarie for a Christian prince, to view and behold himselfe in . . . excerpted and chosen out of that most Christian, and vertuous βασιλικον Δῶρον, or his maiesties instructions to his dearest sonne Henrie the prince, and translated into Latin and

English verse . . . by William Willymat.
4° [Cambridge,] J. Legat for S. Waterson, 1603.
STC 14357   EUL

Daimonologia regis [List G]
845* JAMES I, *King*. Daemonologie, in forme of
a dialogue . . .
STC 14364–6

846 JAMES I, *King*. The essayes of a prentise,
in the diuine art of poesie.
4° Edinburgh, T. Vautroullier, 1584.   EUL
STC 14373

847 JAMES I, *King*. The Kings maiesties speach
to the Lords and Commons of this present parliament at Whitehall, on Wednesday the xxj. of
March. anno Dom. 1609.
4° London, R. Barker, [1609.]   EUL
STC 14396

848 JOHNSON, Robert. Essaies, or rather imperfect offers, by Rob. Iohnson gent.
8° London, J. Windet for J. Barnes, 1601. EUL
STC 14695

849 JONSON, Benjamin. Ben: Ionson his
Volpone or the foxe.
4° London, for T. Thorppe, 1607.   EUL
STC 14783. Greg 259

850 JONSON, Benjamin. The workes of Benia-
min Jonson.
2° London, W. Stansby, 1616.   DUL
STC 14751. Greg 339–49. This is the first volume
of Jonson's works; the second was not printed
until 1640. Title wanting.

851 KEEP. Keepe within compasse: or, the
worthy legacie of a wise father to his beloued
sonne; teaching him how to liue richly in this
world, and eternally happy in the world to come.
Meete for all sorts of people whatsoeuer. The
fift impression.
8° London, for J. Trundle, [c. 1620].   EUL
STC² 14899.3
Date cropped.

852 KELLIE, *Sir* Thomas. Pallas armata, or
militarie instructions for the learned: and all
generous spirits, who affect the profession of
armes. The first part. Containing the exercise of
infanterie, as well antient, as moderne: wherein
are clearlie set downe all the postures and motions,
belonging to battaillions of foote.
4° Edinburgh, heirs of A. Hart, 1627. EUL
STC 14906
Among the commendatory verses are some titled
'Paraineticon' by Drummond.

853 KER, George *and* GRAHAME, David. A
discouerie of the vnnaturall and traiterous conspiracie of Scottissh papistes, against God, his
kirk, their natiue cuntry, the kingis maiesties
persone and estate. Set downe as it was confessed
and subscriued bee M. George Ker, yet remaining
in prison, and Dauid Grahame of Fentrie, iustly
executed for his treason in Edinburgh, the 15. of
Februarie 1592. Wherevnto are annexed, certaine
intercepted letters, writen by sundrie of that
faction, to the same purpose.
4° Edinburgh, R. Waldegraue [J. Wreittoun,
1626?]   EUL
STC 14940

exhortation to repentence by Samson Lennard
[Eng. 9]
854* LENNARD, Sampson. An exhortatory
instruction to a speedy repentance . . .
STC 15460

Mr. Leonardos chirurgie [List F]
855* LEONARD.
Not identified. STC 11408? (Leonard Fuchs,
A most worthy practise.)

856 LEVER, Christopher. Queene Elizabeths
teares: or, her resolute bearing the Christian
crosse, inflicted on her by the persecuting hands
of Steuen Gardner Bishop of Winchester, in the
bloodie time of Queene Marie.
4° London, V. S[ims] for M. Lownes, 1607.
STC 15540   EUL

857 LLOYD, Lodovick. The tragicocomedie of
serpents.
4° London, T. Purfoot for A. Johnson, 1607.
STC 16631   EUL

858 LODGE, Thomas. Phillis: honoured with
pastorall sonnets, elegies, and amorous delights.
VVhere-vnto is annexed, the tragicall complaynt
of Elstred.
4° London, for J. Busbie, 1593.   EUL
STC 16662
Bought in London, 1606.

859 [LODGE, Thomas.] Prosopopeia the teares
of the holy, blessed and sanctified Marie, the
Mother of God.
8° London, for E. White, 1596.   EUL
STC 16662b

860* LUCANUS, Marcus Annaeus. Lucan's
Pharsalia: or the ciuill warres of Rome betweene
Pompey the great and Iulius Cæsar. The first
three books. [*Tr.* T. May.]
8° London, J. N[orton] and A. M[atthews],
sold by M. Law, 1626.   AUCT
STC 16886

Euphues and his England [List F]
861* LYLY, John. Euphues and his England.
STC 17068–79

862 MALYNES, Gerard de. The maintenance
of free trade, according to the three essentiall
parts of traffique; namely, commodities, moneys,
and exchange of moneys, by bills of exchanges
for other countries. Or, an answer to a treatise
of free trade, or the meanes to make trade
flourish, lately published.
8° London, J. L[egatt] for W. Sheffard, 1622.
STC 17226   EUL
The treatise referred to in the title is by Edward
Misselden.

863 [MARCELLINE, George.] The triumphs of
King Iames the first, of Great Brittaine, France,
and Ireland, king; defender of the faith. Published
vpon his maiesties aduertisement to all the kings,
princes, and potentates of Christendome, and
confirmed by the wonderfull workes of God,
declared in his life.
4° London, for J. Budge, 1610.   EUL
STC 17309

hero and leander by Marloe & Chapman [Eng. 14]
864* MARLOWE, Christopher. Hero and Leander.
Begun by C. Marloe and finished by G. Chapman.
STC 17413–7

865* MARLOWE, Christopher. The massacre at
Paris: with the death of the Duke of Guise.
8° London, E. A[llde] for E. White, [1600?]
STC 17423. Greg 133   AUCT

Insatiat countesse [List B]
866* MARSTON, John. The insatiate countesse.
A tragedie.
STC 17476–7. Greg 315

867 MARSTON, John. Parasitaster, or the fawne,
as it hath been diuers times presented at the
blacke Friars, by the children of the queenes
maiesties reuels, and since at Powles . . .
And now corrected of many faults, which by
reason of the authors absence, were let slip in the
first edition.
4° London, T. P[urfoot] for W. C[otton], 1606.
STC 17484. Greg 230   EUL

868 MASON, Henry. The new art of lying,
couered by Iesuites vnder the vaile of equiuoca-
tion, discouered and disproued . . .
4° London, G. Purslowe for J. Clarke, 1624.
STC 17610   EUL

869 MIDDLETON, Richard. Epigrams and
satyres . . .
4° London, N. Okes for J. Harison, 1608.   EUL
STC 17874
And *Times metamorphosis*.

870 MIDDLETON, Thomas. A game at chesse
as it hath bine sundrey times acted at the Globe
on the banck side.
4° [London? 1625?]   EUL
STC 17884. Greg 412
The engraved title has *Jan Masse, Lydden*,
(Leyden) but although the engraving was thus
made in the Low Countries the book itself was
probably printed in England (see Greg, II, 565).

Midleton your 5 gallants [List B]
871* MIDDLETON, Thomas. Your five gallants.
As it hath beene often in action at the Blacke-
friers.
STC 17907. Greg 266

The Guide into Tongues or Thesaurus [List D]
872* MINSHEU, John. Ἡγεμὼν εἰς τὰς γλωσσας,
id est, ductor in linguas, the guide into tongues.
In undecim linguis.
STC 17944
Ordered in List I.

Diana of Montemaior by B. Zong. [Eng. 38]
873* MONTEMAYOR, Jorge de. Diane. [Tr.
B. Yong.]
STC 18044
In 3 parts, the second being Yong's translation
of the continuation of *Diana* by Alonso Perez,
the third his translation of Gaspar Gil Polo's
Diana Enamorado. Also in List C.

874 MURRAY, *Sir* David. A paraphrase of the
civ. psalme.
4° Edinburgh, A. Hart, 1615.   EUL
STC 18294

875 MURRAY, *Sir* David. The tragicall death
of Sophonisba.
8° London, [G. Eld] for J. Smethwick, 1611.
STC 18296. Greg 231   EUL
And the sonnets titled 'Cœlia'.

The Muses Garland [Eng. 20]
876* MUSES.
Not identified. A work with this title was entered
in the *Stationers' Register* to T. Archer on 7 Feb.
1603.

877* MYNSHUL, Geffray. Essays and characters
of a prison and prisoners.
STC 18319   AUCT

Naper on the Reuelation [Eng. 32]
878* NAPIER, John. A plaine discouery of the
whole Reuelation of Saint John.
STC 18354–6

engliss metamorphosis of ouid [List F]
879* OVIDIUS NASO, Publius. The xv. bookes
of P. Ouidius Naso, entytuled Metamorphosis . . .

[*Tr.*] into Englishe meeter by A. Golding.
STC 18956

880* OVIDIUS NASO, Publius. Ovid's Metamorphosis. Englished by G[eorge] S[andys].
2° London, W. Stansby, 1626.   AUCT
STC 18964
Copy in EUL.

the key of the spanish tongue [Eng. 13]
881* OWEN, Lewis. The key of the Spanish tongue.
STC 18995

Peachames emblems [List C]
882* PEACHAM, Henry, *the Younger*. Minerva Britannia, or a garden of heroical deuises.
STC 19511

George Peel [List B]
883 PEELE, George. Polyhymnia describing, the honourable triumph at tylt, before her maiestie . . .
4° London, R. Jhones, 1590.   EUL
STC 19546
Possibly Drummond's entry in List B refers to Peele's *Hunting of Cupid*, on which he took notes in his manuscripts.

884 PERCYVALL, Richard. A dictionarie in Spanish and English, first published into the English tongue by Ric. Perciuale gent. Now enlarged and amplified . . . by J. Minsheu . . . Hereunto . . . is annexed an ample English dictionarie . . . with the Spanish words . . . adjoyned . . .
2° London, E. Bollifant, 1599.   DUL
STC 19620. Bound with Percyvall's *Spanish grammar* (STC 19622). With the motto, in Drummond's hand: 'Petit ardua virtuo'.

885 PERCYVALL, Richard. A Spanish grammar. Augmented and increased . . . by Iohn Minsheu.
2° London, E. Bollifant, 1599.   DUL
STC 19622. And John Minsheu's *Pleasant and delightful dialogues in Spanish and English, profitable to the learner, and not unpleasant to any other reader*. Bound with Percyvall's *Dictionarie*.

lectours on the Reuel. by Perkins [Eng. 26]
886* PERKINS, William. Lectures upon the first three chapters of the Reuelation.
STC 19731

887 PERSIUS FLACCUS, Aulus. Aulus Persius Flaccus his satyres: translated into English, by Barten Holyday . . . And now newly by him reviewed and amended.
8° London, W. Stansby for W. Arondell, 1617.
STC 19779   EUL

art of english poesie [Eng. 7]
888* [PUTTENHAM, George.] The arte of English poesie.
STC 20519
This book is also listed in List B, with after it the words *Parthinade stiles*. This clearly refers to Puttenham's *Partheniades*, either to the 'style' of the poems or to the poems themselves (if the latter, then this must have been partly in MS., for the *Partheniades* were never printed). The entry is interesting, for it shows that the fact of the two works' common authorship was generally well known.

889 QUARLES, Francis. Hadassa: or the history of Queene Ester: with meditations thereupon, diuine and morall.
4° London, for R. Moore, 1621.   EUL
STC 20546

890 RAMSEY, Laurence. The practise of the diuell. The auncient poisoned practises of the diuell, in his papistes, against the true professors of Gods holy worde, in these our latter dayes . . .
4° London, for T. Rider, [1577?]   EUL
STC 20665

891* RAMUS, Petrus. The logike . . . newly translated and diuers places corrected after the mynde of the author per M Roll Makylmenaeum Scotum . . .
8° London, T. Vautrollier, 1574.   AUCT
STC 15246

892 RAMUS, Petrus. The Latine grammar . . . translated into English. (The rudiments of P. Ramus his Latine grammar. Englished and newly corrected.) [In 2 parts.]
8° London, R. Waldegraue, 1585.   EUL
STC 15252
Ong distinguishes the *Grammar* and the *Rudiments* as separate works; bibliographically, they are distinct (see Ong, pp. 318, 328).

Thule or vertews historie [Eng. 47]
893 ROUS, Francis, *the Elder*. Thule, or vertues historie. To the honourable and vertuous Mistris Amy Audely . . . The first booke. [With the second book.]
4° London, F. Kingston for H. Lownes, 1598.
STC 21348   EUL

894 ROWLANDS, Samuel. Humors looking glasse.
4° London, E. Allde for W. Ferebrand, 1608.
STC 21386   EUL

895* SALERNO. The Englishmans doctor. Or, the Schoole of Salerne. [*Tr.* Sir J. Harington.]
STC 21605–7   AUCT

896 SALUSTE DU BARTAS, Guillaume de. The historye of Iudith, in forme of a poeme, in six bookes . . . Englished by T. Hudson.
8° Edinburgh, T. Vautroullier, 1584.   EUL
STC 21671.
Title wanting, but supplied in Drummond's hand, and taken from his transcription.

897 SANSOVINO, Francesco. The quintesence of wit, being a corrant comfort of conceites, maximies, and poleticke deuises . . . Translated out of the Italian tung . . . [by Captain R. Hitchcock].
4° London, E. Allde, 1590.   EUL
STC 21744

Diaphantus [Eng. 31]
898* SCOLOKER, Anthony. Diaphantus, or the passions of love.
STC 21853

899 [SCOT, Patrick.] Calderwoods recantation: or a tripartite discourse. Directed to such of the ministerie, and others in Scotland, that refuse conformitie to the ordinances of the church . . .
4° London, B. Alsop, 1622.   EUL
STC 21857

900 SCOTLAND. *Statutes.* The actis and con-stitutiounis of the realme of Scotland maid in parliamentis haldin be the rycht excellent, hie and mychtie princeis kingis James the first, secund, thrid, feird, fyft, and in tyme of Marie now quene of Scottis, viseit, correctit, and extractit furth of the registers be the lordis depute be hir maiesteis speciall commissioun thairto. Anno. Do. 1566.
2° Edinburgh, R. Lekpreuik, 1566.   EUL
STC 21876
Wanting ff. 132–3.

901 SCOTLAND. A declaration of the parliament of Scotland, to all his majesties good subjects . . . concerning their resolutions for religion king . . . in ends of the covenant . . . 20 April 1648.
8° Edinburgh, E. Tyler, 1648.   DUL
Wing S 1224 (Donald Wing, *Short-title catalogue of books printed . . . 1641–1700*).
With the words, in Drummond's hand: 'Rex vindicabo me de immicis undis per immicos meos'.

902 [SCOTT, Thomas, *B.D.*] Newes from Pernassus. The political touchstone, taken from mount Pernassus: whereon the governments of the greatest monarchies of the world are touched.
4° Helicon [Utrecht?], 1622.   EUL
STC 22080

903 [SCOTT, Thomas, *B.D.*] Vox populi. Or nevves from Spayne, translated according to the Spanish coppie. Which may serve to forewarn

both England and the United Provinces how farre to trust Spanish pretences.
4° [Gorcum?], 1620.   EUL
STC 22098

904 [SCOTT, Thomas, *B.D.*] Vox populi.   EUL
STC 22098
Another copy. Title wanting.

905 SCOTT, Thomas, *Poet.* Foure paradoxes Of art. Of law. Of warre. Of seruice . . .
8° London, T.S. for R. Redmer, 1611.   EUL
STC² 22107.5

906 SELMAN, John. The araignment of Iohn Selman, who was executed neere Charing-Crosse the 7. of Ianuary, 1612. for a fellony by him committed in the kings chappell at White-Hall vpon Christmas day last, in presence of the king and diuers of the nobility.
4° London, W. H[all] for T. Archer, 1612.
STC 22183   EUL

907 SHAKESPEARE, William. A pleasant conceited comedie called, Loues labors lost. As it was presented before her highnes this last Christmas. Newly corrected and augmented . . .
4° London, W. W[hite] for C. Burby, 1598.
STC 22294. Greg 150a   EUL

a midsumers night dreame [Eng. 48]
908* SHAKESPEARE, William. A midsommer nights dreame.
STC 22302. Greg 170

the tragedie of Romeo & Iulieta [Eng. 30]
909 [SHAKESPEARE, William.] The most excellent and lamentable tragedie, of Romeo and Iuliet. Newly corrected, augmented, and amended . . .
4° London, T. Creede for C. Burby, 1599.   EUL
STC 22323. Greg 143

the rap of Lucrece idem [i.e. Shakespeare] [Eng. 19]
910* SHAKESPEARE, William. The rape of Lucrece.
STC 22345–9

Venus & Adon. by Schaksp. [Eng. 18]
911* SHAKESPEARE, William. Venus and Adonis.
STC 22354–60b

cupids whirlegeg [List B]
912* SHARPHAM, Edward. Cupids whirligig.
STC 22380–2. Greg 247

Edward Sharpham the fleire [List B]
913* SHARPHAM, Edward. The Fleire.
STC 22384–6. Greg 255

914 SIDNEY, *Sir* Philip. An apologie for poetrie. Written by the right noble, vertuous, and learned, Sir Phillip Sidney, knight.
4° London, for H. Olney, 1595.   EUL
STC 22534

of his defence of poesie SPS [List F]
915* SIDNEY, *Sir* Philip. The defence of poesie.
STC 22535
Or 915* = 914.

S.P.S. Arcadia [Eng. 1]
916* SIDNEY, *Sir* Philip. The Countesse of Pembrokes Arcadia.
STC 22539–43a
Also in Lists C and F.

917 SMITH, John. A description of New England: or the obseruations, and discoueries, of Captain Iohn Smith (admirall of that country) in the north of America . . . and the accidents befell him among the French men of warre: with the proofs of the present benefit this countrey affoords . . .
4° London, H. Lownes for R. Clerke, 1616.
STC 22788   EUL
With an inset: a map of New England with a portrait of Smith.

918 SMITH, John. A map of Virginia. VVith a description of the countrey, the commodities, people, gouernment and religion . . . Whereunto is annexed the preceedings of those colonies, since their first departure from England, with the discourses, orations, and relations of the saluages, and the accidents that befell them in all their iournies and discoueries. Taken faithfully as they were written out of the writings of Doctor Russell. Richard Wiefin. Tho. Studley. Will. Phettiplace. Anas Todkill. Nathaniel Povvell. Ieffra Abot. Richard Pots. And the relations of diuers other diligent obseruers there present then, and now many of them in England.
4° Oxford, J. Barnes, 1612.   EUL
STC 22791
The map and the second part are both wanting.

Smyths militarie art [List C]
919* ? SMITH, Thomas. ? The arte of gunnerie.
STC 28855?

920* SPELMAN, *Sir* Henry. De non temerandis ecclesiis. A tracte of the rights and respect due unto churches.
8° Edinburgh, A. Hart, 1616.   AUCT
STC 23069

Spenser's amoretti [Eng. 5]
921 SPENSER, Edmund. Amoretti and Epithalamion . . .
8° London, P. S[hort] for W. Ponsonby, 1595.
STC 23076   EUL

E. Spensers farie queene [Eng. 2]
922* SPENSER, Edmund. The Faerie Queene.
STC 23080–3
Copy, reported as Drummond's, at Hawthornden Castle.

Spensers Hȳmes [Eng. 4]
923* SPENSER, Edmund. Fowre hymnes. (Daphnaida.)
STC 23086

Spenser's schephard calender [Eng. 3]
924* [SPENSER, Edmund.] The shepheardes calender. Conteyning twelve æglogues.
STC 23089–93
Under the pseudonym *Immerito.*

925 STUBBES, Philip. A chrystall glasse for Christian women. Containing a most excellent discourse of the godly life and Christian death of Mistris Katherine Stubs, who departed this life in Burton vpon Trent in Stafford-shire, the fourteenth of December. With a most heauenly confession of the Christian faith, which shee made a little before her departure, as also a most wonderfull combat betwixt Satan, and her soule: worthy to be printed in letters of gold . . .
8° London, for J. Wright, 1635 [or 1625?].
STC 23394, another ed.?   EUL

926* STUBBES, Philip. A christal glasse for christian women.   AUCT
AUCT has London, 1607, an edition not listed in STC.

927 [STUBBS, John.] The discouerie of a gaping gulf vvhereinto England is like to be swallovved by an other French mariage, if the Lord forbid not the banes, by letting her maiestie see the sin and punishment thereof.
8° [London, H. Singleton for W. Page,] 1579.
STC 23400   EUL

928 STUCKLEY, *Sir* Lewis. To the Kings most excellent maiestie. The humble petition and information of Sir Lewis Stucley, knight, vice-admirall of Deuon, touching his owne behauiour in the charge committed vnto him, for the bring-ing vp of Sir Walter Raleigh, and the scandalous aspersions cast vpon him for the same.
4° London, B. Norton and J. Bill, 1618.   EUL
STC 23401
Title-leaf wanting (title taken from head-title).

929 STURTEVANT, Simon. Metallica. Or the treatise of metallica. Briefly comprehending the doctrine of diuerse new metallical inuentions . . . Also a transcript of his maiesties letters pattents of priuiledge, granted vnto Simon Sturteuant for the said metallical businesses, for one and thirty

yeares . . .
4° London, G. Eld, 1612.   EUL
STC 23411

930   SYLVESTER, Joshua. Lachrimae lachri-
marum. or the distillation of teares shede for the
vntymely death of the incomparable prince
Panaretus [Henry, Prince of Wales] . . .
4° London, H. Lownes, 1612.   EUL
STC 23576

Godefrey de Bouillon by Eduard Fairefax [Eng. 11]
931   [TASSO, Torquato.] Godfrey of Bulloigne,
or the recouerie of Ierusalem. Done into English
heroicall verse, by Edward Fairefax gent.
2° London, A. Hatfield for J. Jaggard, 1600.   PR
STC 23698
With the cancel slip for the first stanza: 'I sing
the warre made in the Holy land, . . .' With
Drummond's signature in anagram: 'Don Murmidumilla', and also in his hand the motto 'Paix
et peu'.

932   TATIUS, Titus. Rapta Tatio. The mirrour
of his maiesties present gouernment, tending to
the vnion of his whole iland of Brittonie martiall.
4° London, W. W[hite] for S. Waterson, 1604.
STC 23705   EUL

933   [TISSOT, Jacques.] A true relation of a
mighty giant, named Theutobocus, somtimes
king of the Theutons and Cimbrians, ouerthrowne
by Consul Marius, 1700. yeares agone. Buried
then by the castle of Langon, neere the towne of
Romans in the prouince of Daufiné in Fraunce;
whose bones were found of by chaunce, an. 1613.
in a place called to this day, the giants-ground;
and vpon his tombe ingrauen in old letters Theutobocus Rex.
4° London, E. Allde, 1615.   EUL
STC² 24091+

934   TURBERVILE, George. Tragical tales,
translated by Turberuile out of sundrie Italians,
with the argument and lenuoye to each tale.
8° London, A. Jeffs, 1587.   EULC
STC 24330
Reported missing from EUL in 1934.

the amourouss passions of paurino [Eng. 34]
935 * TURNER, Richard. Constant Lusina: the
amorous passions of Paurinio.
STC 24344

936   VERSTEGAN, Richard, *pseud.* [ROW-
LANDS, Richard.] A restitution of decayed intelligence: in antiquities. Concerning the most
noble and renowned English nation.
4° Antwerp, R. Bruney, to be sold at London
by J. Norton and J. Bill, 1605.   FOLG
STC 21361. A and R 846
Bought in London, 1610.

937   VIRGILIUS MARO, Publius. The .xiii.
bukes of Eneados of the famose poete Virgill
translatet out of Latyne verses into Scottish metir,
bi the reuerend father in God, Mayster Gawin
Douglas Bishop of Dunkel & vnkil to the Erle
of Angus. Euery buke hauing hys perticular
prologe.
4° [London, W. Copland,] 1553.   EUL
STC 24797

938   VIRGILIUS MARO, Publius. The first
foure bookes of Virgils Æneis, translated into
English heroicall verse, by Richard Stanyhurst:
with other poëticll deuises thereto annexed.
8° London, H. Bynneman, 1583.   EUL
STC 24807
The 'other poëticll deuises' consist of 'Certaine
psalmes of David', 'Conceites' and 'Epitaphes'.

939   VIRGILIUS MARO, Publius. The Bucoliks
of Publius Virgilius Maro, prince of all Latine
poets; otherwise called his pastoralls, or shepe-
herds meetings. Together with his Georgiks or
ruralls, otherwise called his husbandrie, conteyning foure books. All newly translated into English
verse by A[braham] F[raunce].
4° London, T. O[rwin] for T. Woodcocke, 1589.
STC 24817   EUL

940 * W., R. Papistogelastes.   AUCT
An early edition of STC 21510? (*Merry jests,
concerning popes, monks and friers.* By N.S. Tr.
R. Willet.) Madan, in his *Early Oxford Press*
mentions the 1614 edition and describes it as
'written first in Ital. by N.S. and thence translated into French by S.J. and now out of French
into English by R.W. ut supr. Oxon, 1614 . . .'
(p. 97). AUCT has 'Oxford, 1614'.

941   [WARFORD, William.] A briefe instruction,
by vvay of dialogue, concerninge the principall
poyntes of christian religiõ, gathered out of the
holy scriptures, fathers, and councels. By the
reuerẽde M. George Doulye priest.
8° Louvain [Seville?], L. Kellam, 1604.   EUL
STC 25068. A and R 877

Warner his hexameters [List B]
942 * WARNER.
Not identified, but not William Warner's *Albion's
England*, which was written in fourteeners.

Warners yuie church [List B]
943 * WARNER.
Not identified. Confused with Abraham Fraunce's
Yuychurch?

A touchstone to know truth [in] *falshood* [List A]
944 * ? WARRE, James. ? The touch-stone of
truth.
STC 25090?

945   WILLIS, Timothy. The search of causes. Containing a theophysicall inuestigation of the possibilitie of transmutatorie alchemie . . .
8° London, J. Legatt, 1616.   EUL
STC 25754

946   WITHER, George. Abuses stript, and whipt: or satirical essayes.
8° London, T. S[nodham] for F. Burton, 1614.
STC 25895   EUL

947   WITHER, George. The schollers purgatory, discouered in the stationers common-wealth, and discribed in a discourse apologeticall asvvell for the publike aduantage of the church, the state &. vvhole common-vvealth of England, as for the remedy of priuate iniuryes.
8° [London?] for the honest stationers, [1625?]
STC 25919   EUL

948*   WITHER, George. Cantica sacra.   AUCT
Not identified. STC 25923? (*The songs of the old testament.*)

949*   WITHER, George. Exercises upon the first psalme.
8° London, E. Griffin for J. Harrison, 1620.
STC 25902   AUCT

950*   WRIGHT, Edward. The description and use of the sphære. [In 3 parts.]
4° London, [E. Allde] for J. Tap, 1613.   AUCT
STC 26021
Copy in EUL.

951   WYRLEY, William. The true vse of armorie, shewed by historie, and plainly proued by example . . . with other matters of antiquitie, incident to the aduancing of banners, ensignes, and marks of noblenesse and cheualrie . . .
4° London, J. Jackson for G. Cawood, 1592.
STC 26062   EUL

952   YARROW, Robert. Soueraigne comforts for a troubled conscience. Wherein the subtilties of Satan are discouered, his reasons and obiections fully answered . . .
8° London, for R. Rounthwaite, 1619.   EUL
STC 26077

953   YATES, John. A modell of diuinitie, catechistically composed. VVherein is deliuered the matter and methode of religion, according to the creed, tenne commandements, Lords prayer, and the sacraments . . . The second edition corrected and inlarged by the authors deliberate iudgement.
4° London, J. Legatt for F. Clifton, 1623.   EUL
STC 26086
With an inset: 'A briefe map of Gods election'.

954   YONGE, Nicholas. Musica transalpina. Quintus. The second booke of madrigalles, to 5. & 6. voices: translated out of sundrie Italian authors & newly published . . .
4° London, T. Este, 1597.   EUL
STC 26095

955   ZANCHIUS, Hieronymus. Speculum Christianum or a Christian suruey for the conscience. Containing, three tractates . . . 1 Of the end of the world. 2 Of the perseuerance of the saints. 3 A summarie abridgement of his prælections. Englished for the good of Gods church, and for a warning to wicked and impenitent men. By H.N.
8° London, G. Eld, 1614.   EUL
STC² 26121a+

956   ZEPHERIA. Zepheria.
4° London, widow Orwin for N. L[ing] and J. Busbie, 1594.   EUL
STC 26124
Bought in London, 1606.

Translations: (into French). See 1071, 1117.

recreation poet. de M.I. Allery [Fr. 98]
957* ALARY, Jean d'. Le premier recueil des récréations poétiques . . .

958 ALBERUS, Erasmus. L'alorcan des cordeliers, tant en Latin qu'en François : c'est a dire, la mer des blasphemes & mensonges de cest idole stigmatizé, qu'on appelle S. Fráçois : lequel liure a este recueilli mot a mot par le Docteur Erasme Albere, du liure des conformitez de ce beau S. François a Iesus Christ : liure meschant & abominable s'il en fut oncq, composé par vn cordelier, & imprimé a Milan, l'an M.D.X. Nouuellement y a este adiousté le second liure prins au mesme retraict, afin de mieux descouurir la sainctete de ceste secte infernale, que le monde adore.
8° Geneva, C. Badius, 1560.   EUL
Gathering A is wanting.

les illustres auentures [Fr. 76] *d'amadis* [Fr. 77]
959 AMADIS, *de Gaula.* Le premier liure d'Amadis de Gaule, mis en francoys par le seigneur des Essars Nicolas de Herberay . . .
8° Paris, E. Groulleau, 1548.   EUL
Drummond's price (4 sous, 16 sous) indicates that he bought several volumes, perhaps even the whole set. The set listed in EULC marked *Drummond Collection*—with the exception of the volumes given here—was not Drummond's. The entry occupies two lines, and two prices are given, so the first part may possibly refer to another work.

960 AMADIS, *de Gaula.* Le quatreiesme liure d'Amadis de Gaule, mis en francoys par le Seigneur des Essars Nicolas de Herberay . . .
8° Paris, E. Groulleau for J. Longis, 1548.   EUL

961 AMADIS, *de Gaula.* Le cinquieiesme liure d'Amadis de Gaule, mis en francoys par le Seigneur des Essars Nicolas de Herberay . . .
8° Paris, E. Groulleau for J. Longis, 1548.   EUL

962 AMADIS, *de Gaula.* Le douzieme liure d'Amadis de Gaule. Contenant quelle fin prindrent les loyalles amours d'Agesilan de Colchos, & de la princesse Diane, & par quel moyen la royne Sidonie se rapaisa, apres auoir longuement pourchassé la mort de dom Florisel de Niquee ; auec plusieurs estranges auãtures non moins recreatiues que singulieres, & ingenieuses sur toutes celles

qui ont esté traitees es liures precedents. Traduits d'Espaignol en François par G. Aubert de Poitiers.
16° Lyons, F. Didier, 1577.   EUL
With Drummond's signature in anagram : 'Don Murmidumilla'.

Roland furieux [Fr. 2]
963* ARIOSTO, Lodovico. Le Roland furieux . . . traduit . . . en François.
Drummond might have meant Philippe Des Portes' imitation of Ariosto, with the same title. Also in List E.

964 ARISTOTLE. [*Supposititious work.*] Le miroir des melancholicques descript en la. xxxe. section dés problemes d'aristote concernant, ce qui appartient à prudence entendement, & sapience, traduict de Grec en Francoys, par Meury Riflant.
8° [Rouen,] J. Petit for N. de Burges, 1543.   EUL

965 ARTEMIDORUS, *Daldianus.* Cinq liures d'Artemidore, de l'interpretation des songes. Traduits en François, & reduits en epitome, par Charles Fontaine. Plus vn brief recueil de Valere Maxime, touchant certains songes.
16° Lyons, J. De Tournes, 1581.   EUL

l'Hermaphrodite [Fr. 108]
966 ARTUS, Thomas, *Sieur d'Embry.* Les Hermaphrodites. (Discours de Iacophile a Limne.) [In 2 parts.]
12° n.p., [1605].   FOLG

amours de Baiff [Fr. 107]
967 BAÏF, Jan Antoine de. Les amours . . .
8° Paris, widow of M. de La Porte, 1552.   EUL
Bought in Paris, 1607.

oeuures poetiq. de N. Barged [Fr. 15]
968* BARGEDÉ, Nicolas. Oeuvres poétiques.

969* BARLEMENT, Noel. Les devis familiers.
          AUCT
AUCT gives : 'Gal. & Germ. in Strasburg, 1619'. The first edition of this highly popular dictionary and phrase book was printed in Antwerp in 1530, and it continued to be published in polyglott versions (which included, finally, most of the European languages) for the next hundred years.

angeliq. comedie [Fr. 31]
970* BAZIRE D'AMBLAINVILLE, Gervais de.
Angélique délivrée, à l'imitation d'Arioste ... ;

971   BAZIRE D'AMBLAINVILLE, Gervais de.
La bergere de la Palestine.
12° Paris, A. du Brueill, 1601.   EUL

tragedie de Regulus [Fr. 117]
972* BEAUBRUEIL, Jean de. Regulus, tragédie
...
8° Limoges, H. Barbou, 1582.   AUCT

Histoire de la guerre d'escosse [Fr. 92]
973* BEAUGUÉ, Jean de. L'histoire de la guerre
d'Escosse, traitant comme le royaume fut assailly
... et en grand' partie occupé par les Anglois et
depuis rendu paisible à sa reyne et réduit en son
ancien estat et dignité ...
First printed 1556. Scott, no. 9.

974   BELLEAU, Remi. La bergerie ... diuisee
en vne premiere & seconde iournee.
8° Paris, G. Gilles, 1572.   EUL

975* BELLOT, J. Le guide francois qui conduit
par un assure sentier, au certain usaige de la
langue Francoise, faict, & mis en lumiere, par
J. Bellot gent. Cadomois.   PRESS
'Imprimè a Londres 1582, in french and english'.
Not in STC.

les infortunes du fidell berger [Fr. 101]
976   BELOT. Jehan. Les infortunes du fidelle
berger ou ses afflictions en la ville de Mante ...
8° Paris, F. Huby, 1603.   EUL
Bought in Paris, 1607.

les azolaines de Bembe [Fr. 40]
977   BEMBO, Pietro, *Card.* Les Azolains ...
De la nature d'amour. Traduictz d'Italien ...

Instruction pour tous estats [Fr. 54]
978* [BENOIST, René, *Bp.*] Instruction pour
tous estatz: en laquelle est sommairement déclaré
comme chacun en son estat se doit gouverner, et
vivre selon Dieu.
Barbier gives an Antwerp, 1565 edition.

979   BENOIST, René, *Bp.* Remonstrance a
messieurs de l'assemblee tenue a Rouen, par le
commandement du roy, au moys de Nouembre,
1596 ...
8° Paris, for S. Moreau, (1596).   EUL

980   BERGERON, Nicolas. Sommaire des temps,
hommes illustres, et choses plus memorables
aduenues depuis la creation du monde, iusques à
present ... Auec l'ordre que lon doit tenir à lire,
& cognoistre l'histoire du monde ...
16° Rouen, G. L'Oyselet, 1580.   EUL

meditationes sur huit pseaumes [Fr. 99]
981* BÈZE, Théodore de. Chrestiennes meditations sur huict pseaumes du prophete David.
Composees & nouuellement mises en lumiere ...
See Frédéric Gardy, *Bibliographie des oeuvres ...
de Théodore de Bèze* (Geneva, 1960), pp. 185–6.

982   [BÈZE, Théodore de.] Response aux cinq
premieres et principales demandes de F. Iean Hay,
moine Iesuite aux ministres Escossois.
8° [Geneva,] J. Le Preux, 1586.   EUL
See Frédéric Gardy, *Bibliographie des oeuvres ...
de Theodore de Bèze* (Geneva, 1960), pp. 192–3.
With the signature of Andrew Melville.

Bible en francoise [Fr. 113]
983* BIBLE. La Bible.

984* BIBLE. Psalms. Les Pseaumes de David,
mis en rime françoise par Clement Marot &
Theodore de Beze.   AUCT

985* BIEN-VENU, Gabriel. Foucade aux Estats
...   PRESS
BN has an edition of 1615.

Martir de la Royne d'escosse [Fr. 93]
986   [BLACKWOOD, Adam.] Martyre de la
royne d'Escosse ...
8° Edinburgh [Paris], J. Nafeild, 1587.   BODL
STC 3107. A and R 119

987   [BLACKWOOD, Adam.] Martyre de la
royne d'Escosse, douairiere de France. Contenãt
le vray discours des trahisons à elle faictes à la
suscitation d'Elizabet Angloise, par lequel les
mensonges, calomnies & faulses accusations
dressees contre ceste tres-vertueuse, tres-Catholique
& tres-illustre princesse sont esclarcies & son
innocence auerée. Auec son oraison funebre
prononcée en l'eglise nostre dame de Paris ...
12° Edinburgh [Paris], J. Nafeild, 1588.   EUL
STC 3108. A and R 120

988   BOAISTUAU, Pierre. Le theatre du monde,
ou il est fait vn ample discours des miseres
humaines, composé en Latin par P. Boystuau ...
puis traduit par luy mesme en François. Auec vn
brief discours de l'excellence & dignité de
l'homme.
12° Rouen, T. Reinsart, [*c.* 1590].   EUL

le philocope de Boccace [Fr. 32]
989* BOCCACCIO, Giovanni. Le Philocope ...
contenãt l'histoire de Fleury & Blanchefleur,
diuisé en sept liures; traduictz ... par Adrian
Seuin.

la daimonie de I. Bodin [Fr. 78]
990* BODIN, Jean. De la demonomanie des
sorciers. (Refutation des opinions de Jean Wier.)

Imitations tirees du latin de Iean bonnefois
[Fr. 42]
991* BONNEFONS, Jean. Imitations du latin . . .
avec autres gayetez amoureuses, de l'invention de
l'autheur. [By Gilles Durant.]

Maximes d'estat de I. Botero [Fr. 4]
992* BOTERO, Giovanni. Maximes d'estat,
militaires et politiques, traduites de l'italien . . .
et augmentées . . . par Pierre de Deimier . . .

les dialogues de Guy de Brues [Fr. 97]
993* BRUÈS, Guy de. Les dialogues . . . contre
les nouveaux académiciens . . .

les institutiones de Caluin [Fr. 118]
994* CALVIN, Jean. Institution de la religion
chrestienne.

995 CASA, Giovanni della, *Abp.* Le Galatee,
premierement composé en Italien . . . & depuis
mis en François, Latin, & Espagnol par diuers
auteurs . . . [*Tr.* N. Chytraeus, J. du Peyrat and
D. de Bezerra.]
16° [Lyons,] J. De Tournes, 1598.   EUL

996 CHAMIER, Daniel. La confusion des
disputes papistes . . .
8° Geneva, for F. Lepreux, 1600.   EUL
Title mutilated, with Drummond's signature across
the repair.

997 CHAMPIER, Symphorien. Le myrouel des
appothicaires & pharmacopoles par lequel est
demonstre comment appothiquaires communemēt
errent en plusieurs simples medicines contre lin-
tention des Grectz de Hypocras, Galien, Oribase,
Paule, Egynette, & autres Grectz. Et par la mauluaise & faulse intelligence des autheurs arabes,
lesquelz ont falcifie la doctrine des grectz par leur
mauluaise & non entendue interpretatiō et intelligence faulce. Item les lunettes des cyrurgiens
& barbiers . . .
8° Paris, [1533].   EUL
This is the third part of the Paris edition of 1533,
described (in error) by Brunet as printed in 1538.

Chansons nouuelles [Fr. 71]
998* CHANSONS.
Not identified.

petit tractè de la sagesse de charron [Fr. 115]
999* CHARRON, Pierre. Traicté de sagesse.
A summary of the three books of *De la sagesse*.

1000 CHASSANION, Jean. De la secte des
Iesuites, combien elle est contraire & à la doctrine
de nostre Seigneur Iesus, & à la conuersation
d'icelui . . .
8° [Geneva?] J. Le Preux, 1592.   EUL

encheridion des chirurgens [Fr. 114]
1001* CHAUMETTE, Antoine. La suyte de
l'enchiridion des chirurgiens . . . divisé en quatre
traictés descrivant . . . la vraye nature, essence
causes, signes . . . des fiebvres tant continues
qu'intermittantes, avec leurs curations, traduict
du latin par M. Jean Vigier.

1002 CHAUVET, Jacques. Les institutions de
l'arithmetique . . . diuisees en quatre parties : auec
vn petit traicté des fractions astronomiques.
8° Paris, J. de Marnef, 1578.   EUL

1003 CHEFFONTAINES, Christophe de, *Abp.*
Defense de la foy de noz ancestres contre les
heretiques de nostre temps, auec declaration des
ruses & stratagémes, desquels ils ont vsé pour
seduire les Catholiques.
8° Paris, C. Frémy, 1564.   EUL

1004 CICERO, Marcus Tullius. Les epistres
familieres de M. T. Ciceron, pere d'eloquence.
Latin-Francois par E. Dolet, & F. de Belleforest :
ensemble toutes celles des seigneurs Romains à
Ciceron, l'vn correspondant à l'autre fidelement
. . .
16° Paris, G. Buon, 1572.   EUL

1005 [CLICHTOVEUS, Jodocus.] Le traite de
la vraye noblesse translate nouuellement de latin
en francoys.
8° Paris, A. Bonnemere, [c. 1530].   EUL

propos memorables [Fr. 28]
1006* CORROZET, Gilles. Les diuers propos
memorables des nobles & illustres hommes de
la chrestienté.

accord de plus. passages de la S. escri [Fr. 48]
1007* CRESPIN, Jean. Accord de plusieurs
passages des Sainctes Escritures.
An edition of this work was printed in Geneva,
1561.

traittè de l'estat honest des christienes en leur
[Fr. 50]
1008* [DANEAU, Lambert.] Traité de l'estat
honneste des chrestiens en leur accoustrement.
BM has an edition, Geneva, 1580.

trauaux sans trauaill [Fr. 60]
1009* DAVITY, Pierre. Les travaux sans travail
. . . Avec le tombeau de Mme. la duchesse de
Beaufort . . .

l'austriade [Fr. 74]
1010* DEIMIER, Pierre de. L'Austriade . . .

le Seigneur des accords [Fr. 100]
1011* DES ACCORDS, *Le Seigneur, pseud.*
[Étienne Tabourot.] Les bigarrures et les touches

du Seigneur des Accords.
Also in List E.

les Muses ralliees [Fr. 25]

1012* DESPINELLE,? Les muses r'alliees.
Barbier gives some account of the first editions of
this work, which was presumably compiled by
Despinelle, whose name signed the dedication to
the first edition (*c.* 1599) and appeared on the
title of later editions.

oeuures poet. de des Portes [Fr. 44]

1013   DES PORTES, Philippe. Les premieres
oeuures . . . Reueues, corrigees, & augmentees.
12° Antwerp, N. Soolmans, 1582.   EUL

prieres christiennes [Fr. 19]

1014* ? DES PORTES, Philippe. Quelques
prieres & meditations chrestiennes.
Issued (1598, 1603) with Des Portes' translation
of the Psalms.

oeuures poet. de Mesdames de la Roche [Fr. 18]

1015* DES ROCHES, Magdaleine *and* Catherine.
Les oeuvres . . .

Dialogues [Fr. 56]

1016* DIALOGUES.? Dialogues et deuis des
damoiselles pour les rendre vertueuses.
[Imitated by F. d'Amboise after A. Piccolomini.]

1017   DORÉ, Pierre. Les allumettes du feu diuin
pour faire ardre les cueurs humains en lamour de
dieu, ou sont declarez les principaulx articles et
mysteres de la passion de nostre saulueur Iesus.
Auec les voyes de paradis que a enseignees nostre
benoist Saulueur Iesus en son euangile . . .
[In 2 parts.]
8° Paris, E. Caveiller, 1539.   EUL
Les voyes de paradis is dated 1538.

1018   DU BELLAY, Joachim. Diuers ieux rusti-
ques, et autres oeuures poetiques . . .
4° Paris, F. Morel [the first], 1558.   EUL
Bought in Paris, 1608.

1019   DU BRUEIL, Anthoine. Petit dictionnaire
de l'ortographe Françoise.
16° Paris, A. Du Brueil, 1608.   EUL
Bought in Paris, 1608.

1020   DU CHESNE, Joseph. Le grand miroir du
monde . . . Deuxiesme edition, reueuë, corrigee
& augmentee en diuers endroits, & d'vn liure
entier, par l'auteur. A la fin de chasque liure sont
de nouueau adioustees ample annotations &
obseruations sur le texte . . . Par S[imon]
G[oulart de] S[enlis].
8° Lyons, for the heirs of E. Vignon, 1593. EUL

l'amour de la beaute du S. Croset [Fr. 88]

1021* DU CROSET, *le Sieur*. L'amour de la
beauté.

1022   DU FAIL, Noël. Les contes et discours
d'Eutrapel, reueus et augmentées par le feu seigneur de la Hérissaye . . .
16° Rennes, N. Glamet, 1586.   EUL
Title-leaf mutilated; title written in by Drummond.

1023* DU FAUR, Gui, *Seigneur de Pibrac*. Les
plaisirs de la vie rustique.   AUCT
AUCT has 'Bergerac, 1611'. Cotton says that the
printer Gilbert Vernoy was working in Bergerac
in 1611.

ouranologie [Fr. 57]

1024* DU MONIN, Jean Edouard. L'vranologie,
ou le ciel contenant, outre l'ordinaire doctrine de
la sphære, plusieurs beaux discours . . .
A paraphrase of Buchanan's *De sphœra*, published
before the original Latin.

1025   DU MOULIN, Pierre, *the Elder*. Apologie
pour la sainte cene du Seigneur. Contre la presence
corporelle, & transsubstantiation. Item contre les
messes sans communians. Et contre la cōmunion
sous vne espece . . . Derniere edition, en laquelle
est satisfait à toutes les accusations des aduersaires.
8° Geneva, M. Berjon, 1609.   EUL

1026   DU MOULIN, Pierre, *the Elder*. Familiere
instruction pour consoler les malades. Auec
plusieurs prieres sur ce sujet.
8° Niort, J. Moussat, 1613.   EUL

les amours de Lozie [Fr. 23]

1027* DUPERRIER, Antoine, *Sieur de la Salargue*.
Les amours de Lozie.

1028   DU PERRON, Jacques Davy, *Card*.
Replique a la response de quelques ministres sur
vn certain escript touchant leur vocation.
12° Paris, M. Patisson, 1597.   EUL

essaies poet. de du pyrrat [Fr. 33]

1029* DU PEYRAT, Guillaume. Les essais
poétiques . . .

la curiositè Naturalle de Scipion du Plai [Fr. 22]

1030* DU PLEIX, Scipion. La curiosité naturelle,
redigée en questions selon l'ordre alphabétique.

letteres de Tronchet [Fr. 43]

1031   DU TRONCHET, Estienne. Lettres missiues
et familieres . . . Auec le monologue de la proui-
dence diuine, au peuple François . . . Reueües,
corrigees & augmentees de plusieurs lettres
amoureuses, tirees tant de l'Italien du Bembe,
que de plusieurs autres autheurs.

16° Paris, A. L'Angelier, 1588.   EUL
Bought in Paris, 1608.

epistres d'amour [Fr. 116]
1032 * EPISTRES.
Not identified.

apologue de Herodote [List C]
1033   ESTIENNE, Henri, *le Grand*. L'introduction
au traite de la conformite des merueilles anciennes
auec les modernes: ou, traite preparatif à l'apologie pour Herodote . . .
8° [Montbéliard, J. Foillet,] 1607.   EUL

deux dialogues du nouueau langage [Fr. 38]
1034 * ESTIENNE, Henri, *le Grand*. Deux
dialogues du nouveau langage françois italianizé
et autrement desguizé, principalement entre les
courtisans de ce temps . . .

*traittè de la conformitè du langage françois
auec le Grec par H. Estienne* [Fr. 49]
1035 * ESTIENNE, Henri, *le Grand*. Traicté de
la conformité du langage François avec le Grec . . .

*Traittè de la precellence du langage Françoise
par H. Estienne* [Fr. 27]
1036 * ESTIENNE, Henri, *le Grand*. La pré-
cellence du langage françois.

1037   ESTIENNE, Robert, *the Elder*. Les mots
francois selon lordre des lettres, ainsi que les
fault escrire: tournez en latin, pour les enfans.
4° Paris, R. Estienne [the first], 1544.   EUL
Heavily annotated by Drummond.

declinations françois [Fr. 66]
1038 * ? ESTIENNE, Robert, *the Elder*. Les
declinaisons des noms & verbes.

1039   [FERRIÈRES, Henri de.] Le roy modus
deduitz de la chace, venerie et fauconnerie.
8° Paris, G. Corrozet, 1560.   EUL

1040   [FLORES, Juan de.] Le iugement damour,
auquel est racōptee lhystoire de Ysabel, fille du
roy descoce, trāslatee de Espaignol en Frācoys.
8° Paris, for J. Denis, [1530].   EUL

1041 * FRANCE. Francis I, *King*. Ordonnances
royaulx sur le faict de la iustice & abbreuiatiō
des proces par tout le royaulme de France, faictes
par le roy . . .
12° [Paris,] 1539.   AUCT
Copy in EUL.

1042   FRANCE. Henry III, *King*. Ordonnances
du roy Henry III. de ce nom, roy de France &
de Pologne, sur les plainctes & & doleances
faictes par les deputez des estats de son royaume,
conuoquez & assemblez en la ville de Bloys.
8° Angoulême, J. De Minières, 1580.   EUL

1043   FREDERICK I, *King of Bohemia*. Continuation et confirmation de l'armee du conte Palatin
en Boheme auec aulcunes aultres choses remar-
quables.
4° Brussels, H. Anthoine, 1620.   EUL

le ris de democrit [Fr. 61]
1044 * FREGOSO, Antonio. Le ris de Démocrite:
et le pleur de Héraclite, sur les follies & misères
de ce monde; . . . interprétée en ryme Françoise,
par noble homme Michel d'Amboyse [from the
Italian].

1045   FUCHS, Leonard. Histoire generale des
plantes et herbes auec leur proprieté . . . La figure
& vertu du petum, ou nicotiane vulgairement
appellée herbe à la royne. Auec vn nouueau
preseruatif contre la peste: ensemble vn recueil
d'excellentes receptes tirees de diuers autheurs . . .
12° Rouen, A. Morront, 1612.   EUL

la fuyte du peche [Fr. 110]
1046 * FUITE.
Not identified.

1047   GALENUS, Claudius. Lanatomie des os du
corps humain . . . Nouuellement traduicte de
Latin en francoys, par monsieur Iehan Canappe
docteur en medecine.
8° Lyons, E. Dolet, 1541.   EUL

1048   GALENUS, Claudius. De la raison de
curer par euacuation de sang . . .
8° Lyons, S. Sabon, for A. Constantin, [c. 1542].
                    EUL

1049   GAMON, Christophe de. La semaine, ou
creation du monde . . . contre celle du sieur du
Bartas.
12° Geneva, G. Petit, 1609.   EUL

Tragedies de Garnier [Fr. 72]
1050 * GARNIER, Robert. Les tragedies.

la Rhodomontade [Fr. 26]
1051 * ? GAULTIER, Jacques. Rodomontades
Espagnolles. Recueillies de diuers autheurs, &
notamment du Capitaine Bonbardon, compagnon
du soldat François . . .
An early edition?
Or the *Rodomontades Espaignolles* of Pierre de
Bourdeille de Brantôme—although they do not
seem to have appeared under his name in this
form before 1611.

Pastorelle d'A. Gautier [Fr. 13]
1052   GAUTIER, Albin. L'vnion d'amour et de
chasteté. Pastorale . . .
8° Poitiers, J. Blanchet, 1606.   EUL
Bought in Bourges, 1608.

Circe de Gello [Fr. 96]
1053   GELLI, Giovanni Battista. La Circé . . .
nouuellement mise en françois par le seigneur du
Parc [Denis Sauvage].
8° Lyons, G. Rouillé, 1550.   EUL
Title-leaf wanting; title supplied in MS. by
Drummond. Bought in Paris, 1607.

discours fantastiques de Iustin Tonnellier [Fr. 82]
1054*   GELLI, Giovanni Battista. Les discours
fantastiques de Iustin Tonnelier . . . Nouvellement
traduits en Francois par C[laude] D[e]
K[erquifinen] . . .

antimachiuel [Fr. 9]
1055*   [GENTILLET, Innocent.] Discours sur les
moyens de bien gouverner et maintenir en bonne
paix un royaume ou autre principauté contre
Nicolas Machiavel . . .

*Memoires de l'estat de france sous Charles
Neuueme* [Fr. 1]
1056*   [GOULART, Simon.] Memoires de l'estat
de France, sous Charles Neufiesme. Contenans les
choses plus notables, faites & publiees tant par les
Catholiques que par ceux de la religion, depuis le
troisiesme edit de pacification fait au mois d'Aoust
1570, jusques au regne de Henry troisiesme et
reduits en trois volumes.
A Protestant work. (See Scott, no. 103.)

1057   GRENIER, Jacques. Hymne de I.G.S.D.P.
sur les perfections de sa maistresse.
4° n.p.d. [not before 1588].   EUL
With twenty-three sonnets. Title taken from
head-title.

la Dieronomie comed. [Fr. 91]
1058*   GROTO, Luigi. Le repentir d'amour de
Diéromène, pastorale imitée de l'italien de
L.G.C.D.H. par R[olland] B[risset] G[entil-
homme] T[ourangeau].

bergere fidelle [Fr. 75]
1059*   GUARINI, Giovanni Battista. Le berger
fidelle, pastorale, de l'italien . . .

epistres dorees [Fr. 34]
1060*   GUEVARA, Antonio de, *Bp.* Les épistres
dorées et discours salutaires . . . traduictes
d'espaignol en françois par le seigneur de Guterry
. . .

le mespris de la Court [Fr. 41]
1061   GUEVARA, Antonio de, *Bp.* Le mespris
de la court, auec la commendation de la vie
rustique, nouuellement traduict d'Espaignol en
François. L'amye de court. La parfecte amye.
La contr' amye. L'androgyne de Platon. L'experience de l'amye de court contre la contr' amye.
L'honneste amant. Le nouuel amour. Auec plu-

sieurs epistres, elegies, & dizains, au propos que
dessus.
16° Paris, J. Longis, 1556.   EUL
Bought in Paris, 1608.
After the main work (*tr.* A. Alaigre) the other
pieces (in verse) are by le Seigneur de Borderie,
A. Héroët, C. Fontaine, A. Héroët (translating
'L'androgyne de Platon' from the Latin),
P. Angier, Seigneur Papillon, *et al.*

1062   GUIDO, *de Cauliaco.* Les fleurs . . . ou
sont contenues plusieurs quæstions tresvtiles,
pour ceulx qui sont amateurs de chirurgie, ex-
traictes par maistre Iehan Raoul chirurgiē . . .
8° Paris, B. Prévost, 1547.   EUL

oraison de M.S.G. cardinal de Lorraine [Fr. 94]
1063*   GUISE, Charles de, *Card.*
L'Oraison de Mgr le . . . cardinal de Lorraine,
faite en l'assemblée de Poissy, le roy y estant
présent, le 16 . . . de septembre 1561.

1064*   HABERT, François. Le different du corps
& d'esprit, avec les cantiques extraictz de l'oraison
dominicale, ensemble le IIII liure des visions
fantastiques, une eclogue de la parfaicte amour,
epistres, dixains & ballades, joinct l'epithaphe
de verite . . .
Press has 'Paris. 1542'. Edition not traced. PRESS

1065*   HAMILTON. M. le Marquis d'Hamiltoun.
Discours, par lequel est esclaircy le droit qu'il
ha au duchè de Chastelheraud, & oe utres revenuz
transportez, & assignez a defunct mounsieur le
duc son ayeul en Poictou 1611.   AUCT
Not traced. Refers to James Hamilton, Marquis
of Hamilton (1584–1624/5), the subject of
Donne's poem. The Duchy of Châtelherault was
granted to James, 2nd Earl of Arran, in 1548/9,
but the estates were lost to the family by 1597.
See *Scots Peerage* (Edinburgh, 1907), IV, 367–72.

1066   HANGEST, Jérome de. Contre les tene-
briõs lumiere euuangelicque . . . Secunde et
ampliee edition.
8° Paris, [1535].   EUL

1067   HAY, John, *Jesuit.* Demandes, faictes aux
ministres d'Escosse: touchant la religion chrestienne . . . Reueuës, & de l'Escossois mises en
langue Françoise.
16° Lyons, J. Phillehotte, 1584.   EUL

le miroir du prince Christiene [Fr. 102]
1068*   [HELVIS, Jean.] Le mirouer du prince
chrestien, posé sur les deux colonnes de piété
et justice.

1069   HERODIAN. L'histoire de Herodian, des
empereurs Romains depuis Marcus. Tournee de
Grec, en Latin, par Ange Politian, & de Latin, en

François par Iean Collin. Auec l'exposition de
plusieurs dictions, histoires, fables, situations de
lieux, & descriptions de pais, seruans à entendre
plus facilement les histoires.
16° Paris, C. Micard, 1572. EUL

examen des esprits [Fr. 52]
1070* HUARTE, Juan. Examen des esprits pro-
pres et naix aux sciences . . . traduict d'espaignol
. . .
Also in List F.

1071 JAMES I, *King.* La Lepanthe . . . faicte
francoise par le sieur Du Bartas.
4° Edinburgh, R. Waldegraue, 1591. EUL
STC 14379
The third part of *His maiesties poeticall exercises.*

1072 JESUS CHRIST. Les quinze effusions du
sang de nostre saulueur & redempteur Ieuschrist.
En la fin desquelles est adioustée vne deuote
oraison à la vierge Marie, laquelle on dict auoir
esté trouuée sur son sepulchre en la vallée de
Iosaphat. Auec les douze vendredis blās.
16° Paris, J. Amazeur for G. Merlin, 1553. EUL

1073 [LA MESCHINIÈRE,] Pierre Enoc de.
Opuscules poetiques . . .
8° [Geneva,] J. Stoer, 1572. EUL

discours po. de la Noue [Fr. 47]
1074* LA NOUE, François de. Discours politiques
et militaires . . .

Poesies christienes de M. odet la Noue [Fr. 6]
1075 LA NOUE, Odet de. Poesies chrestiennes
. . . Nouuellement mises en lumiere par le sieur
de la Violette.
8° [Geneva,] heirs of E. Vignon, 1594. EUL
Bought in Paris, 1608.

ouures poet. de I. de la peruse [Fr. 30]
1076* LA PÉRUSE, Jean Bastier de. Les oeuures
. . .

1077 LA PRIMAUDAYE, Pierre de. Aduis sur
la necessite et forme d'vn S. concile, pour l'vnion
des eglises chrestiennes en la foy catholique, &
sainct exercise d'icelle. Seconde edition.
8° Saumur, for C. Girard and J. Moussat, 1611.
EUL

comedies de l'arriuey [Fr. 79]
1078 LARIVEY, Pierre de. Les comedies face-
cieuses . . . A l'imitation des anciens Grecs,
Latins, & modernes Italiens. A sçavoir le laquais.
La vefue. Les esprits. Le morfondu. Les ialoux.
Les escolliers. Seconde edition.
12° Rouen, R. Du Petit-Val, 1601. EUL

les oeuures poetiques de Iean de la Taille [Fr. 14]
1079* LA TAILLE, Jean de. Les oeuvres poétiques . . .

1080 LATIN GRAMMAR. La premiere (–seconde)
partie de la grammaire latine et francoise. (*And*
Tertia (–quarta) pars Latinae grammatices.)
8° Geneva, J. Durant, 1571, 1568, 1568, 1571. EUL

1081 LA TOUCHE, Gervais de. Art nouueau,
et familiere industrie d'interpreter, tourner et
translater de Latin en François, selon le vray
ordre de nature, pour r'accorder & sympathizer
l'eloquence Latine à la Françoise. Nouuellement
recherche & compose . . .
8° Paris, R. Colombel, 1587. EUL
Bought in Paris, 1608.

1082 LAUNOY, Matthieu de *and* PENNETIER,
Henry. La declaration et refutation des fausses
suppositions, et peruerses applications d'aucunes
sentences des sainctes ecritures, desquelles les
ministres se sont seruis en ce dernier temps, à
diuiser la chrêtienté.
8° Paris, G. de La Noue [and J. Du Carroy],
1578. EUL

la Walleterie [Fr. 59]
1083* LA VALLETTRIE, [?] de. ? Ses œuvres
poétiques . . .

la philosophie de l. de Charon [Fr. 69]
1084* LE CARON, Louis. La philosophie . . .

Iean le Maire de Belges [Fr. 112]
1085* LE MAIRE, Jean. ? Les illustrations de
Gaule et singularitez de Troye.

1086 [LE MOYNE, Jean.] Le stile et maniere de
composer, dicter, et escrire toute sorte d'epistre,
ou lettres missiues, tant par response, que autrement, auec epitome de la poinctuation, & accents
de la langue Françoise : liure tres-vtile & profitable. Nouuellement reueu & augmenté.
16° Lyons, T. Payen, 1566. EUL

1087 LÉRY, Jean de. Histoire memorable de la
ville de Sancerre. Contenant les entreprinses,
siege, approches, bateries, assaus & autres efforts
des assiegeans : les resistances, faits magnanimes,
la famine extreme & deliurance notable des
assiegez. Le nombre des coups de canons par
iournees distinguees. Le catalogue des morts &
blessez à la guerre . . .
8° [La Rochelle,] 1574. EUL

1088 [LE TELLIER, Jean-Baptiste.] Memoires
et instructions pour l'establissement des meuriers;
& art de faire la soye en France.
4° Paris, J. and P. Mettayer, 1603. EUL

1089 LITURGIES. Directories. Lordinaire des
crestiens.
2° Paris, Le Petit Laurens for F. Regnault, [n.d.].
EUL

Brunet describes this edition and dates it to between 1497 and 1505 (see Brunet Suppl. II, 87). It may however have been printed later, between 1510 and 1515.

1090 LITURGIES. Hours. Heures de Nostre Dame à l'vsage de Romme en Latin & en François, nouuellement imprimées . . .
16° Paris, J. Amazeur for G. Merlin, 1555.   EUL
Colophon has 1553.

les discours . . . de Machiuelli [Fr. 7]
1091 MACHIAVELLI, Niccolò. Discours de Nic. Macchiauel sur la première décade de Tite-Liue dez l'édification de la ville, traduitz d'italien en françois et de nouueau reueuz et augmentez, par Jacques Gohory . . .
8° Paris, R. Le Mangnier, 1571.   BODL
Bound with Machiavelli's *Le Prince*.

. . . Prince de Machiuelli [Fr. 7]
1092 MACHIAVELLI, Niccolò. Le Prince, de Nicolas Machiauel . . . traduit d'italien en françois, auec la vie de l'auteur mesme par Jaq. Gohory . . .
8° Paris, R. Le Mangnier, 1571.   BODL
Bound with Machiavelli's *Discours*.

1093 [MAILLI, Charles de.] Traicte du nom de Iesus, extraict de la saincte escripture & des anciens docteurs de l'eglise. Nouuellement imprimé . . .
16° Paris, 1588.   EUL

Heptameron de la Royne de Nau. [Fr. 111]
1094 MARGARET, d'Angoulême. L'heptameron ou histoires des amans fortunez, des nouuelles de tres-illustre & tres-excellente princesse, Marguerite de Valois, royne de Nauarre . . .
12° Paris, C. Chappellain, 1607.   EUL

les Margarites de la Margaret [Fr. 20]
1095 MARGARET, d'Angoulême. Les Marguerites de la Marguerite des princesses, tresillustre royne de Nauarre.
16° Paris, widow of F. Regnauld, 1554.   EUL
Bought in Paris, 1608.

la Mariane de Philomen [Fr. 85]
1096* MARIANE. La Mariane du Filomene.
An edition of this anonymous work was printed by Claude de Monstreuil and Jean Richer, Paris, 1596.

les oeuures poet. de Cl. Marot [Fr. 65]
1097* MAROT, Clément. Les oeuures poëtiques.

Histoire de dernieres troubles [Fr. 35]
1098* [MATTHIEU, Pierre.] Histoire des derniers troubles de France, sous les règnes des rois . . . Henry III . . . et Henry IIII.

1099 MATTHIEU, Pierre. Tablettes, ou quatrains de la vie et de la mort. [2 parts in 1.]
16° Rouen, P. Valentin, [c. 1620].   EUL

1100 MÉCONTENTEMENT. Le mécontenttement arriué aux dames d'amour, suiuant la cour.
8° Paris, 1625.   EUL
And 'Le pot aux roses des-couuert, en forme de dialogue'.

1101 MEIGRET, Louis. La response de Louïs Meigręt a l'apolojie de Iáqes Pelletier.
4° Paris, C. Wechel, 1550.   EUL

1102 MEIGRET, Louis. Reponse de Louïs Meigręt a la dezesperée repliqe de Glaomalis de Vezelęt . . .
4° Paris, C. Wechel, 1551.   EUL

tretté de la grammaire françois par Louis Maigret [Fr. 5]
1103 MEIGRET, Louis. Le tretté de la grammęre francoęze, fęt par Louis Meigręt Lionoęs.
4° Paris, C. Wechel, 1550.   EUL
Bought in Paris, 1608.

1104 MELLEMA, Elcie Édouard Léon. Dictionaire ou promptuaire flameng-francoys, tres-ample et tres-copieu: de nouueau composé . . . [In 2 parts.]
4° Antwerp, J. van Waesberghe, 1587.   EUL
Part 2 wanting.

Grammer Italien [Fr. 70]
1105 M[ESMES], Jean Pierre de. La grammaire Italienne, composée en Françoys.
8° Paris, for G. Corrozet, 1548.   EUL
Bought in Paris, 1607.

1106 MERLIN. Les prophecies de Merlin.
4° Paris, [P. Le Noir,] 1526.   EUL
Wanting the title and the following five leaves. In this edition the prophecies only were printed. See Brunet, III, 1655.

1107 MERLIN. Le second volume de Merlin, nouuellement imprime a Paris.
4° Paris, [P. Le Noir, 15]28.   EUL
One of the three volumes which made up the edition of 1528. See Brunet, III, 1655.

Responce a Gentian Heruet [Fr. 55]
1108* MICQUEAU, Jean-Loys. Response au discours de M. Gentian Hervet, sur ce que les pilleurs, voleurs et brusleurs d'églises disent qu'ils n'en veulent qu'aux prestres . . .

1109 MONTAIGNE, Michel de. Les essais de Michel, seigneur de Montagne, divisez en trois livres. Contenants un riche et rare thrésor de plusieurs beaux et notables discours . . .

12° Lyons, for F. Le Febvre, 1595. HUL
Wanting the last leaf.

cõmentaires de Monluc [Fr. 10]
1110 MONTLUC, Blaise de. Commentaires de
messire Blaise de Montluc . . . ou sont descris les
combats, rancontres . . . avecques plusieurs autres
faicts de guerre signalez et remarcables, esquels ce
grand et renommé guerrier s'est trouvé . . .
ensemble diverses instructions qui ne doivent
estre ignorées de ceux qui veulent parvenir par
les armes à quelqu'honneur . . . [2 vols. in 1.]
8° Paris, N. Lescuyer, 1607. UTL
Wanting all save title-leaf. Bought in Paris, 1608.

1111 MORNAY, Philippe de. De la verité de la
religion Chrestienne. Contre les athées, épicuriens,
payens, Iuifs, Mahumedistes, et autres infideles.
4° Antwerp, C. Plantin, 1581. SAUL

1112 MORNAY, Philippe de. De la verité de la
religion chrestienne: contre les athées, epicuriens,
payens, Iuifs, Mahumedistes, & autres infideles
. . . Seconde edition reueue par l'autheur.
8° Antwerp, house of Plantin, 1590. EUL

1113 MORNAY, Philippe de. Traicté de l'eglise,
auquel sont disputees les principales questions,
qui ont esté meuës sur ce poinct en nostre temps
. . . Reueu & augmenté par le mesme aucteur.
8° Frankfort, heirs of A. Wechel, 1582. EUL

1114 [MUHAMMAD Ibn Sirin, *al Basrï*.]
Apomazar des significations et evenemens des
songes, selon la doctrine des Indiens, Perses, &
Egyptiens. Pris de la bibliotheque de Iean
Sambucus. Puis tourné du Grec en Latin, par
Iean Leunclaius. Et mis de nouueau en Françoys
[by Denis Du Val].
8° Paris, D. Du Val, 1581. EUL
The table is wanting.

muse folâtre [List C]
1115 MUSE FOLÂTRE. Le premier (–troisiesme)
liure de la muse folastre. Recherchee des plus
beaux esprits de ce temps. De nouueau reueu,
corrigé, & augmenté. [3 parts in 1.]
24° Rouen, C. Le Villain, 1605. EUL
Edited by Paul de L'Écluse? See Barbier, III, 379.

le combat de Mutio Iustinopolit. [Fr. 87]
1116* MUZIO, Girolamo. Le combat . . . avec les
responses chevaleresses, traduit nouvellement
d'Italien en Françoys par A. Chapuis.

exposition sur l'apocalips [Fr. 58]
1117 NAPIER, John, *of Merchiston.* Ouuerture
de tous les secrets de l'apocalypse ou reuelation
de S. Iean. Par deux traités, l'vn recherchant &
prouuant la vraye interpretation d'icelle: l'autre
appliquant au texte ceste interpretation para-

phrastiquement & historiquement, par Iean
Napeir . . . reueue par lui-mesme: et mise en
Francois par Georges Thomson Escossois.
4° La Rochelle, J. Brenouzet, 1602. EUL
With 2 insets.

1118 NIPHUS, Augustinus, *Suesanus.*
Augustin Niphe, des augures, ou, diuinations.
Traduict par maistre Antoine du Moulin Masconnis.
16° Lyons, J. De Tournes, 1581. EUL

1119 NORMANDY. L'histoire et cronique de
Normandie. Reueuë & augmentee . . . Auec les
figures tant que la dite Normandie que de la
ville de Rouen, metropolitaine d'icelle prouince.
8° Rouen, M. le Mesgissier, 1589. EUL
At the end: 'Description du pays et duché . . .
extraict de la cronique de Normandie'. The
'figures' are wanting.

les Amours de Cleandre par Olenix [Fr. 39]
1120* OLLENIX DU MONT-SACRÉ, *pseud.*
[Nicolas de Montreux]. Les amours de Cleandre
et Domiphille. Par lesquelles se remarque la
perfection de la vertu de chasteté.

Alcee comedie marine [Fr. 89]
1121* ONGARO, Antonio. Alcée pescherie ou
comœdie marine. [*Tr.* from the Italian.]

1122 ONGOYS, Jean d'. Le promptuaire de
tout ce qui est aduenu plus digne de memoire,
depuis la creation du monde iusques à present.
Auquel ont esté adioustez (à ceste seconde
edition) les cathalogues de papes, empereurs &
roys de France, auec trois genealogies & descentes
des roys d'Angleterre, Espagne & Portugal . . .
16° Paris, J. de Bordeaux [the second], 1579.
 EUL

1123 PARIS, University. A la roine regente, et
a nosseigneurs les princes, et seigneurs du conseil.
8° [Paris? 1610?] EUL
A remonstrance from the university against the
Jesuits. Mary de' Medici is the queen addressed.

la maine d'estienne Pasquier [Fr. 106]
1124* PASQUIER, Étienne. La main, ou
œuvres poétiques faits sur la main d' E. Pasquier
aux grands jours de Troyes, 1583.

1125 PASQUIER, Étienne. Les memoires et
recherches de la France. Liure premier et second.
L'vn pour parler du prince, & quelques dialogues
de nouueau reueu.
16° Paris, G. Robinot [the second], 1594. EUL

le Monophile de Pasquier [Fr. 37]
1126 PASQUIER, Étienne. Le Monophile,
auecq' quelques autres oeuures d'amour . . .

augmenté de plusieurs sonets, elegies & chansons, non encor imprimées.
16° Paris, A. L'Angelier, 1578.   BM

consolation a Madame Giury [Fr. 103]
1127* PASSERAT, Jean. Consolation à madame de Givry.

poemes de passerat [List F]
1128* PASSERAT, Jean. Le premier livre des poëmes . . .

1129 PATROCLE ET PHILOMELLE. La naissance d'vn bel amour. Sous les noms de Patrocle et Philomelle histoire veritable & aduenue.
12° Paris, G. Robinot [the second], 1602.   EUL
The dedication is signed I.I.D.M.P.

l'art Poetique de Iacques Pelletier [Fr. 12]
1130* PELETIER, Jacques. L'art poëtique . . .

oeuures poetiques de pelletier [Fr. 67]
1131 PELETIER, Jacques. Les oeuures poetiques . . .
8° Paris, G. Corrozet, 1547.   EUL

Histoire de Albigeois [Fr. 53]
1132* PETER, *a monk of the Abbey of Vaux-de-Cernay*. Histoire des Albigeois, et gestes de noble Simon de Montfort . . . Rendue de Latin en François par M.A. Sorbin . . .

1133 PETRARCA, Francesco. [*Canzoniere.*] Le Petrarque en rime françoise auecq ses commentaires, traduict par Philippe de Maldeghem . . .
8° Brussels, R. Velpius [the younger], 1600.
Bought in Paris, 1608.   EUL

1134 POLLOT, Laurent. Dialogues contre la pluralite des religions, et l'atheisme. 1. De la religion de Dieu. 2. Des religions des hommes. 3. Contre l'atheisme. Sur la fin est adiousté, par occasion tres-necessaire, dernier siecle de fer.
8° La Rochelle, H. Haultin, 1595.   EUL
Bought in Rouen, 1608.

1135 PRAGUE. Relation de la forme en laquelle a este donnee la bataille de la ville de Prague, et de quelques particularitez qui l'ont ensuiuy.
4° Brussels, H. Anthoine, 1620.   EUL

1136 PROTOCOLE. Le pthocolle des notaires, tabellions, greffiers, et sergens conteñat la forme et maniere de faire to⁹ contractz, actes de iustice, commissions & rapportz de sergens a cheualer verge, innuentaires, comptes, demandes: et aultres choses singulieres.
8° Paris, for D. Gerlier, 1518.   EUL
'Extraitz partie de la somme Rouladine, partie du prothocolle de feu maistre Loys Barthelemy . . .'

Rablais [Fr. 8]
1137* RABELAIS, François. Les œuvres . . . contenant la vie, faicts et dicts héroïques de Gargantua, et son filz Pantagruel. Avec la prognostication pantagrueline.

1138 RAMUS, Petrus. La Dialectique de M.P. de la Ramée . . .
8° Paris, G. Auvray, 1577.   BM

1139 REBOUL, Guillaume de. Du schisme des pretendus reformez. Augmenté de quatre parties. Pour replique à la response des ministres du Languedoc, assemblez à Mompellier.
12° Lyons, J. Roussin, 1597.   EUL

dialogue de la vie et de la mort traduit de tuscan par Innocen Rungean [Fr. 95]
1140* RINGHIERI, Innocenzio. Dialogue de la vie et de la mort . . . traduit . . . par J. Louveau [from the Italian].

la celestine [Fr. 36]
1141* [ROJAS, Fernando de.] La Celestine. Tragicomedie, traduit d'Espagnol en François. Où se voyent les ruses & tromperies, dont les maquerelles vsent enuers les fols amoureux.

la Franciade de Ronsard [Fr. 119]
1142* RONSARD, Pierre de. Les quatre premiers liures de la Franciade . . .

epistres de Prince [Fr. 73]
1143 RUSCELLI, Girolamo. Epistres des princes, lesquelles, ou sont addresses aux princes, ou traitent les affaires des princes, ou parlent des princes. Mises en François par F. de Belle-forest.
8° Paris, J. Ruelle, 1574.   PR
Bought in Paris, 1608.

1144 SAINCTES, Claude de, *Bp*. Discours sur le saccagement des eglises catholiques par les heretiques anciens, & nouueaux caluinistes, en l'an 1562.
8° Verdun, for N. Bacquenois, 1562.   EUL
All after M5 wanting.

les oeuures de G. Salust [Fr. 109]
1145 SALUSTE DU BARTAS, Guillaume de. Suite des œuures . . . contenant les peres. La loy. Ionas. Iudit. L'Vranie. Le triomphe de la foy. Les neuf muses. Cantique sur la victoire d'Yury. Edition nouuelle, augmentee d'vn liure entier, reueuë, auec les prefaces, sommaires & annotations de S[imon] G[oulart de] S[enlis].
12° [Geneva,] A. Blanc for J. Chouet, 1596.   EUL

1146 SALUSTE DU BARTAS, Guillaume de. II. partie de la suite des oeuures . . . contenant les trophees, ou premiere partie du iiij. iour de la ij. sepmaine. La magnificence . . . La Lepanthe de:

Iacques VI. roy d'Escosse, faite Françoise . . .
Fragment, ou commencement de la preface sur
la ij. partie du iij. iour de la mesme ij. sepmaine.
Edition nouuelle, reueue, & augmentee des
prefaces, sommaires & annotations de S[imon]
G[oulart de] S[enlis].
8° [Geneva,] A. Blanc for J. Chouet, 1598. EUL

1147   SALUSTE DU BARTAS, Guillaume de.
Suite des oeuures, contenant les peres. La loy.
Les trophees. La magnificence. L'histoire de Ionas.
Plus un fragment ou commencement de preface.
La Lepanthe. Cantique de la victoire d'Iury. Auec
les prefaces, sommaires et annotations de S[imon]
G[oulart de] S[enlis].
12° [Geneva,] for J. Chouet, 1601.   SALE
Present location unknown. Bound with another
part of this 4 part edition, containing: *La Judith,
l'Vranie, le triomphe de la paix, les neuf muses.*

Arcadia de sanazar [Fr. 16]
1148* SANNAZARO, Jacopo. L'Arcadie . . . mise
d'italien en françoys . . .
Also in List F.

Satyre Menippee [Fr. 29]
1149* SATYRE MÉNIPPÉE. Satyre Menippee
de la vertu du catholicon d'Espagne, et de la
tenue des estatz de Paris . . .
Attributed to Pierre Le Roy, Jacques Gillot, J.
Passerat, N. Rapin, F. Chrestien and P. Pithou.

1150* SCOTLAND. L'escosse françoise. Discours
des alliances . . . entre les couronnes de France
et d'Escosse.
8° Paris, 1608.   AUCT
Copy in EUL.

1151   SEBASTIAN, *King of Portugal.* Histoire
veritable des dernieres guerres aduenues en
Barbarie: & du succéz pitoyable du roy de
Portugal dernier, Don Sebastien (que Dieu
absolue) qui mourut en bataille le quatriesme
Aoust, M.D. LXXVIII. Auec l'origine & descente
des roys qui de nostre temps ont commandé és
royaumes de la ditte Barbarie. Traduitte de
l'Espagnol en François.
8° Paris, N. Chesneau, 1579.   EUL
With an inset: a map showing the scene of the
action.

1152   SERRES, Jean de. Inuentaire général de
l'histoire de France . . . [In 2 vols.]
8° [Paris,] for the heirs of E. Vignon, 1603.
Both vols. signed by Drummond.   DUL

le Tombeau de Margarit de Vallois [Fr. 104]
1153* SEYMOUR, *Lady* Anne. Le tombeau de
Marguerite de Valois royne de Navarre. Faict
premierement en disticques Latins par les trois
soeurs (Anne, Marguerite, Jane de Seymour) . . .

Depuis traduictz en Grec, Italiẽ, François par
plusieurs des excellentz poëtes de la Frãce.
Avecques plusieurs odes, hymnes, cantiques,
epitathes, sur le mesme subject.

1154   SIMSON, Alexander. Responce claire et
solide a vn discours sur la presence du corps du
Seigneur au sacrement, faict par F. Iean Iourné
. . . addressé a vn de l'eglise reformée de Cha-
steaudun.
8° [Châteaudun?] 1605.   EUL

la Puce de madame des Roches [Fr. 46]
1155* SOURDRAI, Jacques de, *ed.* La puce de
madame Des-Roches. Qui est vn recueil de diuers
poemes grecs, latins & françois, composez par
plusieurs personnages aux grans iours tenus à
Poitiers l'an M.D. LXXIX . . .
The authors include Catherine Des Roches and
Étienne Pasquier.

les dialogues de speron sperone [Fr. 51]
1156* SPERONI DEGLI ALVAROTTI, Sperone.
Les dialogues . . . traduitz en françoys [from the
Italian] . . .

le str[atageme?] Amoureux d'Estourneaux [Fr. 86]
1157* STRATAGEME.
Not identified.

Le tableau de la grace [Fr. 11]
1158* TABLEAU.
Not identified.

les Dialo. de Iacques Thureau [Fr. 62]
1159* TAHUREAU, Jacques. Les dialogues . . .
ou les vices d'un châcun sont repris fort apre-
ment . . .

discours des champs fees [Fr. 64]
1160   TAILLEMONT, Claude de. Le discours des
champs faëz, à l'honneur & exaltation de l'amour,
& des dames. Contenant plusieurs chansons,
quatrains, dialogues, complaintes, & autres
joyeusetez d'amours.
16° Paris, R. Roux, 1557.   BM

1161   TARTARY. Copie d'vne lettre en forme de
relation escripte de Tartarie par vn gentil-homme
françois à vn sien amy, sur le subject de l'enleue-
ment faict l'année derniere par le prince de
Tartarie de la fille vnique du roy de Narsingue.
8° Paris, C. Touchart, 1612.   EUL
A romance which was the subject of an entertainment performed before Louis XIII and the Queen
Regent.

aminte de T. Tasso [Fr. 83]
1162* TASSO, Torquato. Aminte, pastorale . . .

dialogue de la Noblesse de Tasso [Fr. 24]
1163* TASSO, Torquato. Dialogue de la noblesse, pris de l'italien . . .

1164 [TELESPHORUS, *of Cosenza.*] Liure merueilleux contenant en bref la fleur et substance de plusieurs traictez tant des propheties & reuelations, qu'anciennes croniques, faisant mention de tous les faictz de l'eglise vniuerselle, cõme des schismes, discords & tribulations aduenir en l'eglise de Rome . . . Reueu & corrigé par messieurs de la faculté de theologie de Paris, l'an 1566. [*Tr.* from the Latin.]
8° Paris, T. Bessault, 1566.   EUL

1165 THEOPHILE [DE VIAU], *Sieur.* Recueil de toutes les pieces faites par Theophile, depuis sa prise iusques à present.
8° Paris, 1625.   EUL
Wanting all after L4.

1166 [THIBAULT, Jean.] La physionomie des songes et visions fantasticques des personnes, auec l'expositiõ d'iceulx selon. le vray cours de la lune en, ensuyuant la reigle de viure des anciens astrologues, cerchee & calculee par plusieurs medecins & astrologues les plus excellentz de ce regne.
8° Paris, N. Buffet, 1545.   EUL

1167* THOU, Jacques Auguste de. Épistre de monsieur le président de Thou au roy.   HEND
An edition was printed by P. Chevalier, Paris, 1614.

1168 THUCYDIDES. Lhistoire de Thucydide Athenien, de la guerre, qui fut entre les Peloponnesiens et Atheniens, translatee en langue francoyse par feu messire Claude de Seyssel [from the Latin of Laurentius Valla] . . .
2° Paris, J. Badius, 1527.   EUL

epistres argentees [Fr. 17]
1169* TOLOMEI, Claudio. Les Epistres argentees, ou recueil des principalles lettres des sept livres . . . [*Tr.* Pierre Vidal.]

la flamme d'amour [Fr. 68]
1170* TRELLON, Claude, *Sieur de.* Le premier livre de la flamme d'amour.
Brunet records two editions in this form: Paris, 1591 and Lyons, 1592. The work was afterwards printed with *La muse guerrière.* Also in List F.

1171 [TRELLON, Claude, *Sieur de.*] La muse guerriere.
12° Rouen, L. Costé, 1598.   EUL
And *L'hermitage.*

Tresor de vertu Italien fran. [Fr. 84]
1172* TRESOR. Tresor de vertu, où sont contenues toutes les plus nobles et excellentes sentences et enseignements de tous les premiers auteurs hebreux, grecs et latins . . .
Several possible editions in French and Italian (see Brunet, V, 938–9, Barbier, IV, 824).

les oeuures poet. de Pontus de Tyard [Fr. 90]
1173 TYARD, Pontus de, *Bp.* Les oeuures poetiques . . . a sçavoir, trois livres des erreurs amoureuses. Un livre de vers liriques. Plus un recueil des nouvelles oeuvres pöetiques. [4 vols.]
4° Paris, G. Du Pré [the second], 1573.   SALE
And *Ponti Thyardei . . . de coelestibus asterismis, poëmatium*; *Mantice ou discours de la verité de diuination par astrologie*; and *Solitaire premier, ou dialogue de la fureur poetique.*
Present location unknown.

l'vniuers [Fr. 81]
1174* [TYARD, Pontus de, *Bp.*] L'vniuers, ou discours des parties, et de la nature du monde.

1175 URANIE. Lettres douces pleines de desirs et imaginations d'amour. A Vranie.
16° Lyons, A. Martin, 1589.   EUL

1176 URFÉ, Honoré d'. Le sireine . . .
12° Paris, J. Micard, 1606.   EUL

1177 VALDÉS, Juan de. Cent et dix consyderations divines . . . Traduites premierement, d'Espaignol en langue Italienne, & de neuueau mises en François, par C.K.P.
16° Paris, M. Prévost, 1565.   EUL

l'amant resussite [Fr. 63]
1178* VALENTINIAN, Théodose. Histoire de l'amant résuscité de la mort d'amour.

1179 VASSÉE, Loys. L'anatomie du corps humain, reduite en tables, premierement composées en Latin . . . et depuis traduites par maistre Iean Canappe. Reueu & corrigé auec l'indice.
16° Paris, J. Ruelle [the first], 1554.   EUL

la monstre speriq. de P. de Villier's [Fr. 21]
1180* VILLIERS, Hubert Philippe de. Le premier liure sus la composition de la monstre sphæricȝ du roy, avec une eclogue sus la naissance de monseigneur Charles de Burbon prince du sang, Comte de Soissons . . .   PRESS
PRESS has 'Paris, M.D. XCVII'. Edition not traced.

les Intelligences de Iean de Villiers [Fr. 105]
1181* VILLIERS, Jean de. Les intelligences . . . exhibantes une figure remplie d'infinitez de dictions, langages & sciences, tant separément que conjonctivement . . .

l'apologie du prince d'orange [Fr. 45]
1182* WILLIAM I, *Prince of Orange*. Apologie ou defense de tres illustre Prince Guillaume . . . contre le ban & edict publié par le roy d'espagne . . .

le printemps d'Hyuer [Fr. 80]
1183 YVER, Jacques. Le printemps d'Yuer, contenant cinq histoires, discourues par cinq iournees, en vne noble compagnie, au chasteau du printemps.
16° Lyons, B. Rigaud, 1578.   EUL

Translations: (into English) See 695, 716, 739, 770, 771, 788, 804, 805, 896, 933.
(into Italian) See 1251, 1276, 1277.

ITALIAN BOOKS

academia perrigrina [It. 59]
1184* Not identified.
Possibly Drummond's title refers to *La moral' filosophia del Doni* (1201). Cf. 709.

1185 ALESSIO, *Piemontese, pseud.* [Girolamo Ruscelli?] De' secreti del reuerendo Donno Alessio Piemontese, prima parte, diuisa in sei libri . . . Ora in questa seconda editione dall' autor medesimo tutta ricorretta, & migliorata. Et aggiuntoui nel fine de ogni libro molti bellissimi secreti noui.
16° Lyons, T. Payen, 1558.   EUL

1186* AMMIRATO, Scipione. ?
A work by Ammirato was given to Drummond by Sir David Lindsay some time before 1622. See his letter of thanks, printed in Lord Lindsay's *Lives of the Lindsays* (London, 1849), II, 4–5.

le Brauure del Capitano spauento [It. 26]
1187* ANDREINI, Francesco. Le Brauure del Capitano Spauento; diuise in molti ragionamenti in forma di dialogo . . .

Mirtilla Pastorale [It. 55]
1188* ANDREINI, Isabella. La Mirtilla. Pastorale.

Orlando furioso di M. Lodiuico Ariosto [It. 6]
1189 ARIOSTO, Lodovico. Orlando Furioso . . . reuisto et ristampato, sopra le correttioni di Ieronimo Ruscelli: con l'aggiunta de i cinque canti nuoui . . .
12° Lyons, G. Rouille, 1570.   DUL
Presumably not the copy listed in AUCT (1190*), for this copy must have stayed at Hawthornden.

1190* ARIOSTO, Lodovico. Orlando Furioso.
    AUCT

Rime di M.L. Ariosto [It. 7]
1191* ARIOSTO, Lodovico. Le rime.

I suppositi comedia di l. Ariosto [It. 22]
1192* ARIOSTO, Lodovico. I Suppositi, comedia.

Perla Tragicomedia di Simone Balsamino [It. 39]
1193* BALSAMINO, Simone. Perla: tragicomedia in rima libera . . .

1193.5 BANDELLO, Matteo, *Bp.* Il primo volume delle novelle.
8° Milan, 1560.   SALE

Gli asolini di M. Pietro Bembo [It. 8]
1194* BEMBO, Pietro, *Card.* Gli Asolani.

1195 BEMBO, Pietro, *Card.* Prose . . .
8° Venice, 1540.   EUL

Rime di Pietro Bembo [It. 9]
1196 BEMBO, Pietro, *Card.* Delle rime . . . Terza impressione. (Stanze . . .)
4° Rome, V. and L. Dorico for C. Gualteruzzi, 1548.   JR
Bought in Paris, 1608.

1197 BESSARION, *Card.* Lettere, et orationi . . . tradotte in lingua Italiana. Nelle quali esorta i prencipi d'Italia alla lega, & à prendere la guerra contra il Turco. [*Tr. and ed.* Filippo Pigafetta.]
4° Venice, Comin da Trino, 1573.   EUL

1198* BIANCHI, Lodovico. Le cento e quindici conclusioni. In ottaua rima. Del plusquamperfetto Dottor Gratiano Partesana da Francolin, comico geloso.
4° [Venice? 1587?]   AUCT

1199 BIBLE. Psalms. Sessanta salmi di Dauid. Tradotti in rime volgari Italiane, secondo la verità del testo Hebreo, col cantico di Simeone, e i dieci comandamenti de la legge: ogni cosa insieme col canto.
16° [Geneva,] G. B. Pinerolio, 1564.   EUL
With 'Confessione di fede fatta di comun consentimento de la chiese che sono disperse per la Francia'.

Il Nuouo testamento [It. 52]
1200* BIBLE. New Testament. Il Nuouo Testamento.

1201 BIDPAI. La moral' filosophia del Doni. Tratta dagli antichi scrittori. [In 2 parts.]
4° Venice, F. Marcolini [Academia Peregrina], 1552.   EUL
Title and all before P4 wanting. Translated from Joannes de Capua's Latin version of Bidpai's fables by Antonio Francesco Doni.

1202 BIDPAI. La moral' filosophia del Doni. Another copy of part 2: *Trattati diversi di Sendebar*.   EUL

1203 BOCCACCIO, Giovanni. L'amorosa fiametta . . . di nuoua ristampata, & con diligenza ricorretta.
12° Venice, G. Alberti, 1501.   EUL

dui libri del Veneto senato di Guilielmo Boccarini [It. 30]
1204 BOCCARINI, Guglielmo. Dui libri del Veneto senato . . . doue si tratta in ottaua rima della edificatione di Venetia, & delli fatti heroi della sereniss. republica.
4° Venice, Di Farri, 1583.   SALE
Present location unknown.

1205 BONARDO, Giovanni Maria. Della miseria et eccellenza della vita humana, ragionamenti due . . . nuouamente dati in luce da Luigi Groto Cieco d'Hadria.
8° Venice, F. and A. Zoppini, 1586.   EUL
With the signature of William Fowler.

1206 BONARDO, Giovanni Maria. La minera del mondo . . . nella qual si tratta delle cose più secrete, e più rare de'corpi semplici nel mondo elementare, e de'corpi composti, inanimati, & animati d'anima uegetatiua, sensitiua, e ragioneuole. Diuisa in quattro libri . . .
8° Venice, F. and A. Zoppini, 1585.   EUL

la seconda parte delle lettere del S. Diomede Borgesi [It. 36]
1207* BORGHESI, Diomede. La seconda parte delle lettere nelle quali si danno ammaestramenti intorno al scriuer Toscano.

la institutiona di vna Fanciulla di M. Giou. Michele Bruto [It. 50]
1208* BRUTO, Giovanni Michele. La institutione di vna fanciulla nata nobilmente.

Galateo [It. 56]
1209* CASA, Giovanni della, *Abp.* Il Galatheo . . . o vero trattato de' costumi, e modi . . . Same as 995?

1210 CASA, Giovanni della, *Abp.* Rime, et prose . . . Riscontrate con li migliori originali, & ricorrette con grandissima diligenza . . . [*Ed.* G. Spini.]
12° Venice, G. B. Bonfadino, 1590.   EUL

Rime di Iacomo Castellano [It. 12]
1211* CASTELLANI, Giacomo. I Giovanili scherzi, **rime** varie . . . (Rime spirituali, et morali, . . .)

Il Cortegiano [It. 57]
1212 CASTIGLIONE, Baldassare, *Count.* Il Cortegiano . . . [*Ed.* Lodovico Dolce.]
16° Lyons, G. Rouille, 1562.   PR
Also in List C.

Gabrielo Chiabrera [It. 28]
1213* CHIABRERA, Gabriello. ? Rime.

Merlini Cocaii Macaronica [It. 17]
1214 COCAIUS, Merlinus, *pseud.* [Teofilo Folengo.] Opus Merlini Cocaii poetæ Mantuani macaronicorum, totum in pristinam formam per me Magistrum Acquarium Lodolam optime redactum . . .
12° Venice, D. de Imbertis, 1585.   EUL
Bought in London, 1610.
With the motto in Drummond's hand: 'O cipresso ò palma'.

la lesina [It. 47]
1215* ? COMPAGNIA DELLA LESINA. Capitoli da osseruarsi inuiolabilmente da tutti i confrati della venerabile Compagnia della Lesina.

Madrigali di Francesco Contarini [It. 20]
1216* CONTARINI, Francesco. Madrigale . . . Amorose proposte . . .

Madrigali del S. Carolo Coquinato [It. 24]
1217* COQUINATO.
Not identified.

1218 CRESCI, Pietro. Le vergini, e sante descritte in forma d'elogii . . .
4° Venice, G. B. Somascho, 1589.   EUL
Gathering 'A' (4 leaves) wanting.

la comedia di Dante [It. 13]
1219* DANTE ALIGHIERI. La Divina Commedia.

According to Kastner, Drummond had the edition printed by Giolito, Venice, 1555, in 12°. This had the life of Dante by Dolce (see Kastner, I, 202).

1220 DOLCE, Lodovico. Amorosi ragionamenti. Dialogo, nel quale si racconta vncompassioneuole amore di due amanti, tradoto per M. Lodouico Dolce, da i fragmenti d'vno antico scrittor Greco. 8° Venice, G. Giolito, 1546.   EUL

Modi affigurati M. L. Dolce [It. 45]
1221* DOLCE, Lodovico. Modi affigurati e voci scelte et eleganti della volgar lingua, con un discorso sopra a mutamenti e diversi ornamenti dell' Ariosto . . .

1222 DONI, Antonio Francesco. Inferni del Doni libro secondo de mondi. 4° Venice, (1553).   EUL
Imperfect. Book I and all after C3 wanting.

Cecaria Tragic. del Epicuro Napolitano [It. 41]
1223 EPICURO, *Napolitano, pseud.* Tragicomedia del Epicuro Napolitano, intitulata la Cecaria, nuouamente aggiuntoui un bellissimo lamento del geloso con la luminaria non pui posta in luce, con ogni diligentia reuista, corretta, & ristampata. 8° Venice, V. de Ravanni, 1532.   EUL
Bought in Paris, 1608.

1224 GEOPONICA. Constantino Cesare di li scelti et utilissimi documēti de l'agricoltura . . . [*Tr.* N. Vitelli.] 8° Venice, G.B. da Borgofranco, 1542.   EUL
Title wanting.

1225 GESUALDO, Filippo. Plutosofia . . . nella quale si spiega l'arte della memoria con altre cose notabili pertinenti . . . 4° Padua, P. Megietti, 1592.   EUL
With the signature of William Fowler.

1226* GIOVIO, Paolo, *Bp.* Commentario de le cose de Turchi . . . 8° [Venice,] 1538.   AUCT
Copy in EUL.

1227 GIOVIO, Paolo, *Bp.* Dialogo dell' imprese militari e amorose . . . et del S.G. Symeneoni . . . Con vn ragionamento di M.L. Domenichi, nel medesimo soggetto . . . 8° Lyons, G. Rouille, 1574.   PR

1228 GROTO, Luigi. La dalida tragedia noua . . . Nouamente stampata. 12° Venice, A. Zoppini and nephews, 1595.   EUL
Bought in Edinburgh, 1609.

Rime del Luigi Groto cieco d'Adria [It. 19]
1229* GROTO, Luigi. Delle rime . . .

1230 GROTO, Luigi. Il thesoro comedia noua . . . Nuouamente stampata. 12° Venice, A. Zoppini and nephews, 1599. EUL
Bought in Edinburgh, 1609.

Il pastor fido Madrigali di Baptista Guarini [It. 15]
1231 GUARINI, Giovanni Battista. Il pastor fido, tragicomedia pastorale . . . Nuouamente ricorretto, espurgato . . . 12° Treviso, F. Zanetti, 1603.   EUL

1232 GUAZZO, Stefano. La ciuil conuersatione . . . diuisa in quattro libri . . . Nouamente dall' istesso auttore corretta, & in diuersi luoghi di molte cose, non meno vtili che piaceuoli, ampliata. 8° Venice, G. B. Somasco, 1580.   EUL

l'Hore di ricreatione di M. lud. Guicciardini [It. 16]
1233* GUICCIARDINI, Lodovico. L'hore di ricreatione.

1234 HERODOTUS. Herodoto Alicarnaseo historico delle guerre de Greci & de Persi, tradotto di Greco in lingua Italiana per il conte Mattheo Maria Boiardo, di nouo ristampata, & con summa diligentia reuisto & corretto . . . 8° Venice, B. de Bindoni for M. Sessa, 1539.   EUL

Leone Hibreo [It. 14]
1235* LEONE, *Ebreo* [Judah Abravanel]. ? Dialoghi d'amore.

Lesione della Gelosia [It. 34]
1236 LEZZIONE. Lessione della gelosia letta nella Academia Fiorentina. 4°? Orvieto, 1585.   SALE
Present location unknown.

della eccellenza libri due d'Horatio Lombordelli senese [It. 37]
1237* LOMBARDELLI, Orazio. Della eccellenza libri due.

Berinice comedia del S. Giou. Francasto [It. 40]
1238* LOREDANO, Giovanni Francesco, *the Elder.* Berenice. Comedia.

1239 MACHIAVELLI, Niccolò. Discorsi . . . Sopra la prima deca di Tito Liuio . . . 8° Venice [house of Aldus ?], 1552.   EUL
Many passages marked, probably by Drummond. Not recorded in Renouard, *Alde,* or in his list of Aldine forgeries.

1240 MACHIAVELLI, Niccolò. Historie . . . 8° Venice, Comin da Trino, 1540.   EUL
Date on colophon is 1541. Title mutilated, with Drummond's signature over the repair.

il contrasto Amoroso di Mutio Manfredi [It. 60]
1241* MANFREDI, Muzio. Il Contrasto Amoroso, pastorale.

Le maniere di versi Toscani [It. 27]
1242* MANIERE.
Not identified.

Manutius of Critoun [?] [List E]
1243* ? MANUZIO, Aldo, *the Younger.*
Manutius wrote at least one short piece on James Crichton (the Admirable Crichton).

lettere volgari di diuersi nobilissimi huomini [It. 29]
1244* MANUZIO, Paolo, *ed.* Lettere volgari di diuersi nobilissimi huomini, et excellentissimi ingegni, scritte in diuerse materie . . .

Arcadia de Felice Morinella [It. 58]
1245* MARINELLA, Lucrezia. Arcadia felice.

Creatione del mondo del S. Gasparo Murtola [It. 11]
1246* MURTOLA, Gasparo. Della creatione del mondo, poema sacro . . . Giorni sette, canti sedici.

Battaglie di Hier. Mutio Guistiopolitan [It. 44]
1247* MUZIO, Girolamo. Battaglie di H. Mutio (in diffesa dell' Ital. lingua) . . .

1248 [NOE [BIANCHI], *a Franciscan.*] Viagio da Venetia al sancto sepulchro & al mõte Synai piu copiosamẽte descritto de li altri cõ disegni de paesi: citade: porti: & chiesie & li sancti loghi con molte altre sanctimo nie che qui si trouano designate & descritte come sono nelli luoghi lor proprij.
8° Venice, J. Tacuino de Trino for A. Grimano, 1523.   EUL

Discorso di Iason Denores intorna la poesia [It. 35]
1249 NORES, Giasone di. Discorso . . . intorno à que' principii, cause et accrescimenti, che la comedia, la tragedia, et il poema heroico riceuono dalla, philosophia morale, et ciuile, e da governatori delle republiche.
4° Padua, P. Meieto, 1587.   SALE
Present location unknown. Colophon has 1536.

1250 NOSSENIO, Johan Maria. Annali suopra la statua di Nabuchodonosore monarcha di Babilonia, ne la quale sono inserte molte figure con la loro esplicatione . . .
4° Dresden, H. Schütz, 1602.   EUL
With twelve plates and an inset.

1251 NOSTREDAME, Jean de. Le vite delli piu celebri et antichi primi poeti prouenzali che fiorir-

no nel tempo delli ré di Napoli, & conti di Prouenza, liquali hanno insegnato à tutti il poetar vulgare. Raccolte dall'opere de diuersi excellenti scrittori, ch'in quella lingua le scrissero: in lingua Franzese da Gio: di Nostra Dama poste: & hora da Gio: Giudici in Italiana tradotte, e date in luce.
8° Lyons, A. Marsilij, 1575.   EUL

1252 OCHINO, Bernardino. Il catechismo, o vero institutione Christiana . . . in forma di dialogo . . .
8° Basle, [P. Perna,] 1561.   EUL

1253 OCHINO, Bernardino. Disputa . . . intorno alla presenza del corpo di Giesu Christo nel sacramento della cena.
8° Basle, [P. Perna,] 1561.   EUL

1254 OCHINO, Bernardino. Prediche . . . Nouellamente ristampate & con grande diligenta riuedute & corrette. [In 2 parts.]
8° [Geneva, 1548?]   EUL
The first part has an inscription in Drummond's hand; the second part, which was given to EUL in 1826 by David Laing, has some annotations in what may be Drummond's hand.

1255 OCHINO, Bernardino. Prediche . . . nomate laberinti del libero, o ver seruo arbitrio, prescienza, predestinatione, & libertà diuina, & del modo per vscirne.
8° Basle, [1569].   EUL

1256 PANCIERA, Bartholomeo. Paradosso delle imperfettioni e miserie del 'huomo . . .
8° [Late 16th cent.?]   EUL
Imperfect. Title and all after E8 wanting. Title taken from the head-title.

1257 PANIGAROLA, Francesco, *Bp.* Cento ragionamenti sopra la passione di n. Signore . . . Diuisi in quattro parti . . .
8° Venice, P. Dusinelli, 1597.   EUL

Le Nuoue fiamme di L. paterno [It. 46]
1258* PATERNO, Lodovico. Le nuoue fiamme . . . partiti in cinque libri. Il primo di sonnetti, e canzoni pastorali. Il secondo di stanze. Il terzo di elegie. Il quarto di nenie, e tumuli; e l'ultimo di egloghe marittime, amorose . . .

Della poetica di Fr. Patrici [It. 42]
1259 PATRIZI, Francesco. Della poetica di F. Patrici, la deca istoriale, nella quale . . . oltre a' poeti, e lor poemi . . . si fan palesi, tutte le cose compagne, e seguaci dell' antiche poesie . . .
4° Ferrara, V. Baldini, 1586.   WORC
Bought in Paris, 1608.

1260 PENSA, Girolamo. Epigrammi toscani . . .
4° Monteregale, [L. Torrentino,] 1570.   EUL

Il Petrarcha [It. 10]
1261   PETRARCHA, Francesco. [*Canzoniere.*]
Il Petrarca di nuouo ristampato et diligentemente
corretto.
24° Venice, N. Misserino, 1596.   EUL

*Chronica del le vite de pontifici par
M. F. Petrarcha* [It. 49]
1262* PETRARCHA, Francesco. [*Supposititious
work.*] Chronica delle vite de Pontefici et Impera-
tori Romani . . .

1263   PIETRO, Aretino. Il capitolo . . . in laude
de lo Imperatore, & à sua maesta da lui proprio
recitato.
8° [Venice? 1543?]   PR
Title wanting. Bound with 1264, 1266.

Dialogo di Pietro Aretino [It. 51]
1264   PIETRO, Aretino. Le carte parlanti,
dialogo.
8° Venice, B. detto l'Imperadore for M. Sessa,
1545.   PR
Title and all after s6 wanting. Bought in Bourges,
1608. Bound with 1263, 1266.

1265   PIETRO, Aretino. Quattro comedie del
diuino Pietro Aretino. Cioè il marescalco. La
talanta. La cortegiana l'hipocrito. Nouellamente
ritornate . . .
8° [Venice?] 1588.   EUL

1266   PIETRO, Aretino. La uita di San Tomaso,
signor d'Aquino . . .
8° Venice, G. de Farri and brothers for M. Biago
of Perugia, 1543.   PR
Title wanting. Bound with 1263, 1264.

I Romanzi di M. Giou. battista Pigna [It. 43]
1267* PIGNA, Giovanni Battista. I romanzi . . .
divisi in tre libri, ne quali della poesia et della
vita dell' Ariosto con nuovo modo si tratta.

1268* POMI, David de'. Discorso intorno a
l'humana miseria, e sopr'al modo di fuggirla . . .
Composto . . . à maggior intelligenza dell' Ecclesi-
aste di Salomone; da esso autore tradotto e
dichiarato.
8° Venice, G. Ziletti, 1572.   AUCT

la cinthia comedia di G. Baptista della Porta
[It. 21]
1269* PORTA, Giovanni Battista della. La
Cintia; comedia.

ciriffo Caluaneo di luca Pulci [It. 31]
1270   PULCI, Luca. Ciriffo Caluaneo . . . con la
giostra del magnifico Lorenzo de Medici, insieme
con le epistole composte dal medesimo Pulci.
Nouamente ristampate.
4° Florence, house of Giunta, 1572.   SALE
Present location unknown.

1271* RICCI, Francesco. Descrittione della nati-
vita, & morte di Carlo Quinto Imperatore, &
trionfo fatto nella mag. citta di Bologna nella sua
coronatione; con la pompa funerale fatta in
Brusselle alli 29 de Decembre 1558 per la felice,
& immortal memoria di sua S.M.C. tradotta di
lingua fiammenga in Italiana, per M. Francesco
Ricci di Padoua.   PRESS
PRESS has 'Vinegia. 1591'. Not traced.

Rime del Sig. Cesare Rinaldi [It. 18]
1272* RINALDI, Cesare. Delle Rime . . . parte
terza . . .

Discorsi del conte Annibale Romei [It. 61]
1273* ROMEI, Annibale, *Count.* Discorsi . . .

1274   RUGGERI, Carlo. La reina di Scotia.
Tragedia . . .
4°? Naples, 1604.   SALE
Bound with: Nicolo Rossi, *Discorsi intorno alla
tragedia* (Vicenza, 1590) and Antonfrancesco
Cirni Corso, *Discorso . . . come si possano in buona
parte rimovere sei principali abusi de Christiane-
simo* (Rome, 1564). Ruggeri's work is not listed
in Scott. Present location unknown.

Orationi di Ruzzante [It. 54]
1275* RUZZANTE, *pseud.* [Angelo Beolco.]
Tre orationi di Ruzzante recitate in lingua rustica
alli illustris. Signori Cardinali Cornali & Pisani . . .

1276   SALUSTE DU BARTAS, Guillaume de.
La diuina settimana: cioè i sette giorni della
creation del mondo. Tradotta di rima Francese in
verso sciolto Italiano [by Ferrante Guisone].
12° Venice, G.B. Ciotti, 1593.   EUL
With the signature of William Fowler.

1277   SALUSTE DU BARTAS, Guillaume de. La
diuina settimana; cioè, i sette giorni della creatione
del mondo . . . tradotta in rima Francese in verso
sciolto Italiano dal Sig. Ferrante Guisone. Et in
questa quinta impressione ricorretta, con le sue
figure adornata.
12° Venice, G.B. Ciotti, 1601.   EUL
Leaves H1 and H2 are uncut.

Arcadia di Iacobo Sanazaro [It. 53]
1278   SANNAZARO, Jacopo. Arcadia . . . di
nuouo ristampata, con le annotationi di Thomaso
Porcacchi, & ripurgata per M. Borgarutio Bor-
garucci. Con la vita dell' auttore, descritta dal
medesmo, & con la dichiaratione di tutte le uoci
oscure, che son nell' opera.
12° Venice, P. Marinelli, 1589.   EUL

1279   SCOGLI. Scogli del Christiano naufragio,
quali va scoprendo la santa chiesa di Christo. Alli
suoi diletti figliuoli, perche da quelli possano
allontanarsi.
8° n.p., 1618.   EUL

Le Troiane Tragedia di l. Dolce [It. 23]
1280 SENECA, Lucius Annaeus. Le Troiane
tragedia di M. Lodovico Dolce. Recitata in
Venetia l'anno MD LXVI. Di nuouo ristampata,
& con somma diligenza ricorretta.
8° Venice, P. Ugolino, 1593.   EUL

1281 STRASOLINI, Nicolo. Discorso . . .
4° [Venice, c. 1591].   EUL
Title wanting; title taken from head-title.

Discorsi sopra Tacit de Cauriana [List E]
1282* TACITUS, Publius Cornelius. Discorsi del
Signor F. Cavriana . . . sopra i primi cinque libri
[of the Annals] di Cornelio Tacito. Nelli quali
si trattano molte cose al governo del publico, &
delle corte appertinenti, & insieme varii casi
seguiti, nelle presenti guerre civili di Francia . . .
Almost certainly the edition of Florence, 1600
(from which the title is taken) which has Tacitus'
text in Latin and Italian.

1283 TARSIA, Giovanni Maria, *ed.* Historia del
beatissimo Gregorio Papa; nella quale, oltre alla
santa dottrina, si truouano ancora, ad essempio di
tutti i Christiani, assai vite, cosi di buoni come
di cattiui: altrimenti chiamata dialoghi. Di nuouo
ristampata, & riordinata . . .
8° Venice, 1582.   EUL

Rime et prose del sig. T. Tasso foure Tomes [It. 4]
1284 TASSO, Torquato. Opere.
12° Ferrara, G. Vasalini, 1583–7.   SALE
6 vols. (in 4?). In a letter the bookseller Constable
mentions this work as offered for sale in 1815,
and due to be restored 'to its old abode at Hawthornden'. NLS, Constable Letter Books, MS 7,89
f. 311.
Bought in London, 1610. Present location unknown.

*Gierusalem conquistata del sig. T. Tasso of the
edition of Paris* [It. 1]
1285 TASSO, Torquato. Di Gerusalemme conquistata . . . libri xxiiii [ed. Angelo Ingegneri].
12° Paris, A. L'Angelier, (1595).   HUL
The date is given on the title-page as 'MDLCXV'.

Gierusalem & [conquistata?] printet at [ ] with [ ]
[It. 2]
1286* TASSO, Torquato. ? Di Gerusalemme
conquistata.
Presumably Drummond had not the book by
him while making this entry, and intended to fill
in the blanks later.

1287* TASSO, Torquato. La Gerusalemme
liberata.   AUCT

lettere famigliar del S. T. Tasso [It. 5]
1288* TASSO, Torquato. Delle lettere familiari.

Il Re Torismond del S. T. Tasso [It. 32]
1289 TASSO, Torquato. Il Re Torrismondo,
tragedia, accomodata di nuouo in molti luochi
secondo la intentione dell'autore con una gionta
del medesimo.
4° Ferrara, G. C. Cagnacini and brothers, 1587.
Present location unknown.   SALE

1290 TASSO, Torquato. Il Rinaldo . . . Di
nuouo riueduto, & con diligenza corretto: aggiun-
teui gli argomenti, & allegorie à ciascun canto.
12° Ferrara, G. C. Cagnaccini and brothers, [1590?]
Part 2 of a collection.   EUL

le sette giornate de S. T. Tasso [It. 3]
1291* TASSO, Torquato. Le sette giornate de
Mondo creato.

lettere di M. C. Tolemei [It. 25]
1292* TOLOMEI, Claudio. Delle lettere . . .
libri sette . . .

1293 TOMAI, Tomaso. Idea del giardino del
mondo . . .
8° Venice, D. Farri, 1603.   EUL

1294 UBALDINI, Petruccio. La vita di Carlo
Magno imperadore: scritta in lingua Italiana, &
di nueuo corretta & ristampata . . .
4° [London, R. Field,] 1599.   EUL
STC 24487

Dictionario di p. venuti [It. 48]
1295 VENUTI, Filippo. Dictionarium Latinum
. . .
8° Venice, G. D. Micheli, 1589.   EUL
With the register of the complete dictionary,
of which this volume forms only the second part.

*Trattato di Pietro Vettori delle lodi de gli
vliui* [It. 38]
1296 VETTORI, Pietro. Trattato . . . delle lodi,
et della coltiuatione de gl'vliui. Di nuouo ristampato.
4° Florence, house of Giunta, 1574.   EUL
Bought in Paris, 1607.

Discorso d'intorno Tumori di Nicolao Viti [It. 33]
1297 VITI, Nicolao. Discorso d'intorno a
tumori ed ossi frontespiziali.
4° Rome, A. Gardano and F. Coattini, 1585.
Bought in Paris, 1608.   WELL

1298* ZANOBI, Antonio. Lamento di caprarola
& conforto d'amaranto ambi pastori nella morte
dell. illustrissimo Card. Farnese di F. Antonio
Zanobi Servita, da Fiorenza.   PRESS
PRESS has 'Rome, 1589'. Not traced.

1299 * ZINO, Benedetto, *Trevigiano*. Sonetti fatti ad imitatione del Petracha.   AUCT
AUCT has 'Treuigi 1589'. Not traced.

Translations: (into English) See 709, 719, 800, 817, 897, 931, 934, 940, 954, 1384. (into French) See 963, 977, 989, 992, 995, 1044, 1053, 1054, 1058, 1059, 1091, 1092, 1116, 1121, 1132, 1139, 1143, 1148, 1156, 1162, 1163, 1169.

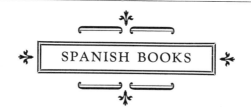

SPANISH BOOKS

1300 ALEMÁN, Mateo. Primera parte de Guzman de Alfarache.
12° Madrid, V. de Castro, 1600.   SALE
Present location unknown.

1301 BIBLE. La Biblia, que es, los sacros libros del vieio y nueuo testamento. Trasladada en Español [by Casiodoro de Reyna].
4° [Basle, T. Guarin,] 1569.   EUL

1302 BIBLE. Psalms. Los Psalmos de Dauid. Metrificados en lengua castellana por Iuan le Quesne [Juan de Enzinas]. Conforme a la traducion verdadera d'el texto hebreo.
8° [Geneva,] 1606.   EUL
And 'Los mandamientos de Dios' (in verse), and 'El cantico de Simeon'.

Boscan [Sp. 7]
1303 BOSCAN ALMOGAVER, Juan. Las obras de Boscan y algunas de Garcilasso dela Vega, repartidas en quatro libros. De nueuo enmendadas . . .
12° Antwerp, G. Smits for P. Bellère, 1576. EUL

1304 CARION, Johann. Suma y compendio de todas las chronicas del mundo, desde su principio hasta el año presente, traduzida por el Bachiller Francisco Thamara . . .
12° Antwerp, M. Nuyts, 1555.   EUL
And *Tabla y repertorio de todas las personas y cosas memorables, desde el principio del mundo, hasta el año presente de M.D.LV.*

1305 CASAS, Christoval de las. Vocabulario de las dos lenguas toscana y castellana. [In 2 parts.]
4° Seville, A. Escriuano for F. de Aguilar, 1570.   EUL
Title, all before A1, and all after 2D8 wanting. With the signature of Simion Grahame, author of *The anatomie of humors*.

1306 CATECISMO. Catechismo à saber es formulario para instruyr los mochachos en la Christiandad: hecho a manera de dialogo, donde el ministro de la y glesia pregunta, y el mochacho responde, transladado de frances en Español.
1550.   PRESS
Not traced.

Galatea [Sp. 8]
1307 * CERVANTES SAAVEDRA, Miguel de. Galatea, diuida en seys libros.
Or a translation of Giovanni della Casa's *Galatea?*

1308 CIEZA DE LEON, Pedro de. Parte primera de la chronica del Peru.
8° Antwerp, J. Laet for J. Bellère, 1554. SALE
Present location unknown. Quaritch (in error) gives this edition as a 12°.

1309 HUARTE, Juan. Examen de ingenios para las sciencias, donde se muestra la differencia de habiliades que ay en los hombres, y el genero de letras que à cada uno responde en particular . . .
8° Leyden, J.J. Paets, 1591.   MORG

1310 HUARTE, Juan. Examen de ingenios para las sciencias. Donde se muestra la diferencia de habilidades, que ay enlos hombres; y el genere de letras, que a cada vno responde en particular.
12° [Antwerp,] house of Plantin, 1603.   EUL

1311 LAZARILLO, de Tormes. La vida de Lazarillo de Tormes, y de sus fortunas y aduersidades.
12° [Antwerp,] house of Plantin, 1602.   EUL

1312 * LUIS, de Granada, Dominican. Oraciones y exercicios de devoción, recopilados de diversos graves autores . . .   AUCT
AUCT has 'Seville, 1599', an edition not listed by Palau.

1313 MENESES, Alonso de. Reportorio de caminos . . . Añadido el camino de Madrid a Roma . . .
24° Alcala, S. Martinez, 1576.   EUL
Colophon dated 1579. A reprint of the first edition? Not recorded in Palau.

la Diana de George De Montemayor [Sp. 1]
1314* MONTEMAYOR, Jorge de. Los siete libros de la Diana.

1315 OVIDIUS NASO, Publius. Las transformaciones de Ouidio en lengua Española, repartidas en quinze libros, con las allegorias al fin dellos, y sus figuras, para prouecho de los artifices . . . [Tr. Jorge Bustamente.]
8° Antwerp, P. Bellère, 1595.   EUL

Dictionario por el doctor Ian Pallet [Sp. 6]
1316* PALET, Jean. Diccionario . . . de la lengua española y francesa . . . Dictionarie . . . de la langue espagnole et françoise (Dictionarie . . . de la lengue françoise et espagnole . . .) [In 2 parts.]

1317 PINEDA, Hernando de. Flor de las rosas. Tratado de la cofradia d'el Sancto Rosario.
8° Antwerp, D. Vervliet, 1571.   EUL

1318 PREGUNTAS. Preguntas y respuestas sobre la importancia del acto de contricion: y la diferencia que ay entre ella, y la atricion: y los actos particulares, que en la contricion se hazen. Agradables, y muy prouechoses para todo genero de gente.
16° Madrid, J. de la Cuesta, 1608.   EUL

1319* REPORTORIO. Reportorio de los tiempos, el mas copioso que hasta agora se ha impresso: en q̃ va añadido muchas cosas de memoria acontecidas en espanna. 1545.   PRESS
Edition not traced. AUCT has 'Medina del Campo. 1545'.

1320 [ROJAS, Fernando de.] Celestina. Tragicomedia de Calisto y Melibea. En la qual se contienen . . . muchas sententias filosofales, y auisos muy necessarios para mancebos . . .
16° Antwerp, house of Plantin, 1599.   EUL
With the motto, in Drummond's hand:
'Ò cipresso ò palma'.

1321 SANDOVAL, Prudencio de, *Bp.* Primera parte de la vida y hechos del emperador Carlos quinto . . .
2° Valladolid, S. de Canas, 1604.   GUL
With the motto, in Drummond's hand:
'Ò cipresso ò palma'.

Carcel de amor [Sp. 2]
1322* SAN PEDRO, Diego de. Carcel de amor.

Floresta [Sp. 4]
1323* SANTA CRUZ DE DUEÑAS, Melchior de. Floresta española de apotegmas, o sentencias fabia y graciosamente dichas de algunos Españoles . . .

Silua de varios Romancez [Sp. 5]
1324* SILVA. Silua de varios romances . . .

1325 VARGAS, Balthazar de. Breue relacion en octaua rima de la iornada que a hecho el ill^mo y ex^mo señor duque d'Alua desde España hasta los estados de Flandes.
8° Antwerp, A. Tavernier for the author, 1568.
     EUL

Arcadia y versos de Vega Carpio [Sp. 3]
1326* VEGA CARPIO, Lope Felix de. Arcadia. Prosas y versos.

1327 XIMENEZ AYLLON, Diego. Sonetos a illustres varones deste felicissimo y catholico excercito y corte de su excelencia . . .
8° Antwerp, J. Laet, 1569.   EUL

Translations: (into English) See 790, 822, 873.
(into French) See 959, 960, 961, 962, 1040, 1060, 1061, 1070, 1140, 1151, 1177.

MANUSCRIPTS

1328 ALEXANDER, William, *Earl of Stirling.*
Doomesday or the Great day of the Lords Iudgement by Sir William Alexander knight.   EUL
Paper, 249×171 mm., ff. 62. Secretary hand. Described in Alexander's *Works* (STS), II, xliv-xlvi, where it is designated MS. H, and dated to c. 1613. The annotations are not in Drummond's hand.

1329* ALEXANDER, William, *Earl of Stirling.*
A Relation of the Conspiracie of Gowrie.   AUCT

1330 ANDERSON, Henry, *of Perth.* Amaryllis ingrata. Musarum querimonia. Ad sereniss. potentissimumque regem Ia. 6. Perthanam urbem ingredientem 5. cal. Iunias 1580 panegyris.   EUL
Paper, 304×203 mm., ff. 22. In three different hands (one italic, two secretary).
There are two copies of the first two poems.

1331 ANHALT, *family of.* Geonologia illustrissimę familię Anhaltinę quatuorcentis quinquaginta tantum annorum incipiens ab Alberto Urso, et sequens usq ad presens.   EUL
Paper, 570×433 mm., s. sh.
Latest date on pedigree 1603.

1332* ANSWER. An Answere to the Chamelion.
                                           AUCT

1333 ASHBY, William, *English Ambassador in Scotland.* The offers mad by her Ma^tties Embassador of England in her ma^tties name and her counsell.   EUL
Paper, 462×340 mm., s. sh. Signed 'W. Asheby'. Dated on endorsement in another hand 4 August 1588.

1334 BASTON, William. Villielmi Bastone A⟨ ⟩ in Bellum de Banockburne. Carmen. [With other verses on Bannockburn.]   EUL
Paper, 179×128 mm., ff. 8. Cropped.
Printed in Goodall's edition (Edinburgh, 1759) of Joannes de Fordun's Scotichronicon, II, 251-5.

1335 BELRINNES, *Battle of.* The discourse of the battell of Belrinness.   EUL
Paper, 324×264 mm., s. sh.

1336 BOTHWELL, Francis Stewart, *5th Earl of.* [Letter to David Black, Minister of St. Andrews, urging him not to heed lies and rumour; describing Bothwell's own pitiful state, and his present innocence of intrigues with the 'papist Lords'.] Paper, 384×300 mm., s. sh. Described on endorsement as 'Letter Apologetick 1594'.   EUL

1337 BOTHWELL, James Hepburn, *4th Earl of.* The testament and latter will of the Lord Bodwell. Paper, 311×210 mm, s. sh.   EUL
Another copy, in another hand: paper, 247× 212 mm, s. sh. This death-bed confession at Malmö, in which Bothwell confesses to witchcraft, treachery and seduction, is considered to be a forgery. See R. Gore-Brown, *Lord Bothwell,* p. 454.

1338* BUCHANAN, George. Epistola ad Regem Iacobum 6.   AUCT

1339* CAMDEN, William. Nuntius Scoto-Britannus, or, a paire of Spectacles for W. Camden, to looke vpon North-Britain.   AUCT

1340* COCKBURN, *Sir* William, *Bart.* Anti-Baronius pro Traduce.   AUCT

1341* COWPER, William, *Bp.* Lectures on Josuah.   AUCT

1342* CRASSUS, Nicolaus. Antiparœnesis ad Cæsarem Baronium, pro Venetia Republica.
                                           AUCT

1343* CRICHTON, James. Iacobus Crittonus. Ad Urbem Venetam carmen.   AUCT

1344* CUJACIUS, Jacobus. Testament.   AUCT
There is a copy of this among the Hawthornden MSS, NLS. 2059, f. 132.

1345 DANIEL, Samuel. Hymens Triumph.
                                           EUL
Paper, 197×158 mm, ff. 35. Secretary hand, with corrections and insertions in Daniel's own hand. *Hymens Triumph* was written for the marriage in 1614 of Robert Ker, Lord Roxborough, to Jean Drummond, and this MS., which has Daniel's dedicatory verse to 'the Ladie of Roxborough', was probably a presentation copy to the bride. See Joan Rees, *Samuel Daniel* (Liverpool, 1964), p. 158 and W. W. Greg, '*Hymens Triumph* and the Drummond MS.', *MLQ*, VI (1903), pp. 59-64.

1346* DONNE, John. An Hymne to the Saints, and Marquis Hamilton.   AUCT
Written at the request of Sir Robert Kerr in memory of James Hamilton, Marquis of Hamilton, who died 1624/5 apparently of poison. The poem is printed in H.J.C. Grierson's edition of Donne's *Poems* (Oxford, 1912 & reprints), II, 288–90.

1347* DONNE, John. A Satyre.   AUCT
Donne wrote six satires, including one on Coryat's *Crudities*.

1348* DOUGLAS, William. De Quadratura Circuli tractatus demonstrativus M.S. autog. 1626.   AUCT

1349* DRUMMOND, *family of.* The Genealogie of the House of Drummond.   AUCT

1350 EGLISHAM, George. Georgii Eglis⟨semmii⟩ aduersus Andreæ Meluini cauillum in aram regiam, epigrammata prophylactica.   EUL
Paper, 325×210 mm, s. sh. With the first part of Melville's epigram. Printed in Eglisham's *Duellum Poeticum*, London, 1618.

1351 ELIZABETH I, *Queen of England.* [Letter to Queen Anne, wife of James VI, professing friendship. Signed 'Your verey affectionate sistar Elizabeth R.' Dated Richmond, 28th. January, 1595.]   EUL
Paper, 222×289 mm, s. sh., somewhat mutilated.

1352* ELIZABETH I, *Queen of England.* A Letter to the Earle of Morton. Greenwich 1579.   AUCT

1353* ELIZABETH I, *Queen of England.* Lettre a la Royne d'Escosse, Greenwich, 1594.   AUCT

1354* ELIZABETH I, *Queen of England.* A Register of all that passed between the Commissioners of James Prince of Scotland, and Marie Queene, before Elizabeth Queene of England, and Her Commissioners. 1568 Anno.
                    AUCT

1355* ESSAY. An Essay, Demonstrative of Bounty.   AUCT

1356* ESSEX, Robert Devereux, *2nd Earl of.* The Coppie of a Letter to Queene Elizabeth.
                    AUCT

1357* FIVE. The fyve Sences.   AUCT

1358 FORDUN, Joannes de. Johannis de Fordun chronica gentis Scotorum.   BODL
With the inscriptions: 'Mr James Drummond, 1650, Gifted theis book to Coronall Fairfax, the 17 of December anno 1650.' And in Lord Fairfax's hand: 'It was sent to me by Lady Hathornden,

widow to the famous poet, William Drummond, by the hands of her husband's brother, vizt. Mr. James Drummond (here superscribinge).' The work is often known as the *Scotichronicon*, and is a medieval history of Scotland.

1359 FOWLER, William. The Tarantula of loue: by M. William Fowler.   EUL
Paper, 183×155 mm, ff. 36. In Fowler's autograph, with his signature on the last two leaves. The title and author's name is in Drummond's hand. Printed in Fowler's *Works* (STS), I, 136 *et seq.* and described III, xlix.

1360* FOWLER, William. Verses, dedicated to the Ladie Thirlstane.   AUCT

1361 GARNETT, Henry, *Jesuit.* [Document, beginning:] Whether our church be hereticall holding the doctrine of the Scriptures, the three creedes, and the foure first councells.   EUL
Two copies: 1. Paper, 414×306 mm, s. sh. Endorsed 'Garnetus. Depositions'.
2. Paper, 400×305 mm, s. sh. Endorsed 'Garnetts answers to some articles'.

1362* GOWRIE, John Ruthven, *Earl of.* A Letter to the Kingis M. Padua, 1595.   AUCT

1363* HARINGTON, *Sir* John. A New-Yeares Gift to King James.   AUCT
Printed in *Nugæ Antiquæ*, ed. H. Harington (London, 1804), I, 325-35, from a transcription made in 1802 from Drummond's copy.

1364 HENRY, *Prince of Wales.* [Duty letter in Latin to his father James VI showing his ability at the age of nine. Dated Stirling, 18th. February, 1601/2.]   EUL
Paper, 283×193 mm, s. sh. Described by T. Birth, *The life of Henry, Prince of Wales*, p. 411.

1365 JAMES I, *King.* Tabula consanguinitatis inter Christianam Lotharingicam, Ferdinandi, Magni Hetruriæ Ducis, uxorem, et Jacobum Steuartum, ejusdemque conjugem Annam Altiburgicam, Britannorum Reges fœlicissimos.
                    EUL
Paper, 460×335 mm, s. sh.

1366 KALENDAR. [Kalendar and astronomical tables, *etc.*]   EUL
Vellum, 172×150 mm, ff. 40. Latin. Cent. XV [1482?], Scottish (Coupar-Angus). The Kalendar is Cistercian, and the book belonged to the Cistercian Priory of Coupar-Angus. For a full description and list of contents see Catherine R. Borland, *A descriptive catalogue of the Western Medieval manuscripts in Edinburgh University Library* (Edinburgh, 1916), pp. 201–2.

1367* KERR, *Sir* Robert, *1st Earl of Ancram.*
Psalmes in English verses, to the measures of the
French and Dutch.   AUCT

1368* LA GOUTTE, *Le Sieur de.* La Cannelle.   AUCT

1369 LA ROCHE DE CHANDIEU, Antoine,
called Sadeel. [Letter of, to James VI of Scotland,
dated La Rochelle, 20th. July, 1587.]   EUL
Paper, 297×211 mm, ff. 2. In French.

1370 LEICESTER, Robert Dudley, *Earl of.*
[Letter to the Earl of Morton, dated 7th September,
1572, and signed 'Yr L. assured louing frend R.
Leycester'.]   EUL
Paper, 436×320 mm, s. sh.

1371* LINDSAY, *Sir* David. A Satyre of the three
Estates.   AUCT

1372 MAITLAND, *Sir* Richard, *of Lethington.*
The selected poemes of Sr Richard Metellan of
Lydington.   EUL
Paper, 186×143 mm, ff. 72. Secretary hand.
This MS. was used for the Maitland Club edition
of Maitland's poems edited by Joseph Bain, 1830.

1373 MAITLAND, Thomas. Thomæ Metelani ad
serenissimam principem Elizabetha Anglorum
Reginam Epistola.   EUL
Paper, 213×160 mm, ff. 21. Secretary hand.

1374 MARY, *Queen of Scots.* The declaration of
the will of the maist mychty and wertuous prēcess
Marie quene of Scotland, dowarure of france,
duryng the tyme of hir extreme maladie, with the
preirs and exhortations maid be hir.   EUL
Paper, 412×305 mm, s. sh. Printed in J. Small's
article 'Queen Mary at Jedburgh in 1566', *Pro-
ceedings of the Society of Antiquaries of Scotland*
(1880/1), pp. 227–9.

1375 MARY, *Queen of Scots.* [Letter of, to
Queen Elizabeth I. Dated 8th. November, 1582.]   EUL
Paper, 313×230 mm, ff. 6. In French. Printed in
Labanoff, *Lettres, instructions et mémoires de
Marie Stuart* (London, 1844), V, 318–38, from a
Cotton MS. in the B.M.

1376* MARY, *Queen of Scots.* Tetrasticha ou
Quatrains a Son fils.   AUCT

1377 MELVILLE, Andrew. Magistri Andreæ
Melvini Epigramma in aram Regiam interpolatum
& à se castigatum αυτογραφον.   EUL
Paper, 316×216 mm, s. sh.

1378 MELVILLE, Andrew. Epitaphium Alexandri Arbuthneti. In Alexandrum Arbuthnetum &

Thomam Smetoniam, duo nostræ gentis lumina,
ad Septemtriones & Meridiem nuper extincta.   EUL
Paper, 236×200 mm, s. sh. The two pieces are
printed together in the *Delitiæ Poetarum Scotorum*
(Amsterdam, 1637), II, 120–1, from which the
titles are quoted.

1379 MELVILLE, Andrew. A. Melvinus H.
R⟨ollo⟩co S.D. [Latin verses.]   EUL
Paper, 306×208 mm, s. sh.

1380 MELVILLE, Andrew. Præfatio Magistri
Andreæ Melvini in poema de gestis Scotorum ad
Henricum Principem αυτογραφον.   EUL
Paper, 411×333 mm, s. sh.

1381 MONTGOMERY, Alexander. Poems.   EUL
Paper, 181×135 mm, ff. 83. The Margaret Ker
(Kerr, or Cer) MS., the chief source for Mont-
gomery's known work. For a detailed description
see Montgomery's *Poems*, ed. James Cranstoun
(STS), xlvii–xlviii.

1382* MURRAY, John. Certaine Sonnets.   AUCT

1383 PARMA, Alexander Farnese, *Duke of.*
[Letter of, thanking James VI of Scotland for
protection offered to Spanish survivors of the
Armada landed in Scotland. Dated Brussels, 4th
May, 1598.]   EUL
Paper, 412×320 mm, s. sh. In French.

1384 PETRARCA, Francesco. The triumphs of
the most famous poet Mr Frances Petrarke
translated out of italian into inglish by Mr Wm.
Fouler P. of Hauicke.   EUL
Paper, 325×220 mm, ff. 43. Secretary hand, not
in Fowler's autograph.
Printed in Fowler's *Works* (STS), I, 13 *et seq.*
and described III, xlix.

1385* PISSAMIO, S^r *of Buram.* The Copie of a
Letter written by him to the Pope Paulo Quinto.   AUCT

1386* RALEIGH, *Sir* Walter. A Relation of S^r
Walter Ralieghs Speach and Behaviour at the
tyme of his Death.   AUCT

1387* ROLLOCK, Hercules. Apologia contra
Theonis Calumnias.   AUCT

1388* ROLLOCK, Hercules. Paradoxon, quod
Rex est quasi Devs.   AUCT

1389 ROSS, Thomas. Mr. Thomas Ros his
owne hand writting of the famous libell which he
affixed in England and therefore was executed in
Scotland 1618.   EUL

Paper, 400 × 305 mm, s. sh. The libel consisted of a Latin thesis nailed on the door of St. Mary's, Oxford, which claimed that 'all Scotsmen ought to be expelled from the court of England, with the exception of his majesty himself, the prince, and a very few others'. Ross was disappointed in his hopes for an Oxford scholarship. See *DNB*.

1390* SALUSTE DU BARTAS, Guillaume de. Lettre au Roy d'Escosse. M.S. Autog. Nerac. 1. Mars. 1588.   AUCT

1391 SIDNEY, *Sir* Philip. Astrophel and Stella written by Sʳ· Philip Sidny knight.   EUL
Paper, 151 × 205 mm, ff. 60. Secretary hand. Wanting all between sonnet and song ix. Described in William A. Ringler's edition of Sidney's *Poems*

(Oxford, 1962), pp. 539–40. The MS. was written for or by Sir Edward Dymoke, who met and exchanged verses with William Fowler in Padua in 1591 or 1592. The MS. may have come to Drummond through this association of his uncle.

1392* SUFFOLK. A Discourse of the Succession to the &c. in favour of the House of Suffolke. MS.   AUCT

1393* THORIUS, Raphael. Galliæ Pietas in Henricum Walliæ Principem.   AUCT

1394* WILLIAM I, *Prince of Orange*. Lettre a Messieurs du conseil d'Estat du Roy d'Escosse, Delphe, 1581.   AUCT

GIFTS

1395 ARISTOPHANES. Ἀριστοφάνους κωμωδιαι ἔνδεκα . . . Aristophanis comoediae undecim, cum scholiis antiquis, quae studio et opera . . . Odoardi Biseti Carlaei sunt quam plurimis locis . . . emendata et perpetuis novis scholiis illustrata. Ad quae accesserunt ejusdem in duas posteriores novi commentarii, opera tamen et studio . . . D. Aemylii, Francisci Porti . . . filii, ex Biseti autographo exscripti et in ordinem digesti (cum latina interpretatione Nicodemi Frischlini, Florentis Christiani et Andreae Divi).
2° Geneva, for the Caldoriana Societas, 1607.
                                                SAUL
Given by Drummond to Sir John Scot of Scot-starvet for his newly founded class library, St Andrews, 1620.

1396 BOLTON, Edmund. Nero Cæsar, or mon-archie depraued.
2° London, T. Snodham for T. Walkley, 1624.
STC 3221   FOLG
On the title-page, in Drummond's hand: 'To his Noble and Loving freind Wᵐ Drummond of Reckertown W.D.'

1397 BUCHANAN, George. Rerum Scoticarum historia.
2° Edinburgh, house of A. Arbuthnet, 1582.
STC 3991   SALE
Given by Drummond to Ben Jonson.
See Herford and Simpson, *Ben Jonson*, I, 267, who, however, give the date as 1586.

1398 DRUMMOND, William, *of Hawthornden*. Flowres of Sion. By William Drummond of Hawthorne-denne. To which is adjoyned his cypresse grove.
4° Edinburgh, A. Hart, 1623.   AUL
STC 7248
'Giuen to the librarie of Mʳ· Thomas Rheid in Aberdone by the Author. 1627'.
This and the next item are extant examples of the many copies of his own works given by Drummond to his friends.

1399 DRUMMOND, William, *of Hawthornden*. Forth feasting. A panegyricke to the kings most excellent majesty.
4° Edinburgh, A. Hart, 1617.   AUL
STC 7252
'Giuen to the Librarie of Mʳ Thomas Rhed in Aberdone by the Author. 1627.'
Bound with a copy of the *Poems* (1616), which according to Drummond's inscription, he gave to 'the Colledge of king James in Edinburgh', 1624.

1400 RAMUS, Petrus. Petri Rami arithmeticae libri duo: geometriae septem et viginti. A Lazaro Schonero recogniti & aucti.
4° Frankfort, heirs of A. Wechel, 1599.   EUL
Given by Drummond on graduation to the university library in 1605.

ASSOCIATED BOOKS

1401 BRIGGS, HENRY. Arithmetica logarith-mica, siue logarithmorum chiliades centum, pro

numeris naturali serie crescentibus ab vnitate ad 100000. Vna cum canone triangulorum, seu tabula artificialium sinuum, tangentium & secantium, ad radium 10,00000,00000. & ad singula scrupula prima quadrantis. Quibus nouum traditur compendium, quo nullum nec admirabilius, nec utilius soluendi pleraque problemata arithmetica & geometrica. Hos numeros primus inuenit clarissimus vir Iohannes Neperus Baro Merchistonij : eos autem ex ejusdem sententiâ mutauit, eorumque ortum & usum illustrauit Henricus Briggius, in celeberrimâ Academiâ Oxoniensi geometriæ professor Sauilianus. Editio secunda aucta per Adrianum Vlacq Goudanum.
2° Gouda, P. Rammasenius, 1628.   EUL
With the signature of Sir William Alexander, Earl of Stirling, and a note (in the hand of John Adamson, Principal of the University) that this book was given to Drummond to 'be put up in his catalogue for Edinburgh College 1631'.

BIBLIOTHECA IMAGINARIA

These three entries follow the Latin prose books in the 1611 catalogue. Drummond must have meant to compile a list of joke titles (on the lines of John Donne's imaginary library), but ran out of wit after these. The first title plays with William Warner's famous *Albion's England* and the Stuart accession to the crown of England; the second joke is obvious, but the third seems pointless.

1402   *Albions Scotland.*

1403   *Gierosoleme ruinata by Titus.*

1404   *The Battle of Banoch-burne.*

ADDENDUM

1405   GEMISTUS, Georgius. Elegans ac brevis quatuor virtutum explicatio (autore Plethone), Græce et Latine, nunc primum edita, A. Occone . . . interprete; item, de moribus philosophorum locus ex Platonis Theæteto, Græce et Latine, eodem interprete: et Aristotelis de virtutibus & vitiis Libellus, cum Latina quatuor interpretum versione A. Chamaillardi, S. Grynæi, A. a Lacuna, J. Velsii. [*Ed.* A. Occo.]
8° Basle, J. Oporinus, 1552.   PR

Appendixes

I

These lists are taken from the Hawthornden MSS (2059, ff. 359–67). They have appeared in print previously, edited by David Laing in *Archaeologia Scotica, Transactions of the Society of Antiquaries of Scotland* (Edinburgh 1857) IV 73–7, and by French Rowe Fogle *A Critical Study of William Drummond of Hawthornden* (New York 1952), but they are reproduced here revised and corrected, edited directly from the manuscripts. Catalogue and STC numbers, etc., are entered on the side.

Bookes red be me anno 1606
Knox chronicles   STC 15071
S. P. S. Arcadia   916
Baldassers Castios courteour   719
Achilles Statius de amoribus clitophontis
   in latin   398
certaine matters concerning Scotland   STC 18017–8
daphnis polustephanos   714
euphues his england   861
epitome moralium Plutarchi
the anatomie of sin and Genologie of verteu   703

orlando furioso comedie   STC 12265–6
constant calipolis
the paradise of dentie deuises   STC 7516–24
Metaphrasis poetica lepantiados Morray   340
The holie loue of Heuinlie visdome   771
Romeo and Iulieta Tragedie   909
Paurino and lusina   935
loues labors lost comedie   907
The sanctuarie of a troubled soule   829
The malcontent comedie   STC 17479–81
Menstres aurora   STC 337
Dratons oule   760
loues martir   STC 5119
The passionat pilgrime   STC 22342–3
The metamorphosis of ouid in english   879
The 4 part of the miror of knighthead
   c.f. STC 18859–71
Thule or vertues historie   893
The rape of lucrece   910
Dekkars part of the kings entreance in London
   STC 6510–13
A midsommers nights Dreame comedie   908
The 8 booke of the miror of knighthead   STC 18870

Doctor dodipol comedie   STC 6991
alphonsus historie comed   STC 12233
Noua Noui Orbis descriptio Benzonis   418
The Tragedie of Locrine   STC 21528
Guazzaes ciuil conuersation in english   STC 12422
three volumes of Diana in english   873
certaine letters concerning Greene   STC 12900
Cardanus de varietate rerum   103
Dorastus and faunia   STC 12285–8
The 2 volume of amadis de Gaule english   STC 542
Eurialus and lucretia english   STC 19974
Galatea de moribus   995

bookes red be me anno 1607
Aminte de Torquato Tasso in frenche   1162
tragediæ Senicæ
Blacvidii   422
Nicolai crassii iunioris Resp. ad paraenesum
  Baronii
consolation a Madame de Gui   1127
Arcadie de Sanasarre in french   1148
Claudianus
Diane de Montemaior in frenche
Instituta Iustiniani   223
Poemata flaminii, Bembi, castilionis
P. Bembi Ætna
les oeuures poetiques de pontus de Tyard   1173
carpentarii orationes contra Ramum   443
Iuuenilia Mureti   339
Circe de Gello in frenche   1053
le Tombeau de Margarite de Valois   1153
oratio eucharistica G. du val   478
La Medee de Iean de la Peruse   1076
l'Hermaphrodite   966

bookes red be me anno 1608
Troisiesme Tome des Hist. Tragiques
preimier Tome d'Amadis de Gaule   959
second tom. d'Amadis
Neuuiesme tom. d'amadis
Dix septiesme d'amadis
comedies de la Riue   1078
l'enfer d'amour
Ramus de relligione   68
Prince d'orange   1182
exposition sur l'apocalips   1117
Bezæ iuuenilia   c.f. 253
la conformitè du langage fran. auec le grec H. E.
  [Henri Estienne]
les ris de democrite   1044

trauaux sans trauaille   1009
Erastus en François   [Prince Erastus]
Cinsquiesme d'amadis de Gaule   961
Sixsieme d'amadis
les antiquites de France   [Francois Des Rues]
Dernier Tome of de serres   1152
le seigneur des accords   1011
Nilus contra primatum papæ
epistres de Pasquier
histoire des albigeois   1133
la curiositè de du plessix   1030
oracula Sybillæ en grec
la fuite du pechè   1046
Cinthia comedia in Italien   1269
la gazzette françoise
la celestine   1140

bookes red anno 1609 be me
Bartas   1147
13 tome d'Amadis de Gaule
La franciade de Ronsard
Rablais   1137
Hierusalem de Tasso in english   931
Dictionaire de Nicot
Daniel's vorkes   738
Roland furieux in frenche   963
azolains de Bembe in frenche   977
Amours de Ronsard
Monophile d'Estienne pasquier   1126
orlando furioso in english   STC 746–7
The anatomie of humours   STC 12168
Les poemes de passerat   1128
An apologie for the oth of alleagence   STC 14400
Hymnes de Ronsard
les odes de Ronsard
elegies et ecglougues de Ronsard
deux Tragedies de Iodelle
recherches de pasquier   1125
no body comedie   STC 18597
Sir gyles gooscape comedie   STC 12050
A mad vorld comedie   STC 17888
The Ile of Gooles comedie   744
liberalitie and prodigalitie comedie   STC 5593
Sir Ph. Sid. arcadia   916
Parasitaster by Marston comed.   867
The court of ciuil conuersation
The hunting of cupid   [George Peele]
poetical Rapsodie by Dauison   742
Thetis festiual by Daniel   STC 13161

Italien bookes red be me anno 1610
Sanasars Arcadia et en f. [and in French]   1278
first part of the rimes of petrarche et en f.1261, 1132
pastor fido de Guarini et en f.   1231, 1059
Arcadia de Morinella   1245
aminta of Tasso et en f.   1284, 1162
azolins of Bembo ; et en f.   1194, 977
Gierusalem liberata of Tasso & engl.   1287, 931
  english latin, frenche
Spesenrs fayrie Queene   922
lib. poetices I. Scaligeri   373
defence d'Herodote H. E.   1033

Bookes red anno 1611
Histoire macaroniq   1214?
quadrains de Pibracq   [Gui Du Faur]
Heraclite par du moulin   [Pierre Du Moulin]
Responce a tous propos
Six liures de Mario Æquicolo d'Alueto de la
  nature d'amour
amoretti and epithalamion by Spenser   921
anticotton   STC 5861
Remerciement de beurrieres de Paris
pater noster des Iesuites
le pourmenoir de Montagne
desdaine d'amour
Cornelius Tacitus in english   STC 23645
Les Pseaumes de Dauid   984
epistole de gli apostoli
Il padre de famiglia del S. Torquato Tasso
Il Rinaldo del S. T. Tasso   1290
The Death of Sophonisba. by D. M.   875
poemata P. bembi
Rime del Cesare Rinaldi   1272
A discourse of ciuil lyff, by lod. Bryskett out of
  the Italians of Geraldi   STC 3958
delle Rime del S. Torquato Tasso part prime   1284
delle Rime del S. Tasso parte seconda   1284
fatti de gli apostoli
delle Rime del S. T. Tasso parte terza   1284
Traictè de sagesse par pierre Charron   999
Del le rime del T. Tasso parte quarta   1284
Rime de Sanazaro
Discorso di Iason Denores intorno la poesia   1249
Phillis by Thomas Lodge   858
Zephiria by some vncertaine writter   956
Syntagma disputationum theologicarum
  danielis Tileni
Theophile par du Moulin
relatione vniuersale de Botero

Menstries vorkes 4 tragedies Aurora   698
Englands Helicon   STC 3191
Ioshua
Iudges
Ruth
Samuel
Kings
chronicles
Ezra
Nehemiah
Ester
Iob

bookes red be me anno 1612
Philippes de Mornay de la veritè de la
  religion chrestienne   1111
Rime de M. Pietro Bembo   1196
Rime di Luigi Groto cieco d'adria   1229
Madrigali di F. Contarini   1216
Madrigali del S. Carlo Coquinato   1217
le Noue fiamme di lodiuico Paterno   1258
les oeuures poetiques de Passerat   1128
Inglish votaries be I. bale   704
The Prophecie of Isaias
The art of English Poesie   888
The metamorphose of Aiax   STC 12779
Ben Ihonsons epigrams
Heaths epigrams   STC 13018
Beacons essayes   STC 1139–40
Staffords Niobe turned in a Nilus   STC 23130
Becons booke of learning to the king   STC 1164
Draytons Heroical epistles Barons varres,
  legends   762
lettere amorose Girolamo Parabosco

anno 1613
La diuina semana del S. T. Tasso
Bartas   1145
Rime del Marino
Morsolo
Dionysius Africanus de Situ Orbis   119
Dratons Poluolbion   STC 722–7
S. W. A. Doomsday   1328
Ihone Dones lyriques
[Drayton's] Owle   760
petrarcha de contemptu mundi
Bartas Workes   1147
Rime del S. lelio Capilupi
Dialogue de la vie et la mort par maistre
  Innocent Ringhier   1139

Consolation a Madame de Giury   1127
Ben Ihonsons epigrames
Dauies Epigrames   STC 6341
Sr Ihone Daueis nosce te ipsum   741
lamentations of Ieromie and prophecie
il Dante   1219
Rime di Cesare Caporali del Mauro et d'altri
   [Mauritius Moro]
Campions Ayres   STC 4547–8
Nosce te ipsum I. Dauies   741

anno 1614
la semaine de C. Gamon   1049
la Reina di Scotia T.   1274
Ciceronis Tusculanæ quest.   108?
Madrigalli di Mutio Manfredi
il contrasto amoroso   1241
Mirtilla   1188
S.P. Complaint   STC 22353?
perla   1193
la fiametta   1203
Pisides de opifice mundi   [George, of Pisidia]
ezekialls prophecie
La fiametta of Boccace   1023
pastor fido   1231
S.T. Overb. Wyfe   STC 18904–7
Boscan   1303
Garcilasso   1303
Granades 4 extrema   [Luis de Granada]
Dionyse Cathusiano   52

II

This list of comedies — and some tragedies, such as number 21 — appears in the Hawthornden MSS (MS 2060, ff. 122–3), and is presumably a list of plays Drummond had read or plays that he had bought. Judging from the dates these were printed, the catalogue was compiled some time after 1621. Greg numbers are given on the side.

Catalogue of Comedies
1   When you see mee yee know mee.
     Rowley.   212
2   the Two merry milke maides. I.C.   364
3   a Woman is a Weather-cocke. Feild.   299
4   May-day. Chapman   297
5   The Raigne of Edward the second.
     Marlow   129
6   Cæsar and Pompey. Oxford.   232

7   lingua   239
8   the weakest goes to the Walles.   171
9   Doctor faustus. Marlow.   205
10   Antonio and Mellida first part. I.M.   184
11   The Rape of Lucrece. Hey-wood   273
12   Two Wise-men all the rest fooles   361
13   The Ducke of Milane Messenger.   386
14   The faire maide of the exchange.   242
15   a faire Querrell. Midleton Rowley   352
16   a king & no king Beaumont Flesher   360
17   Histriomastike.   290
18   the bondman. Massinger.   408
19   Phylaster Beaumont and Fletcher   363
20   first & second part Edward the 4   153–4
21   Therrie king of france.   368
22   The Wonder of Woemen Sophonisba
      Marston   231
23   the Spanish Tradgedie Hieronimo   110
24   Albumazar cambridge   303
25   the insatiate countesse   315
26   Honest lawer. S.S.   337
27   Mustapha   278
28   Nero   410
29   Swe—Name Araigned.   362
30   If yee know not mee yee know nobody
      Elizabeth.   215
31   The Duchesse of Malfy. Webster.   389
32   Wylle beguyled.   234
33.   a Woman kild wt kyndnesse. Heywood.   258
34   The Virgine Martire Messenger. Decker.   380
35   Cupids WhirleGig.   247
36   the Fleire. Sharpham.   255
37   a Tricke to catch the old one. Midlton.   262
38   The Malcontent Marston. Webster.   203
39   the Mariage of the artes. Holyday.   353
40   the Maides Tragedie   357
41   Greene tu Quoque.   323
42   Byrones conspiracie Chapman.   274–275
43   The Heire. T.M.   384
44   Amendes for ladies Feild.   356
45   orlando furioso.   123
46   Herod & Antipater.   382
47   The Diuelles law case Webster   388
48   Dauid & Bersebe. Peele.   160
49   Wester-Hoe Decker & Webster   257
50   The conuerted Courtesan Dekker   204
51   All fooles chapman   219
52   To choose a good-Wyffe   191
53   The fawn Marston   230
54   Mucedorus   151

ADDENDA IN PROOF

1406   JOHNSTON, John. Heroes ex omni
historia Scotica lectissimi.
4° Leyden, C. Guyotius for A. Hart, 1603.   NLS
STC 14786

1407   JOHNSTON, John. Inscriptiones historicæ
regum Scotorum . . . Præfixus est Gathelus, siue
de gentis origine. Fragmentum A. Meluini.
Additæ sunt icones omnium regum . . .
Stuartorum in ære sculptæ.
4° Amsterdam, C. Claesson for A. Hart, 1602.
                                                NLS
STC 14787
Ben Johnson's book, which, since it is bound with
the previous entry, was probably given by him
to Drummond. With the motto 'tanquā
explorator' and the signature (erased) 'Sū Ben:
Jonsonij.' The portraits are wanting.

Index

Roman numbers refer to text pages
Italic numbers refer to catalogue entries